Arithmetic

for

Commerce

D1477161

By the same author

A COMPLETE "O" LEVEL MATHEMATICS
1st edition 1973   2nd edition 1976

Arithmetic for Commerce

A Greer

Senior Lecturer, Gloucester Technical College

Stanley Thornes (Publishers) Ltd.

First published in 1976 by Stanley Thornes (Publishers) Ltd.,
EDUCA House, Malmesbury Road, Kingsditch, CHELTENHAM, England

Reprinted 1977 with minor corrections

ISBN 0 85950 028 4

Typeset by Avontype, Bristol
Printed at The Pitman Press, Bath

Preface

This is a complete course in Commercial Arithmetic and the contents include all the topics required for the following examinations:

R.S.A.—Arithmetic, Business Calculations and the Certificate of Office Studies.

London Chamber of Commerce—Arithmetic.

National Retail and Distribution Certificate.

A.E.B.—Certificate of Proficiency in Arithmetic.

E.M.E.U., U.L.C.I., N.C.T.E.C. and U.E.I.—Commercial Arithmetic.

It is assumed that for many students it is appropriate to revise the beginnings in the teaching of the subject, hence the starting point is Operations in Arithmetic. The emphasis is on a simple approach and references to all the basic aspects of arithmetic have been included. A teacher and his class may work, if desired, through the book chapter by chapter.

A very large number of graded exercises have been provided in each section of the work, together with answers, and students will find it possible to work from relatively easy problems to a situation in which confidence in dealing with harder problems is acquired.

At the end of each of the chapters there is a summary which gives details of all the important points raised in the Chapter. There is also, at the end of most chapters, a Mental Test and a Self Test. The mental test consists of basically simple problems which can each be solved in a few seconds but which, nevertheless bring out the important points given in the chapter summary. The self tests consist, in the main, of objective type questions. Such tests are growing in popularity with examiners and they give the student a chance to assess his or her progress.

In addition there are five sets of Miscellaneous Exercises placed at strategic intervals throughout the book. All the questions in these exercises are of the type usually found in the examinations for which this book caters. The idea is that the student is given the opportunity of answering examination type questions thus gaining experience in examination technique.

Finally I would like to thank Mr. K. A. Stroud for his invaluable help in correcting the manuscript and checking the answers to the exercises and also for his suggestions for the improvement of the text.

A. Greer *Gloucester*, 1976.

Contents

1. Operations in Arithmetic

Introduction

In this chapter the basic operations of arithmetic are revised. We will add, subtract, multiply and divide numbers. Since arithmetic is all about numbers let us first consider what numbers are and how they are represented.

Some Definitions

Numbers are represented by symbols which are called *digits*. There are nine digits which are 1, 2, 3, 4, 5, 6, 7, 8 and 9. We also use the symbol 0 (i.e. zero) where no digit exists. Digits and zero may be combined together to represent any number.

Numeration expresses numbers in words — zero, one, two, three, four, five, six, seven, eight and nine.

Notation expresses numbers in figures or symbols (0, 1, 2, 3, 4, 5, 6, 7, 8, 9). These are all unit figures. The next number, ten, is 10 which is a combination of one and zero. 11 (eleven) is the combination of one and one and it equals ten plus one. 20 (twenty) is the combination of two and zero and it equals two tens. Ten tens are one hundred and ten hundreds are one thousand and so on.

100 indicates one hundred
900 indicates nine hundreds
954 indicates nine hundreds, five tens and four units
1000 indicates one thousand
8000 indicates eight thousands
9999 indicates nine thousands, nine hundreds, nine tens and nine units

Note that in the case of the number 9999:

9 9 9 9
d c b a

a is a units figure and equals	9
b is a tens figure and equals	9 0
c is a hundreds figure and equals	9 0 0
d is a thousands figure and equals	9 0 0 0

In arithmetic the sign $+$ means plus or add and the sign $=$ means equals. Thus,

$$7+2 = 9$$

The number $9999 = 9000+900+90+9$

If we want to write six hundreds, five tens and seven units then we write 657. If we want to write four hundred and seven units we write 407; the zero keeps the place for the missing tens.

eight thousand and thirty five is written 8035
eight thousand and nine is written 8009
ten thousand is written 10 000
one hundred thousand is written 100 000
one thousand thousand is called one million which is written 1 000 000.
8 000 000 indicates eight million
37 895 762 indicates thirty seven million, eight hundred and ninety five thousand, seven hundred and sixty two.

In the number 37 895 762 we have grouped the digits in threes with a space between them. This space takes the place of the comma which was traditionally used to group the figures of a number into threes. The change has taken place because many foreign countries use a comma instead of a decimal point.

Exercise 1

Write the following in figures:

1) four hundred and fifty seven

2) nine thousand, five hundred and thirty six

3) seven thousand, seven hundred and seventy seven

4) three thousand and eight

5) seven hundred and five

6) thirty thousand and twenty eight

7) five thousand and ninety

8) four thousand nine hundred and four

9) one hundred and twenty five thousand, nine hundred and six

10) three million, eight hundred thousand and seven

11) ninety five million, eight hundred and twenty seven thousand

12) three hundred million and nine

Write the following numbers in words:

13) 225   19) 17 000
14) 8321   20) 198 376
15) 3017   21) 200 005
16) 3960   22) 7 365 231
17) 1807   23) 27 000 309
18) 20 004

Addition

When adding numbers together place the figures in columns making sure that all the units figures are placed under one another, that all the tens figures are placed beneath each other and so on. Thus all the figures having the same place value fall in the same column.

Example 1   Add together 4219, 583, 98 and 1287.

4219 Start off by adding the units column. Thus 7 and 8 make 15
583   and 3 makes 18 and 9 makes 27. Place the 7 in the units
98   column of the answer and carry the 2 forward to the tens
1287 column. Adding this we have 2 and 8 is 10 and 9 is 19 and 8
―――― is 27 and 1 is 28. Place the 8 in the tens column of the answer
6187 and carry the 2 forward to the hundreds column which we
―――― now add. 2 and 2 is 4 and 5 is 9 and 2 is 11. We write a 1 in

the hundreds column of the answer and carry 1 forward to the thousands column which we now add. 1 and 1 is 2 and 4 is 6. Writing the 6 in the thousands column of the answer we see that the answer to the addition is 6187.

Example 2   Find the value of $17638 + 108749 + 1011 + 2345008$.

The + sign simply means add the numbers together and our problem is to add the four numbers. As before we write them in a column so that digits having the same place values are written beneath each other.

    17 638   Add up the units column from bottom to top, saying
   108 749   audibly, 9, 18, 26. Write 6 in the units column of the
     1 011   answer and carry the 2 forwards to the tens column. Add
 2 345 008   the tens column as 2, 3, 7 and 10. Write 0 in the tens
 ─────────   column of the answer and carry the 1 forward to the
 2 472 406   hundreds column. Carry on in this way with the re-
 ─────────   maining columns until the answer is obtained.

Exercise 2

Find the values of each of the following:

1) $96 + 247 + 8$

2) $109 + 57 + 3478 + 926$

3) $35068 + 21007 + 905 + 1178 + 32$

4) $23589 + 7987432 + 234068 + 9871 + 324689$

5) $15437 + 1344 + 1626 + 107924$

Subtraction

Subtraction means taking away. Let us take 5 from 6. We know that 1 is left. We write $6 - 5 = 1$ which we read as six minus five equals 1.

Example 3   Subtract 17 from 59

    59   Place 17 under 59. 7 from 9 leaves 2. Write 2 in the units
    17   column of the answer and then 1 from 5 leaves 4. Writing 4 in
    ──   the tens column of the answer we see that $59 - 17 = 42$.
    42
    ──

There are two methods by which subtraction can be performed. Consider

$$15 - 8 = 7$$

1st method: Take 8 from 15. We have 7 left.

2nd method: If to 7 we add 8 then we obtain 15. 7 is therefore the difference between 15 and 8.

Example 4   Find the difference between 32 and 17.

Which is the greater of 32 and 17? Clearly 32 is the greater. Therefore we subtract 17 from 32.

32 In the units column we cannot take 7 from 2. However if we
17 borrow 1 from the tens place and put it before the 2 we get 12,
—   the 3 in the tens column becoming 2. Now 7 from 12 leaves 5.
15 We write 5 in the tens column of the answer and take 1 from 2 in
—   the tens column leaving 1.

Many people find it easier to work the borrowing method the other
way round and to write the subtraction out in this way:

32 We say that 7 from 2 will not go, so we take 7 from 12 giving 5
17 which we write in the units column of the answer. We now
 1 increase the 1 in the tens column by 1 making it 2 (the small
—   figure 1 is a useful aid to the memory until practice makes it
15 unnecessary). Finally we take 2 from 3 leaving 1 which is written
—   in the tens column of the answer.

Example 5   Subtract 1835 from 5423.

5423 In the units column 5 from 3 will not go, so take 5 from 13
1835 leaving 8. Increase the 3 on the bottom of the tens column by 1
 111 making it 4. 4 from 2 will not go, so take 4 from 12 leaving 8
——   and increase the 8 on the bottom of the hundreds column by 1
3588 making it 9. 9 from 4 will not go, so take 9 from 14 leaving 5.
——   Finally increase the 1 on the bottom of the thousands column
      and take 2 from 5 leaving 3.

Exercise 3

1) Find the difference of 27 and 59.

2) Subtract 258 from 593.

3) Find the value of $53-39$.

4) Subtract 7693 from 9251.

5) What is the difference between 336 and 9562?

Combined Addition and Subtraction

Suppose we want to find the value of
$$18+7-5+3-16+8$$
we pick out all the numbers preceded by a plus sign and add them
together. Thus
$$18+7+3+8 = 36$$
(Note that the first number, it is 18, has no sign in front of it. When this
happens a plus sign is always assumed.)

Next we pick out all the numbers preceded by a minus sign and add
these together. Thus
$$-5-16 = -21$$
Finally we subtract 21 from 36 to give 15.

Hence,
$$18+7-5+3-16+8 = 36-21 = 15$$

Example 6   Find the value of $2+6-3+9-5+11$

$$2+6+9+11 = +28 \qquad 28$$
$$-3-5 = -8 \qquad\quad 8$$

⎫ Subtracting

$$20$$

Exercise 4

Find the value of each of the following:

1) $8-6+7-5+9-2$

2) $21+32-63-58+79+32-11$

3) $152-78+43-81$

4) $27+45+9+7-15-23-41-8+17$

Arithmetical Signs, Terms and Symbols

The result obtained by adding numbers is called the *sum*. Thus the sum of 9 and 6 is 15.

The result obtained by subtracting one number from another is called the *difference*. The difference between 19 and 8 is $19-8 = 11$.

The sign $=$ is the sign of *equality* and means equal to. Thus 4 hours $=$ 240 minutes.

$+$ is the *addition* sign meaning plus. Thus $4+5 = 9$

$-$ is the *subtraction* sign meaning minus. Thus $9-5 = 4$

$\times$ is the *multiplication* sign meaning multiplied by, or times. Thus $6\times 8 = 48$

$\div$ is the *division* sign meaning divided by. There are several ways of indicating division which are as follows:

1) $6\div 3 = 2$ This reads six divided by three equals two.

2) $\dfrac{6}{3} = 2$ This reads six over three (or six divided by three) equals two.

3) $3\overline{)6}$ 2 This reads three into six goes two or six divided by three equals two.

Multiplication

MULTIPLICATION TABLE

1	2	3	4	5	6	7	8	9	10
2	4	6	8	10	12	14	16	18	20
3	6	9	12	15	18	21	24	27	30
4	8	12	16	20	24	28	32	36	40
5	10	15	20	25	30	35	40	45	50
6	12	18	24	30	36	42	48	54	60
7	14	21	28	35	42	49	56	63	70
8	16	24	32	40	48	56	64	72	80
9	18	27	36	45	54	63	72	81	90
10	20	30	40	50	60	70	80	90	100

We can find the value of 6+6+6+6 by adding the four sixes together. The answer is 24. We could, however, do this more rapidly by using the multiplication tables because we know that 4×6 = 24.

When two numbers are multiplied together the result is called the *product*. Thus the product of 5 and 9 is 5×9 = 45.

The multiplication table is shown above. The extreme left hand vertical column, 1 to 10, as well as the top horizontal row, give the numbers whose products we wish to find. Thus to find the product of 6 and 8 (i.e. 6×8) we find 6 in the extreme left hand column. We then run the eye, or a finger, horizontally along this row until we come to the column headed 8 and we find the number 48, which is the required product. Hence 6×8 = 48. Similarly we find that 5×9 = 45 and 9×8 = 72.

You should use this multiplication table to revise the tables you may previously have studied. Try to make sure that you know up to 10×10 without the need to refer to the table.

Exercise 5

Write down the following products:

1) 3×2	3) 9×6	5) 7×9	7) 9×9
2) 5×7	4) 8×4	6) 5×3	8) 6×7

Long Multiplication

Example 7   Multiply 236 by 7.

236 7 times 6 is 42. Place the 2 in the answer and carry the 4. 7
  7 times 3 is 21, plus the 4 carried, is 25. Place 5 in the answer and
─── carry the 2. 7 times 2 is 14, plus the 2 carried is 16.
1652
────

Example 8   Multiply 369 by 527.

369 Write the two numbers with their respective units figures
527 directly underneath each other. Start by multiplying 369
─── by 7 giving 2583. Write the 3 directly beneath the units
2583 figures of the two numbers to be multiplied together. Now
738 multiply 369 by 2 (which is really 20) giving 738. Make sure
1845 that the figures obtained by multiplying are this time moved
─── one place to the left. Finally, when multiplying by 5 (which
194463 is really 500) it is again necessary to move one further place
─── to the left. We now add the three sets of figures obtained by
multiplication, the result being 194463.

Alternatively if you wish, you can start with the left-hand figure in the multiplier as shown below.

369 First multiply 369 by 500 giving 184 500. Then multiply
527 369 by 20 giving 7380 and finally multiply 369 by 7 giving
——— 2583. To obtain the product add these three sets of figures
184500 obtained by multiplication.
7380
2583

——

194463

——

Checking the Accuracy of a Multiplication

There is a simple method of checking the result of a multiplication which is illustrated by considering

$$843 \times 797 = 671\,871$$

Sum of the digits of 843 $= 8+4+3 = 15$; $15 \div 9 = 1$ and remainder 6
Sum of the digits of 797 $= 7+9+7 = 23$; $23 \div 9 = 2$ and remainder 5
Multiplying the remainders: $6 \times 5 = 30$; $30 \div 9 = 3$ and remainder 3
Sum of the digits of the product $=$
$$6+7+1+8+7+1 = 30; \quad 30 \div 9 = 3 \text{ and remainder } 3$$
Since the two remainders are the same the product 671 871 is correct.

Example 9

Multiply 369 by 527 and check the accuracy of the multiplication.

This multiplication has already been performed in Example 8 and we find that
$$369 \times 527 = 194\,463.$$

Sum of the digits of 369 $= 3+6+9 = 18$; $18 \div 9 = 2$ and remainder 0
Sum of the digits of 527 $= 5+2+7 = 14$; $14 \div 9 = 1$ and remainder 5
Multiplying the remainders: $0 \times 5 = 0$
Sum of the digits of the product $=$
$$1+9+4+4+6+3 = 27; \quad 27 \div 9 = 3 \text{ and remainder } 0$$
Since the two remainders are the same the product is correct.

Exercise 6

Obtain the following products and check
your accuracy:

1) 29×32
2) 359×26
3) 3149×321
4) 5683×789
5) $17\,632 \times 58$

Division

Division consists of finding how many times one number is contained in another number.

The *dividend* is the number to be divided.

The *divisor* is the number by which the dividend is divided.

The *quotient* is the result of the division.

Thus, $\dfrac{\text{dividend}}{\text{divisor}} = \text{quotient}$

Short Division

If the divisor is less than 10 it is usual to work by short division.

Example 10   Divide 2625 by 7.

7)2625 7 will not divide into 2. Next try 7 into 26. It goes 3 and a
 375   remainder of 5. Carry the remainder so that the next number
        to be divided is 52. 7 goes into 52, 7 times and remainder 3.
        Carry the 3 so that the next number to be divided is 35.
        7 into 35 goes 5 exactly.

Example 11   Divide 1979 by 9.

9)1979   9 will not divide into 1 so try dividing 9 into
 219 remainder 8   19. It goes 2 remainder 1. Carry the 1 so that
                the next number to be divided is 17. 9 into 17
                goes 1 remainder 8. Carry the 8 so that the
                next number to be divided is 89. 9 goes into 89
                9 remainder 8. There are no more numbers to
                divide so the answer is 219 remainder 8.

Exercise 7

Work out the answers to the following:

1) $1968 \div 8$ 2) $392 \div 7$ 3) $2168 \div 5$ 4) $7369 \div 4$

5) $5621 \div 9$

Long Division

The method is shown in the next example.

Example 12   Divide 3024 by 36.

36)3024(84   36 consists of two digits. Look at the first two digits in
 288   the dividend, i.e. 30. 36 will not divide into 30 because
 ‾‾‾   36 is the larger number. Next look at the first three
 144   figures of the dividend. They are 302. Will 36 divide into
 144   302? It will because 302 is the larger number. How
 ‾‾‾   many times will it go? Let us multiply 36 by 9 the
 . . .   result is 324 which is greater than 302. Now try 36×8.
             The result is 288 which is less than 302. Place 8 in the
             answer (i.e. the quotient) and write the 288 under the
             302. Subtracting 288 from 302 we get a remainder of 14.
             Now bring down the next figure in the dividend, which
             is 4. Now divide 36 into 144. The result is 4 exactly
             because $4 \times 36 = 144$. Write 4 in the quotient and we
             see that $3024 \div 36 = 84$ exactly.

Example 13   Divide 1 000 000 by 250.

250)1000000(4000   250 will not divide into the first three figures of
 1000   the dividend (100) so we try 250 into 1000. It
 ‾‾‾‾   goes 4 times exactly leaving no remainder. To
 . . . .   obtain the quotient the remaining three zeros
                   are written in the quotient giving 4000.

Tests for Divisibility

A number is divisible by:

2 if it is an even number.

4 if its last two figures are divisible by 4. (3024 is divisible by 4 because 24 divided by 4 is 6 exactly.)

8 if its last three figures are divisible by 8. (19 168 is divisible by 8 because 168 divided by 8 is 21 exactly.)

16 if its last four figures are divisible by 16. (32 064 is divisible by 16 because 2064 divided by 16 is 129 exactly.)

5 if the last figure is a zero or a five. (3265 and 4280 are both divisible by 5.)

10 if the last figure is a zero. (198 630 is divisible by 10.)

9 if the sum of the digits of the number are divisible by 9. (5283 is divisible by 9 because $5+2+8+3 = 18$ is divisible by 9.)

11 when the difference between the sum of 1st, 3rd, 5th, 7th etc. digits and the 2nd, 4th, 6th, etc. digits is divisible by 11 or it is zero. (Is the number 4741 divisible by 11? Sum of 1st and 3rd digits $= 4+4 = 8$. Sum of the 2nd and 4th digits $= 7+1 = 8$. Difference is $8-8 = 0$. Therefore 4741 is divisible by 11. Is 64 824 375 divisible by 11? Sum of the odd numbered digits $= 6+8+4+7 = 25$. Sum of the even numbered digits $= 4+2+3+5 = 14$. Difference $= 25-14 = 11$ which is divisible by 11. Hence 64 824 375 is divisible by 11.)

Exercise 8

Work out the answers to the following:

1) $4918 \div 9$ 3) $1237 \div 4$ 5) $15352 \div 17$ 7) $2093595 \div 35$

2) $7584 \div 6$ 4) $10001 \div 11$ 6) $45927 \div 27$ 8) $290227 \div 49$

Sequence of Arithmetical Operations

Numbers are often combined in a series of arithmetical operations. When this happens a definite sequence must be observed.

1) Brackets are used if there is any danger of ambiguity. The contents of the bracket must be evaluated before performing any other operation. Thus:

$$2 \times (7+4) = 2 \times 11 = 22$$
$$15-(8-3) = 15-5 = 10$$

2) Multiplication and division must be done before addition and subtraction. Thus;

$$5 \times 8+7 = 40+7 = 47 \ (\text{not } 5 \times 15)$$
$$8 \div 4+9 = 2+9 = 11 \ (\text{not } 8 \div 13)$$
$$5 \times 4-12 \div 3+7 = 20-4+7 = 27-4 = 23$$

Exercise 9

Find values for the following:

1) $3+5 \times 2$

2) $3 \times 6-8$

3) $7 \times 5-2+4 \times 6$

4) $8 \div 2+3$

5) $7 \times 5 - 12 \div 4 + 3$

6) $11 - 9 \div 3 + 7$

7) $3 \times (8 + 7)$

8) $2 + 8 \times (3 + 6)$

9) $17 - 2 \times (5 - 3)$

10) $11 - 12 \div 4 + 3 \times (6 - 2)$

Mental Test 1

Try to answer the following questions without writing anything down except the answer.

1) Add 3, 7, 4, 9 and 5.

2) Add 2, 4, 6, 8, 10 and 12.

3) Add 20, 30, 40, 50, 60, 70 and 80.

4) Add 12, 15 and 19.

5) Subtract 17 from 28.

6) Take 14 away from 23.

7) Find the sum of 27 and 35.

8) Add 19 and 13 and take away 27 from the sum.

9) Find the difference between 29 and 54.

10) Multiply 13 by 5.

11) Find the product of 14 and 6.

12) Multiply 19 by 7.

13) Multiply 273 by 3.

14) Divide 63 by 3.

15) Divide 515 by 5.

16) Multiply 311 by 9.

17) Add 126, 37 and 54.

18) Divide 572 by 4.

19) Multiply 17 by 5 and then add 23.

20) Divide 164 by 4 and then take away 18.

Self-Test 1

In questions 1 to 4 state the letter corresponding to the correct answer.

1) Thirty thousand and four in figures is:

   a 3004   **b** 30 004

   c 34 000   **d** 30 400

   e 300 004

2) Five thousand and fifteen in figures is:

   a 5015   **b** 5150

   c 5115   **d** 50015

   e 515

3) One hundred and six thousand and sixteen in figures is:

   a 116 000   **b** 106 000

   c 106 160   **d** 116 160

   e 106 016

4) Ten million, seventeen thousand and six in figures is:

   a 10 017 006   **b** 10 170 006

   c 10 017 060   **d** 10 017 600

   e 10 170 060

5) Add up the three sets of figures below:

(a)   5018
      362
   12 894
      268
   4 134
   ——

   ——

(b)   3 263
   8 783
      35
    357
  10 089
   ——

(c)   528
   5 079
   9 867
    61
   356
   ——

6) State the letter corresponding to correct answer to the problems shown below.

(a) $107-104+63-48+137+50-149$

a 65   b 56   c 66

(b) $368-55+378-286+245-254$

a 416   b 395   c 396

(c) $45-764+418-382+1049-689+1000$

a 677   b 605   c 687

7) Subtract the following:

(a) $2092-987$

(b) $2315-999$

(c) $7005-889$

(d) $958-697$

(e) $432-318$

(f) $23\,301-22\,398$

8) Multiply the following:

(a) $16\,398\times7$

(b) $635\,489\times12$

(c) $93\,081\times407$

(d) $51\,365\times450$

(e) 9457×6003

(f) $68\,859\times836$

9) Divide the following:

(a) $46\,348\div4$

(b) $32\,340\div60$

(c) $1536\div32$

(d) $17\,280\div960$

10) In each of the following division problems there is a remainder. Perform the division and state the remainder:

(a) $685\,329\div64$

(b) $61\,385\div13$

(c) $969\,234\div19$

(d) $17\,432\div560$

11) Each of the following numbers is divisible by either 4, 8, 16, 5, 10, 9 or 11. State which number will divide exactly into the given number:

(a) 1404

(b) 8615

(c) 4167

(d) 1564

(e) 102971

(f) 73216

12) State the letter corresponding to the correct answer to the problems shown below.

(a) $3+7\times4$

a 40   b 31   c 84

(b) $6\times5-2+4\times6$

a 52   b 42   c 18

(c) $7\times6-12\div3+1$

a 40   b 39   c 21

(d) $17-2\times(6-4)$

a 30   b 1   c 13

(e) $3\times5-12\div(3+1)$

a 12   b 10   c 8

In questions 13 to 20 decide if the answer is true or false and write the correct answer in your notebook.

13) $7+5\times3 = 22$

14) $7-2\times3 = 15$

15) $6\times5-3+2\times7 = 26$

16) $10\div2+3 = 8$

17) $7\times5-12\div4+2 = 10$

18) $18-10\div2+3\times(5-2) = 22$

19) $36-27+54-58 = 15$

20) The exact value of $(312\times11\times19)\div39$ is 1672

2. Fractions

Introduction

In this chapter we deal with the rules for the addition, subtraction, multiplication and division of fractions.

Vulgar Fractions

The circle in Fig. 2.1 has been divided into eight equal parts. Each part is called one-eighth of the circle and is written as $\frac{1}{8}$. The number 8 below the line shows how many equal parts there are and it is called the *denominator*. The number above the line shows how many of the equal parts are taken and it is called the *numerator*. If five of the eight equal parts are taken then we have taken $\frac{5}{8}$ of the circle.

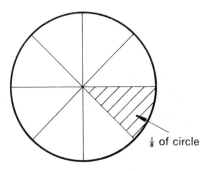

$\frac{1}{8}$ of circle

Fig. 2.1

From what has been said above we see that a fraction is always a part of something. The number below the line (the denominator) gives the fraction its name and tells us the number of equal parts into which the whole has been divided. The top number (the numerator) tells us the number of these equal parts that are to be taken. For example the fraction $\frac{3}{4}$ means that the whole has been divided into four equal parts and that three of these parts are to be taken.

The value of a fraction is unchanged if we multiply or divide both its numerator and denominator by the same amount.

$\frac{3}{5} = \frac{12}{20}$ (by multiplying the numerator and denominator by 4)

$\frac{2}{7} = \frac{10}{35}$ (by multiplying the numerator and denominator by 5)

$\frac{12}{32} = \frac{3}{8}$ (by dividing the numerator and denominator by 4)

$\frac{16}{64} = \frac{1}{4}$ (by dividing the numerator and denominator by 16)

Example 1

Write down the fraction $\frac{2}{7}$ with a denominator of 28.

In order to make the denominator 28, we must multiply the original denominator of 7 by 4 because $7 \times 4 = 28$. Remembering that to leave the value of the fraction unchanged we must multiply both numerator and denominator by the same amount, then

$$\frac{2}{7} = \frac{2 \times 4}{7 \times 4} = \frac{8}{28}$$

Exercise 10

Write down the following fractions with the denominator stated:

1) $\frac{3}{4}$ with denominator 28

2) $\frac{3}{5}$ with denominator 20

3) $\frac{5}{6}$ with denominator 30

4) $\frac{1}{9}$ with denominator 63

5) $\frac{2}{3}$ with denominator 12

6) $\frac{1}{6}$ with denominator 24

7) $\frac{3}{8}$ with denominator 64

8) $\frac{5}{7}$ with denominator 35

Reducing a Fraction to its Lowest Terms

Fractions like $\frac{3}{8}$, $\frac{7}{16}$ and $\frac{5}{32}$ are said to be in their *lowest terms* because it is impossible to find a number which will divide exactly into both the numerator and denominator. However, fractions like $\frac{9}{18}$, $\frac{8}{12}$ and $\frac{21}{24}$ are not in their lowest terms because they can be reduced further by dividing both numerator and denominator by some number which divides exactly into both of them. Thus,

$$\frac{9}{18} = \frac{1}{2} \text{ (by dividing both numerator and denominator by 9)}$$

$$\frac{8}{12} = \frac{2}{3} \text{ (by dividing both numerator and denominator by 4)}$$

$$\frac{21}{24} = \frac{7}{8} \text{ (by dividing both numerator and denominator by 3)}$$

Sometimes we can divide the numerator and denominator by the same number several times.

Example 2

Reduce $\frac{210}{336}$ to its lowest terms.

$$\frac{210}{336} = \frac{105}{168} \text{ (by dividing top and bottom by 2)}$$

$$= \frac{35}{56} \text{ (by dividing top and bottom by 3)}$$

$$= \frac{5}{8} \text{ (by dividing top and bottom by 7)}$$

Hence $\frac{210}{336}$ reduced to its lowest terms is $\frac{5}{8}$

Exercise 11

Reduce the following fractions to their
lowest terms:

1) $\dfrac{8}{16}$ 4) $\dfrac{15}{25}$ 7) $\dfrac{210}{294}$ 10) $\dfrac{210}{315}$

2) $\dfrac{9}{15}$ 5) $\dfrac{42}{48}$ 8) $\dfrac{126}{245}$

3) $\dfrac{8}{64}$ 6) $\dfrac{180}{240}$ 9) $\dfrac{132}{198}$

Types of Fractions

If the numerator of a fraction is less than its denominator the
fraction is called a *proper fraction*. Thus $\frac{2}{3}$, $\frac{5}{8}$ and $\frac{3}{4}$ are all proper
fractions. Note that a proper fraction has a value which is less than 1.

If the numerator of a fraction is greater than its denominator then
the fraction is called an *improper fraction* or a *top heavy fraction*.
Thus $\frac{5}{4}$, $\frac{3}{2}$ and $\frac{9}{7}$ are all top heavy, or improper, fractions. Note that all
top heavy fractions have a value which is greater than 1.

Every top heavy fraction can be expressed as a whole number and
a proper fraction. These are sometimes called *mixed numbers*. Thus
$1\frac{1}{2}$, $5\frac{1}{3}$ and $9\frac{3}{4}$ are all mixed numbers. In order to convert a top heavy
fraction into a mixed number it must be remembered that

$$\frac{\text{numerator}}{\text{denominator}} = \text{numerator} \div \text{denominator}$$

Example 3   Express $\dfrac{15}{8}$ as a mixed number.

$$\frac{15}{8} = 1\frac{7}{8} \ (\text{because } 15 \div 8 = 1 \text{ and remainder } 7)$$

From Example 3 we see that we convert a top heavy fraction into a
mixed number by dividing the denominator into the numerator.
Notice that the remainder becomes the numerator in the fractional
part of the mixed number. To change a mixed number into an improper fraction we multiply the whole number by the denominator of
the fractional part. To this we add the numerator of the fractional part
and this sum then becomes the numerator of the improper fraction.
Its denominator is the same as the denominator of the fractional part
of the mixed number.

Example 4   Express $3\dfrac{5}{8}$ as a top heavy fraction.

$$3\frac{5}{8} = \frac{(8 \times 3) + 5}{8} = \frac{24 + 5}{8} = \frac{29}{8}$$

Exercise 12

Express each of the following as a mixed number:

Express each of the following as top-heavy fractions:

1) $\frac{7}{2}$

4) $\frac{12}{11}$

6) $2\frac{3}{8}$

9) $6\frac{7}{20}$

2) $\frac{8}{4}$

5) $\frac{21}{8}$

7) $5\frac{1}{10}$

10) $4\frac{3}{7}$

3) $\frac{22}{10}$

8) $8\frac{2}{3}$

Lowest Common Multiple (LCM)

The LCM of a set of numbers is the *smallest* number into which each of the given numbers will divide. Thus the LCM of 4, 5 and 10 is 20 because 20 is the smallest number into which the numbers 4, 5 and 10 will divide exactly.

The LCM of a set of numbers can usually be found by inspection.

Exercise 13

Find the LCM of the following sets of numbers:

1) 8 and 12

5) 2, 8 and 10

9) 12, 42, 60 and 70

2) 3, 4 and 5

6) 20 and 25

10) 18, 30, 42 and 48

3) 2, 6 and 12

7) 20 and 32

4) 3, 6 and 8

8) 10, 15 and 40

Lowest Common Denominator

When we wish to compare the values of two or more fractions the easiest way is to express the fractions with the same denominator. This common denominator should be the LCM of the denominators of the fractions to be compared and it is called the *lowest common denominator*.

Example 5   Arrange the fractions $\frac{3}{4}, \frac{5}{8}, \frac{7}{10}$ and $\frac{11}{20}$ in order of size starting with the smallest.

The lowest common denominator of 4, 8, 10 and 20 is 40. Expressing each of the given fractions with a denominator of 40 gives:

$$\frac{3}{4} = \frac{3 \times 10}{4 \times 10} = \frac{30}{40} \qquad \frac{5}{8} = \frac{5 \times 5}{8 \times 5} = \frac{25}{40}$$

$$\frac{7}{10} = \frac{7 \times 4}{10 \times 4} = \frac{28}{40} \qquad \frac{11}{20} = \frac{11 \times 2}{20 \times 2} = \frac{22}{40}$$

Therefore the order is $\frac{22}{40}, \frac{25}{40}, \frac{28}{40}, \frac{30}{40}$ or $\frac{11}{20}, \frac{5}{8}, \frac{7}{10}$ and $\frac{3}{4}$

Exercise 14

Arrange the following sets of fractions in order of size, beginning with the smallest:

1) $\dfrac{1}{2}, \dfrac{5}{6}, \dfrac{2}{3}, \dfrac{7}{12}$

2) $\dfrac{9}{10}, \dfrac{3}{4}, \dfrac{6}{7}, \dfrac{7}{8}$

3) $\dfrac{13}{16}, \dfrac{11}{20}, \dfrac{7}{10}, \dfrac{3}{5}$

4) $\dfrac{3}{4}, \dfrac{5}{8}, \dfrac{3}{5}, \dfrac{13}{20}$

5) $\dfrac{11}{16}, \dfrac{7}{10}, \dfrac{9}{14}, \dfrac{3}{4}$

6) $\dfrac{3}{8}, \dfrac{4}{7}, \dfrac{5}{9}, \dfrac{2}{5}$

Addition of Fractions

The steps when adding fractions are as follows:

(1) Find the lowest common denominator of the fractions to be added.

(2) Express each of the fractions with this common denominator.

(3) Add the numerators of the new fractions to give the numerator of the answer. The denominator of the answer is the lowest common denominator found in (1).

Example 6   Find the sum of $\dfrac{2}{7}$ and $\dfrac{3}{4}$

First find the lowest common denominator (this is the LCM of 7 and 4).

It is 28. Now express $\dfrac{2}{7}$ and $\dfrac{3}{4}$ with a denominator of 28.

$$\frac{2}{7} = \frac{2 \times 4}{7 \times 4} = \frac{8}{28} \qquad\qquad \frac{3}{4} = \frac{3 \times 7}{4 \times 7} = \frac{21}{28}$$

Adding the numerators of the new fractions:

$$\frac{2}{7} + \frac{3}{4} = \frac{8}{28} + \frac{21}{28} = \frac{29}{28} = 1\frac{1}{28}$$

A better way of setting out the work is as follows:

$$\frac{2}{7} + \frac{3}{4} = \frac{2 \times 4 + 3 \times 7}{28} = \frac{8 + 21}{28} = \frac{29}{28} = 1\frac{1}{28}$$

Example 7   Simplify $\dfrac{3}{4} + \dfrac{2}{3} + \dfrac{7}{10}$

The LCM of the denominators 4, 3 and 10 is 60.

$$\frac{3}{4} + \frac{2}{3} + \frac{7}{10} = \frac{3 \times 15 + 2 \times 20 + 7 \times 6}{60} = \frac{45 + 40 + 42}{60} = \frac{127}{60} = 2\frac{7}{60}$$

Example 8   Add together $5\dfrac{1}{2}$, $2\dfrac{2}{3}$ and $3\dfrac{2}{5}$

First add the whole numbers together, $5 + 2 + 3 = 10$. Then add the fractional parts in the usual way. The LCM of 2, 3 and 5 is 30.

$$5\frac{1}{2} + 2\frac{2}{3} + 3\frac{2}{5} = 10 + \frac{15 \times 1 + 10 \times 2 + 6 \times 2}{30} = 10 + \frac{15 + 20 + 12}{30}$$

$$= 10 + \frac{47}{30} = 10 + 1\frac{17}{30} = 11\frac{17}{30}$$

Exercise 15

Add together:

1) $\frac{1}{2}+\frac{1}{3}$

2) $\frac{2}{5}+\frac{9}{10}$

3) $\frac{3}{4}+\frac{3}{8}$

4) $\frac{3}{10}+\frac{1}{4}$

5) $\frac{1}{2}+\frac{3}{4}+\frac{7}{8}$

6) $\frac{1}{8}+\frac{2}{3}+\frac{3}{5}$

7) $1\frac{3}{8}+3\frac{9}{16}$

8) $7\frac{2}{3}+6\frac{3}{5}$

9) $3\frac{3}{8}+5\frac{2}{7}+4\frac{3}{4}$

10) $4\frac{1}{2}+3\frac{5}{6}+2\frac{1}{3}$

11) $7\frac{3}{8}+2\frac{3}{4}+\frac{7}{8}+\frac{5}{16}$

12) $7\frac{2}{3}+\frac{2}{5}+\frac{3}{10}+2\frac{1}{2}$

Subtraction of Fractions

The method is similar to that used in addition. Find the common denominator of the fractions and after expressing each fraction with this common denominator, subtract.

Example 9 Simplify $\frac{5}{8}-\frac{2}{5}$

The LCM of the denominators is 40.

$$\frac{5}{8}-\frac{2}{5}=\frac{5\times5-8\times2}{40}=\frac{25-16}{40}=\frac{9}{40}$$

When mixed numbers have to be subtracted the best way is to turn the mixed numbers into top heavy fractions and then proceed in the way shown in Example 9.

Example 10 Simplify $3\frac{7}{10}-2\frac{3}{4}$

$$3\frac{7}{10}-2\frac{3}{4}=\frac{37}{10}-\frac{11}{4}=\frac{37\times2-11\times5}{20}=\frac{74-55}{20}=\frac{19}{20}$$

Example 11 Simplify $5\frac{2}{5}-3\frac{7}{8}$

$$5\frac{2}{5}-3\frac{7}{8}=\frac{27}{5}-\frac{31}{8}=\frac{27\times8-31\times5}{40}=\frac{216-155}{40}=\frac{61}{40}=1\frac{21}{40}$$

Exercise 16

Simplify the following:

1) $\frac{1}{2}-\frac{1}{3}$

2) $\frac{1}{3}-\frac{1}{5}$

3) $\frac{2}{3}-\frac{1}{2}$

4) $\frac{7}{8}-\frac{3}{8}$

5) $\frac{7}{8}-\frac{5}{6}$

6) $3\frac{1}{4}-2\frac{3}{8}$

7) $3-\frac{5}{7}$

8) $5-3\frac{4}{5}$

9) $5\frac{3}{8}-2\frac{9}{10}$

10) $4\frac{7}{32}-3\frac{9}{10}$

11) $1\frac{5}{16}-\frac{4}{5}$

Combined Addition and Subtraction

Example 12   Simplify $5\frac{3}{8}-1\frac{1}{4}+2\frac{1}{2}-\frac{7}{16}$

$$5\frac{3}{8}-1\frac{1}{4}+2\frac{1}{2}-\frac{7}{16}=\frac{43}{8}-\frac{5}{4}+\frac{5}{2}-\frac{7}{16}=\frac{43\times2-5\times4+5\times8-7\times1}{16}$$

$$=\frac{86-20+40-7}{16}=\frac{(86+40)-(20+7)}{16}$$

$$=\frac{126-27}{16}=\frac{99}{16}=6\frac{3}{16}$$

Exercise 17

Simplify the following:

1) $2\frac{1}{2}+3\frac{1}{4}-4\frac{3}{8}$

2) $5\frac{1}{10}-3\frac{1}{2}-1\frac{1}{4}$

3) $4\frac{3}{8}-2\frac{1}{2}+5$

4) $6\frac{1}{2}-3\frac{1}{6}+2\frac{1}{12}-4\frac{3}{4}$

5) $1\frac{3}{16}-2\frac{2}{5}+3\frac{3}{4}+5\frac{5}{8}$

6) $12\frac{7}{10}-5\frac{1}{8}+3\frac{3}{20}+1\frac{1}{2}$

7) $2\frac{3}{16}-2\frac{3}{10}+\frac{5}{8}+1\frac{3}{4}$

8) $12\frac{3}{4}-6\frac{7}{8}+5\frac{21}{32}-2\frac{13}{16}$

9) $3\frac{9}{20}+1\frac{3}{8}-2\frac{7}{10}+1\frac{3}{4}$

10) $2\frac{9}{25}+3\frac{4}{5}-2\frac{7}{10}-\frac{3}{20}$

Multiplication

When multiplying together two or more fractions we first multiply all the numerators together and then we multiply all the denominators together. Mixed numbers must always be converted into top heavy fractions.

Example 13   Simplify $\frac{5}{8}\times\frac{3}{7}$

$$\frac{5}{8}\times\frac{3}{7}=\frac{5\times3}{8\times7}=\frac{15}{56}$$

Example 14   Simplify $\frac{2}{5}\times3\frac{2}{3}$

$$\frac{2}{5}\times3\frac{2}{3}=\frac{2}{5}\times\frac{11}{3}=\frac{2\times11}{5\times3}=\frac{22}{15}=1\frac{7}{15}$$

Example 15   Simplify $1\frac{3}{8}\times1\frac{1}{4}$

$$1\frac{3}{8}\times1\frac{1}{4}=\frac{11}{8}\times\frac{5}{4}=\frac{11\times5}{8\times4}=\frac{55}{32}=1\frac{23}{32}$$

Exercise 18

Simplify the following:

1) $\dfrac{2}{3} \times \dfrac{4}{5}$ 3) $\dfrac{2}{9} \times 1\dfrac{2}{3}$ 5) $1\dfrac{2}{5} \times 3\dfrac{1}{2}$ 7) $1\dfrac{2}{9} \times 1\dfrac{2}{5}$

2) $\dfrac{3}{4} \times \dfrac{5}{7}$ 4) $\dfrac{5}{9} \times \dfrac{11}{4}$ 6) $2\dfrac{1}{2} \times 2\dfrac{2}{3}$ 8) $1\dfrac{7}{8} \times 1\dfrac{4}{7}$

Cancelling

Example 16   Simplify $\dfrac{2}{3} \times 1\dfrac{7}{8}$

$$\frac{2}{3} \times 1\frac{7}{8} = \frac{2}{3} \times \frac{15}{8} = \frac{2 \times 15}{3 \times 8} = \frac{30}{24} = \frac{5}{4} = 1\frac{1}{4}$$

The step to reducing $\frac{30}{24}$ to its lowest terms has been done by dividing 6 into both the numerator and denominator.

The work can be made easier by *cancelling* before multiplication as shown below.

$$\overset{1}{\underset{1}{\cancel{2}}} \times \overset{5}{\underset{4}{\cancel{15}}} = \frac{1 \times 5}{1 \times 4} = \frac{5}{4} = 1\frac{1}{4}$$

We have divided 2 into 2 (a numerator) and 8 (a denominator) and also we have divided 3 into 15 (a numerator) and 3 (a denominator). You will see that we have divided the numerators and the denominators by the same amount. Notice carefully that we can only cancel between a numerator and a denominator.

Example 17   Simplify $\dfrac{16}{25} \times \dfrac{7}{8} \times 8\dfrac{3}{4}$

$$\overset{1}{\underset{5}{\cancel{16}}} \times \overset{7}{\underset{1}{\cancel{8}}} \times \overset{7}{\underset{2}{\cancel{35}}} = \frac{1 \times 7 \times 7}{5 \times 1 \times 2} = \frac{49}{10} = 4\frac{9}{10}$$

Sometimes in calculations with fractions the word 'of' appears. It should always be taken as meaning multiply. Thus

$$\frac{4}{5} \text{ of } 20 = \overset{}{\underset{1}{\cancel{5}}} \times \overset{4}{\underset{}{\cancel{20}}} = \frac{4 \times 4}{1 \times 1} = \frac{16}{1} = 16$$

Exercise 19

Simplify the following:

1) $\dfrac{3}{4} \times 1\dfrac{7}{9}$ 2) $5\dfrac{1}{5} \times \dfrac{10}{13}$ 3) $1\dfrac{5}{8} \times \dfrac{7}{26}$ 4) $1\dfrac{1}{2} \times \dfrac{2}{5} \times 2\dfrac{1}{2}$

5) $\frac{5}{8} \times \frac{7}{10} \times \frac{2}{21}$ 7) $3\frac{3}{4} \times 1\frac{3}{5} \times 1\frac{1}{8}$ 9) $\frac{3}{4}$ of 16   11) $\frac{2}{3}$ of $4\frac{1}{2}$

6) $2 \times 1\frac{1}{2} \times 1\frac{1}{3}$ 8) $\frac{15}{32} \times \frac{8}{11} \times 24\frac{1}{5}$ 10) $\frac{5}{7}$ of 140   12) $\frac{4}{5}$ of $2\frac{1}{2}$

Division of Fractions

To divide by a fraction, all we have to do is to invert it and multiply. Thus

$$\frac{3}{5} \div \frac{2}{7} = \frac{3}{5} \times \frac{7}{2} = \frac{3 \times 7}{5 \times 2} = \frac{21}{10} = 2\frac{1}{10}$$

Example 18   Divide $1\frac{4}{5}$ by $2\frac{1}{3}$

$$1\frac{4}{5} \div 2\frac{1}{3} = \frac{9}{5} \div \frac{7}{3} = \frac{9}{5} \times \frac{3}{7} = \frac{27}{35}$$

Exercise 20

Simplify the following:

1) $\frac{4}{5} \div 1\frac{1}{3}$ 3) $\frac{5}{8} \div \frac{15}{32}$ 5) $2\frac{1}{2} \div 3\frac{3}{4}$ 7) $3\frac{1}{15} \div 2\frac{5}{9}$

2) $2 \div \frac{1}{4}$ 4) $3\frac{3}{4} \div 2\frac{1}{2}$ 6) $5 \div 5\frac{1}{5}$ 8) $2\frac{3}{10} \div \frac{3}{5}$

Operations With Fractions

The sequence of operations when dealing with fractions is the same as those used with whole numbers. They are, in order:

(1) Work out brackets.
(2) Multiply and divide.
(3) Add and subtract.

Example 19   Simplify $\frac{1}{5} \div \left(\frac{1}{3} \div \frac{1}{2}\right)$

$$\frac{1}{5} \div \left(\frac{1}{3} \div \frac{1}{2}\right) = \frac{1}{5} \div \left(\frac{1}{3} \times \frac{2}{1}\right) = \frac{1}{5} \div \frac{2}{3} = \frac{1}{5} \times \frac{3}{2} = \frac{3}{10}$$

Example 20   Simplify $\dfrac{2\frac{4}{5} + 1\frac{1}{4}}{3\frac{3}{5}} - \dfrac{5}{16}$

With problems of this kind it is best to work in stages as shown below:

$$2\frac{4}{5} + 1\frac{1}{4} = 3\frac{16+5}{20} = 3\frac{21}{20} = 4\frac{1}{20}$$

$$\frac{4\frac{1}{20}}{3\frac{3}{5}} = \frac{81}{20} \div \frac{18}{5} = \frac{81}{20} \times \frac{5}{18} = \frac{9}{8}$$

$$\frac{9}{8} - \frac{5}{16} = \frac{18-5}{16} = \frac{13}{16}$$

Exercise 21

Simplify the following:

1) $3\frac{3}{14} + \left(1\frac{1}{49} \times \frac{7}{10}\right)$

4) $\left(1\frac{7}{8} \times 2\frac{2}{5}\right) - 3\frac{2}{3}$

7) $\dfrac{5\frac{3}{5} - 3\frac{1}{2} \times \frac{2}{3}}{2\frac{1}{3}}$

9) $\dfrac{3\frac{9}{16} \times \frac{4}{9}}{2 + 6\frac{1}{4} \times 1\frac{1}{5}}$

2) $\frac{1}{4} \div \left(\frac{1}{8} \times \frac{2}{5}\right)$

5) $\dfrac{2\frac{2}{3} + 1\frac{1}{5}}{5\frac{4}{5}}$

8) $\frac{2}{5} \times \left(\frac{2}{3} - \frac{1}{4}\right) + \frac{1}{2}$

10) $\dfrac{\frac{5}{9} - \frac{7}{15}}{1 - \left(\frac{5}{9} \times \frac{7}{15}\right)}$

3) $1\frac{2}{3} \div \left(\frac{3}{5} \div \frac{9}{10}\right)$

6) $3\frac{2}{3} \div \left(\frac{2}{3} + \frac{4}{5}\right)$

Summary

1) The denominator (bottom number) gives the fraction its name and gives the number of equal parts into which the whole has been divided. The numerator (top number) gives the number of equal parts that are to be taken.

2) The value of a fraction remains unaltered if both the numerator and the denominator are multiplied or divided by the same number.

3) The LCM of a set of numbers is the smallest number into which each of the numbers of the set will divide exactly.

4) To compare the values of fractions which have different denominators express all the fractions with the lowest common denominator and then compare the numerators of the new fractions.

5) To add fractions express each of them with their lowest common denominator and then add the resulting numerators.

6) To multiply fractions multiply the numerators together and then multiply the denominators together.

7) To divide, invert the divisor and then proceed as in multiplication.

8) The sequence of operations when dealing with fractions is: (i) work out brackets; (ii) multiply and divide; (iii) add and subtract.

Mental Test 2

Try to write down the answer to the questions which follow without writing anything else.

1) Simplify $\frac{3}{8} + \frac{1}{4}$

3) Simplify $\frac{7}{10} - \frac{2}{5}$

5) Add $\frac{3}{4}$ to the difference of $\frac{5}{8}$ and $\frac{3}{8}$

2) Simplify $\frac{2}{5} + \frac{3}{20}$

4) Simplify $\frac{1}{2} + \frac{1}{4} + \frac{1}{8}$

6) Simplify $\frac{1}{2} + \frac{3}{4} - \frac{2}{3}$

7) Simplify $\frac{1}{2} \times \frac{1}{5}$

8) Simplify $\frac{2}{3}\times\frac{3}{7}$ 10) What is $\frac{2}{3}$ of 12?   12) Simplify $\frac{1}{4}\div 2$ 14) Simplify $\frac{1}{4}\div\frac{1}{2}$

9) Multiply $\frac{2}{5}$ and $\frac{15}{16}$ 11) Find $\frac{3}{4}$ of 16   13) Divide $\frac{1}{4}$ by $\frac{3}{4}$ 15) Simplify $\frac{2}{3}\div\frac{4}{5}$

Self-Test 2

In questions 1 to 15 state the letter, or letters, corresponding to the correct answer or answers.

1) When the fraction $\frac{630}{1470}$ is reduced to its lowest terms the answer is

a $\frac{63}{147}$ b $\frac{3}{7}$ c $\frac{21}{49}$ d $\frac{9}{20}$

2) Which of the following fractions is equal to $\frac{4}{9}$?

a $\frac{12}{27}$ b $\frac{4}{36}$ c $\frac{36}{4}$ d $\frac{20}{90}$

e $\frac{52}{117}$

3) The fraction $\frac{3}{4}$ when written with denominator 56 is the same as

a $\frac{3}{56}$ b $\frac{56}{12}$ c $\frac{42}{56}$ d $\frac{56}{42}$

4) The LCM of 5, 15, 40 and 64 is

a 960   b 192 000   c 640
d 64

5) The mixed number $3\frac{5}{6}$ is equal to

a $\frac{15}{6}$ b $\frac{5}{18}$ c $\frac{15}{18}$ d $\frac{23}{6}$

6) The improper fraction $\frac{104}{14}$ is equal to

a $7\frac{3}{7}$ b $\frac{364}{49}$ c $7\frac{6}{14}$ d $\frac{52}{7}$

7) $\frac{1}{4}+\frac{2}{3}+\frac{3}{5}$ is equal to

a $\frac{1}{2}$ b $\frac{1}{10}$ c $\frac{91}{60}$ d $1\frac{31}{60}$

8) $1\frac{3}{8}+2\frac{5}{6}+3\frac{1}{4}$ is equal to

a $6\frac{4}{9}$ b $6\frac{15}{192}$ c $\frac{35}{24}$ d $\frac{21}{40}$

e $7\frac{11}{24}$

9) $1\frac{1}{8}+2\frac{1}{6}+3\frac{3}{4}$ is equal to

a $6\frac{5}{18}$ b $7\frac{1}{24}$ c $1\frac{1}{24}$ d $7\frac{5}{24}$

10) $\frac{7}{8}\times\frac{3}{5}$ is equal to

a $\frac{10}{13}$ b $\frac{4}{3}$ c $\frac{35}{24}$ d $\frac{21}{40}$

11) $\frac{5}{8}\times\frac{4}{15}$ is equal to one of the following, when the answer is expressed in its lowest terms:

a $\frac{20}{120}$ b $\frac{1}{6}$ c $\frac{32}{75}$ d $\frac{9}{23}$

12) $\frac{3}{4}\div\frac{8}{9}$ is equal to

a $\frac{24}{36}$ b $\frac{2}{3}$ c $\frac{27}{32}$ d $\frac{3}{2}$

13) $6\frac{4}{9}\div3\frac{2}{3}$ is equal to

a $2\frac{2}{3}$ b $\frac{638}{27}$ c $\frac{58}{33}$ d $18\frac{8}{27}$

14) $3\times\left(\frac{1}{2}-\frac{1}{3}\right)$ is equal to

a $1\frac{1}{2}-\frac{1}{3}$ b $\frac{1}{2}$

c $3\times\frac{1}{2}-3\times\frac{1}{3}$

15) $\frac{5}{8}+\frac{1}{2}\times\frac{1}{4}$ is equal to

a $\frac{9}{32}$ b $\frac{3}{4}$ c $\frac{9}{16}$ d $\frac{3}{32}$

In questions 16 to 25 decide whether the answer given is true or false.

16) In a fraction the number above the line is called the numerator.

17) In a proper fraction the numerator is always greater than the denominator

18) If the numerator of a fraction is greater than its denominator then the fraction is called an improper fraction.

19) An improper fraction always has a value greater than 1

20) The fraction $6\frac{2}{5}$ is called a mixed number

21) When the fractions $\frac{5}{8}$, $\frac{3}{4}$, $\frac{7}{10}$ and $\frac{3}{5}$ are put in order of size the result is $\frac{3}{5}$, $\frac{5}{8}$, $\frac{7}{10}$ and $\frac{3}{4}$

22) $\frac{27}{9}$ is the same as $27 \div 9$

23) $\frac{28}{35} \div \frac{7}{16}$ is the same as $\frac{28}{35} \times \frac{16}{7}$

24) $3 \times (\frac{1}{2} + \frac{1}{4})$ is the same as $3 \times \frac{3}{4}$

25) $\frac{5}{8} + \frac{1}{4} \times \frac{1}{2}$ is the same as $\frac{7}{8} \times \frac{1}{2}$

3. The Decimal System

Introduction

In this chapter we first deal with the addition, subtraction, multiplication and division of decimal numbers. Then rough checks for calculations are discussed and finally the conversion of fractions to decimals and vice-versa are discussed.

The Decimal System

The decimal system is an extension of our ordinary number system. When we write the number 666 we mean $600+60+6$. Reading from left to right each figure 6 is ten times the value of the next one.

We now have to decide how to deal with fractional quantities, that is, quantities whose values are less than one. If we regard 666·666 as meaning $600+60+6+\frac{6}{10}+\frac{6}{100}+\frac{6}{1000}$ then the dot, called the decimal point, separates the whole numbers from the fractional parts. Notice that with the fractional, or decimal parts, e.g. ·666, each figure 6 is ten times the value of the following one, reading from left to right. Thus $\frac{6}{10}$ is ten times as great as $\frac{6}{100}$, and $\frac{6}{100}$ is ten times as great as $\frac{6}{1000}$ and so on.

Decimals then are fractions which have denominators of 10, 100, 1000 and so on, according to the position of the figure after the decimal point.

If we have to write six hundred and five we write 605; the zero keeps the place for the missing tens. In the same way if we want to write $\frac{3}{10}+\frac{5}{1000}$ we write ·305; the zero keeps the place for the missing hundredths. Also $\frac{6}{100}+\frac{7}{1000}$ would be written ·067; the zero in this case keeps the place for the missing tenths.

When there are no whole numbers it is usual to insert a zero in front of the decimal point so that, for instance, ·35 would be written 0·35.

Exercise 22

Read off as decimals:

1) $\frac{7}{10}$

2) $\frac{3}{10}+\frac{7}{100}$

3) $\frac{5}{10}+\frac{8}{100}+\frac{9}{1000}$

4) $\frac{9}{1000}$

5) $\frac{3}{100}$

6) $\frac{1}{100}+\frac{7}{1000}$

7) $8+\frac{6}{100}$

8) $24+\frac{2}{100}+\frac{9}{10000}$

9) $50+\frac{8}{1000}$

Read off the following with denominators 10, 100, 1000, etc.

10) 0·2

11) 4·6

12) 3·58

13) 437·25

14) 0·004

15) 0·036

16) 400·029

17) 0·001

18) 0·0329

Addition and Subtraction of Decimals

Adding or subtracting decimals is done in exactly the same way as for whole numbers. Care must be taken, however, to write the decimal points directly underneath one another. This makes sure that all the figures having the same place value fall in the same column.

Example 1 Simplify $11·36+2·639+0·047$

$$
\begin{array}{r}
11·36 \\
2·639 \\
0·047 \\
\hline
14·046 \\
\hline
\end{array}
$$

Example 2 Subtract 8·567 from 19·126

$$
\begin{array}{r}
19·126 \\
8·567 \\
\hline
10·559 \\
\hline
\end{array}
$$

Exercise 23

Write down the values of:

1) $2·375+0·625$
2) $4·25+7·25$
3) $3·196+2·475+18·369$
4) $38·267+0·049+20·3$
5) $27·418+0·967+25+1·467$

6) $12·48-8·36$
7) $19·215-3·599$
8) $2·237-1·898$
9) $0·876-0·064$
10) $5·48-0·0691$

Multiplication and Division of Decimals

One of the advantages of decimals is the ease with which they may be multiplied or divided by 10, 100, 1000, etc.

Example 3 Find the value of $1·4 \times 10$

$$1·4 \times 10 = 1 \times 10 + 0·4 \times 10 = 10 + \frac{4}{10} \times 10 = 10 + 4 = 14$$

Example 4 Find the value of $27·532 \times 10$

$$27·532 \times 10 = 27 \times 10 + 0·5 \times 10 + 0·03 \times 10 + 0·002 \times 10$$

$$= 270 + \frac{5}{10} \times 10 + \frac{3}{100} \times 10 + \frac{2}{1000} \times 10$$

$$= 270 + 5 + \frac{3}{10} + \frac{2}{100} = 275·32$$

In both of the above examples you will notice that the figures have not been changed by the multiplication; only the *positions* of the figures have been changed. Thus in Example 3, $1·4 \times 10 = 14$, that is the decimal point has been moved one place to the right. In Example 4,

$27 \cdot 532 \times 10 = 275 \cdot 32$; again the decimal point has been moved one place to the right.

To multiply by 10, then, is the same as shifting the decimal point one place to the right. In the same way to multiply by 100 means shifting the decimal point two places to the right and so on.

Example 5 $17 \cdot 369 \times 100 = 1736 \cdot 9$

The decimal point has been moved two places to the right.

Example 6 $0 \cdot 07895 \times 1000 = 78 \cdot 95$

The decimal point has been moved three places to the right.

Exercise 24

Multiply each of the following numbers by 10, 100 and 1000.

Write down the values of

1) $4 \cdot 1$
2) $2 \cdot 42$
3) $0 \cdot 046$
4) $0 \cdot 35$
5) $0 \cdot 1486$
6) $0 \cdot 001\ 753$

7) $0 \cdot 4853 \times 100$
8) $0 \cdot 009 \times 1000$
9) $170 \cdot 06 \times 10$
10) $0 \cdot 563\ 96 \times 10\ 000$

When dividing by 10 the decimal point is moved one place to the left, by 100, two places to the left and so on. Thus,

$$154 \cdot 26 \div 10 = 15 \cdot 426$$

The decimal point has been moved one place to the left.

$$9 \cdot 432 \div 100 = 0 \cdot 094\ 32$$

The decimal point has been moved two places to the left.

$$35 \div 1000 = 0 \cdot 035$$

The decimal point has been moved three places to the left.

In the above examples note carefully that use has been made of zeros following the decimal point to keep the places for the missing tenths.

Exercise 25

Divide each of the following numbers by 10, 100 and 1000.

Give the value of:

1) $3 \cdot 6$
2) $64 \cdot 198$
3) $0 \cdot 07$
4) $510 \cdot 4$
5) $0 \cdot 352$

6) $5 \cdot 4 \div 100$
7) $2 \cdot 05 \div 1000$
8) $0 \cdot 04 \div 10$
9) $0 \cdot 0086 \div 1000$
10) $627 \cdot 428 \div 10\ 000$

Long Multiplication

Example 7   Find the value of $36 \cdot 5 \times 3 \cdot 504$

First disregard the decimal points and multiply 365 by 3504

$$
\begin{array}{r}
365 \\
3\,504 \\
\hline
1\,095\,000 \\
182\,500 \\
1\,460 \\
\hline
1\,278\,960 \\
\hline
\end{array}
$$

Now count up the total number of figures following the decimal points in both numbers (i.e. $1+3 = 4$). In the answer to the multiplication (the product), count this total number of figures from the right and insert the decimal point. The product is then 127·8960 or 127·896 since the zero does not mean anything.

Exercise 26

Find the values of the following:

1) $25·42 \times 29·23$

2) $0·3618 \times 2·63$

3) $0·76 \times 0·38$

4) $3·025 \times 2·45$

5) $0·043 \times 0·032$

Long Division

Example 8   Find the value of $19·24 \div 2·6$

First convert the divisor (2·6) into a whole number by multiplying it by 10. To compensate multiply the dividend (19·24) by 10 also so that we now have $192·4 \div 26$. Now proceed as in ordinary division.

$$
\begin{array}{r}
26)\overline{192\cdot4}\,(7\cdot4 \\
182 \qquad\quad \\
\hline
10\,4 \\
10\,4 \\
\hline
\cdots \\
\hline
\end{array}
$$

— this line 26×7

— 4 brought down from above. Since 4 lies to the right of the decimal point in the dividend insert a decimal point in the answer (the quotient)

Notice carefully how the decimal point in the quotient was obtained. The 4 brought down from the dividend lies to the right of the decimal point. Before bringing this down put a decimal point in the quotient immediately following the 7.

The division in this case is exact (i.e. there is no remainder) and the answer is 7·4. Now let us see what happens when there is a remainder.

Example 9   Find the value of $15·187 \div 3·57$

As before make the divisor into a whole number by multiplying it by 100 so that it becomes 357. To compensate multiply the dividend also by 100 so that it becomes 1518·7. Now divide.

```
357)1518·7(4·25406
     1428        —         this line 357 × 4

      907        —         7 brought down from the dividend. Since it
      714                  lies to the right of the decimal point insert a
      ——                   decimal point in the quotient.
     1930        —         bring down a zero as all the figures in the
     1785                  dividend have been used up.
     ——
     1450
     1428
     ——
      2200       —         Bring down a zero. The divisor will not go into
      2142                 220 so place 0 in the quotient and bring down
      ——                   another zero.
       58
```

The answer to 5 decimal places is 4·25406. This is not the correct answer because there is a remainder. The division can be continued in the way shown to give as many decimal places as desired, or until there is no remainder.

It is important to realise what is meant by an answer given to so many decimal places. It is the number of figures which follow the decimal point which give the number of decimal places. If the first figure to be discarded is 5 or more then the previous figure is increased by 1. Thus

$$85·7684 = 85·8 \text{ correct to 1 decimal place}$$
$$= 85·77 \text{ correct to 2 decimal places}$$
$$= 85·768 \text{ correct to 3 decimal places}$$

Notice carefully that zeros must be kept:

$$0·007362 = 0·007 \text{ correct to 3 decimal places}$$
$$= 0·01 \text{ correct to 2 decimal places}$$

$$7·601 = 7·60 \text{ correct to 2 decimal places}$$
$$= 7·6 \text{ correct to 1 decimal place}$$

If an answer is required correct to 3 decimal places the division should be continued to 4 decimal places and the answer corrected to 3 decimal places.

Exercise 27

Find the value of:

1) 18·89 ÷ 14·2 correct to 2 decimal places

2) 0·0396 ÷ 2·51 correct to 3 decimal places

3) 7·21 ÷ 0·038 correct to 2 decimal places

4) 13·059 ÷ 3·18 correct to 4 decimal places

5) 0·1382 ÷ 0·0032 correct to 1 decimal place

Significant Figures

Instead of using the number of decimal places to express the accuracy of an answer, significant figures can be used. The number

39·38 is correct to 2 decimal places but it is also correct to 4 significant figures since the number contains four figures. The rules regarding significant figures are as follows:

(i) If the first figure to be discarded is 5 or more the previous figure is increased by 1.

$$8·1925 = 8·193 \text{ correct to 4 significant figures}$$
$$= 8·19 \text{ correct to 3 significant figures}$$
$$= 8·2 \text{ correct to 2 significant figures}$$

(ii) Zeros must be kept to show the position of the decimal point, or to indicate that the zero is a significant figure.

$$24\,392 = 24\,390 \text{ correct to 4 significant figures}$$
$$= 24\,400 \text{ correct to 3 significant figures}$$

$$0·0858 = 0·086 \text{ correct to 2 significant figures}$$

$$425·804 = 425·80 \text{ correct to 5 significant figures}$$
$$= 426 \text{ correct to 3 significant figures}$$

Exercise 28

Write down the following numbers correct to the number of significant figures stated:

1) 24·865 82   i) to 6   ii) to 4   iii) to 2   5) 35·603 to 4

2) 0·008 3571 i) to 4   ii) to 3   iii) to 2   6) 28 387 617 i) to 5   ii) to 2

3) 4·978 48   i) to 5   ii) to 3   iii) to 1   7) 4·149 76   i) to 5   ii) to 4   iii) to 3

4) 21·987 to 2   8) 9·2048 to 3

Rough Checks for Calculations

The worst mistake that can be made in a calculation is that of misplacing the decimal point. To place it wrongly, even by one place, makes the answer ten times too large or ten times too small. To prevent this occurring it is always worth while doing a rough check by using approximate numbers. When doing these rough checks always try to select numbers which are easy to multiply or which will cancel.

Example 10   1) $0·23 \times 0·56$

For a rough check we will take $0·2 \times 0·6$
Product roughly $= 0·2 \times 0·6 = 0·12$
Correct product $= 0·1288$

(The rough check shows that the answer is 0·1288 not 1·288 or 0·012 88)

2) $173·3 \div 27·8$

For a rough check we will take $180 \div 30$
Quotient roughly $= 6$
Correct quotient $= 6·23$

(Note the rough check and the correct answer are of the same order)

3) $\dfrac{8 \cdot 198 \times 19 \cdot 56 \times 30 \cdot 82 \times 0 \cdot 198}{6 \cdot 52 \times 3 \cdot 58 \times 0 \cdot 823}$

Answer roughly $= \dfrac{8 \times 20 \times 30 \times 0 \cdot 2}{6 \times 4 \times 1} = 40$

Correct answer $= 50 \cdot 94$

(Although there is a big difference between the rough answer and the correct answer, the rough check shows that the answer is 50·94 and not 509·4 or 5·094)

Exercise 29

Find rough checks for the following:

1) $223 \cdot 6 \times 0 \cdot 0048$

2) $32 \cdot 7 \times 0 \cdot 259$

3) $0 \cdot 682 \times 0 \cdot 097 \times 2 \cdot 38$

4) $78 \cdot 41 \div 23 \cdot 78$

5) $0 \cdot 059 \div 0 \cdot 002\,68$

6) $33 \cdot 2 \times 29 \cdot 6 \times 0 \cdot 031$

7) $\dfrac{0 \cdot 728 \times 0 \cdot 006\,25}{0 \cdot 0281}$

8) $\dfrac{27 \cdot 5 \times 30 \cdot 52}{11 \cdot 3 \times 2 \cdot 73}$

Fraction to Decimal Conversion

We found, when doing fractions, that the line separating the numerator and the denominator of a fraction takes the place of a division sign. Thus

$$\frac{17}{80} \text{ is the same as } 17 \div 80$$

Therefore to convert a fraction into a decimal we divide the denominator into the numerator.

Example 11   Convert $\dfrac{27}{32}$ to decimals.

$$\frac{27}{32} = 27 \div 32$$

```
32)27·0 (0·84375
   25 6
   ────
    1 40
    1 28
    ────
     120
      96
     ───
     240
     224
     ───
      160
      160
      ───
      · · ·
      ───
```

Therefore $\dfrac{27}{32} = 0 \cdot 843\,75$

Example 12   Convert $2\frac{9}{16}$ into decimals.

When we have a mixed number to convert into decimals we need only deal with the fractional part. Thus to convert $2\frac{9}{16}$ into decimals we only have to deal with $\frac{9}{16}$.

$$\frac{9}{16} = 9 \div 16$$

$$
\begin{array}{r}
16)9{\cdot}0\,(0{\cdot}5625 \\
\underline{8\,0} \\
1\,00 \\
\underline{96} \\
40 \\
\underline{32} \\
80 \\
\underline{80} \\
\cdot\cdot
\end{array}
$$

The division shows that $\frac{9}{16} = 0{\cdot}5625$ and hence $2\frac{9}{16} = 2{\cdot}5625$

Sometimes a fraction will not divide out exactly as shown in Example 13.

Example 13   Convert $\frac{1}{3}$ to decimals.

$$\frac{1}{3} = 1 \div 3$$

$$
\begin{array}{r}
3)1{\cdot}0\,(0{\cdot}333 \\
\underline{9} \\
10 \\
\underline{9} \\
10 \\
\underline{9} \\
1
\end{array}
$$

It is clear that all we shall get from the division is a succession of threes.

This is an example of a recurring decimal and in order to prevent endless repetition the result is written $0{\cdot}\dot{3}$. Therefore $\frac{1}{3} = 0{\cdot}\dot{3}$.

Some further examples of recurring decimals are:

$$\frac{2}{3} = 0{\cdot}\dot{6} \text{ (meaning } 0{\cdot}6666\ldots\ldots \text{ etc.)}$$

$$\frac{1}{6} = 0{\cdot}1\dot{6} \text{ (meaning } 0{\cdot}1666\ldots\ldots \text{ etc.)}$$

$$\frac{5}{11} = 0{\cdot}\dot{4}\dot{5} \text{ (meaning } 0{\cdot}454545\ldots\ldots \text{ etc.)}$$

$$\frac{3}{7} = 0{\cdot}\dot{4}2857\dot{1} \text{ (meaning } 0{\cdot}428571428571\ldots\ldots \text{ etc.)}$$

For all practical purposes we never need recurring decimals; what we need is an answer given to so many significant figures or decimal places. Thus

$$\frac{2}{3} = 0.67 \text{ (correct to 2 decimal places)}$$

$$\frac{5}{11} = 0.455 \text{ (correct to 3 significant figures)}$$

Exercise 30

Convert the following to decimals correcting the answers, where necessary, to 4 decimal places:

1) $\frac{1}{4}$

2) $\frac{3}{4}$

3) $\frac{3}{8}$

4) $\frac{11}{16}$

5) $\frac{1}{2}$

6) $\frac{2}{3}$

7) $\frac{21}{32}$

8) $\frac{29}{64}$

9) $1\frac{5}{6}$

10) $2\frac{7}{16}$

Write down the following recurring decimals correct to 3 decimal places:

11) $0.\dot{3}$

12) $0.\dot{7}$

13) $0.1\dot{3}$

14) $0.1\dot{8}$

15) $0.3\dot{5}$

16) $0.\dot{2}\dot{3}$

17) $0.\dot{5}\dot{2}$

18) $0.3\dot{8}$

19) $0.3\dot{2}\dot{8}$

20) $0.5\dot{6}7\dot{1}$

Conversion of Decimals to Fractions

We know that decimals are fractions with denominators 10, 100, 1000 etc. Using this fact we can always convert a decimal to a fraction.

Example 14   Convert 0·32 to a fraction.

$$0.32 = \frac{32}{100} = \frac{8}{25}$$

When comparing decimals and fractions it is best to convert the fraction into a decimal.

Example 15   Find the difference between $1\frac{3}{16}$ and 1·1632

$$1\frac{3}{16} = 1.1875$$

$$1\frac{3}{16} - 1.1632 = 1.1875 - 1.1632 = 0.0243$$

Exercise 31

Convert the following to fractions in their lowest terms:

1) 0·2

2) 0·45

3) 0·3125

4) 2·55

5) 0·0075

6) 2·125

7) What is the difference between 0·28135 and $\frac{9}{32}$?

8) What is the difference between $\frac{19}{64}$ and 0·295 ?

Summary

1) Decimals are fractions with denominators of 10, 100, 1000 etc. The decimal point separates the whole numbers from the fractional parts.

2) When adding or subtracting decimal numbers the decimal points are written under one another.

3) To multiply by 10 move the decimal point one place to the right, to multiply by 100 move the decimal point two places to the right, etc.

4) To divide by 10 move the decimal point one place to the left, to divide by 100 move the decimal point two places to the left, etc.

5) When multiplying first disregard the decimal points and multiply the two numbers as though they were whole numbers. To place the decimal point in the product, count up the total number of figures after the decimal point in both numbers and then in the product count this number of figures starting from the extreme right.

6) When dividing first make the divisor into a whole number and compensate the dividend.

7) Significant figures and decimal places are used to denote the accuracy of a number.

8) Before multiplying or dividing always perform a rough check which will ensure that the decimal point is placed correctly.

9) To convert a fraction into a decimal divide the numerator by the denominator.

10) When comparing fractions and decimals, convert the fraction into a decimal.

Mental Test 3

Try to write down the answers to the following without writing anything else.

1) Add 1·2, 1·3 and 2·5.

2) Add 0·21, 0·32, 0·73 and 0·51.

3) Add 1·01, 1·20, 31 and 0·20.

4) Subtract 0·64 from 1·86.

5) Take 1·04 from 3·16.

6) Take 3·98 from 4·06.

7) Multiply 2·3 by 5.

8) Multiply 0·83 by 7.

9) Multiply 1·43 by 4.

10) Multiply 0·06 by 8.

11) Multiply 1·03 by 9.

12) Divide 0·84 by 7.

13) Divide 1·35 by 9.

14) Divide 19·2 by 8.

15) Divide 0·091 by 0·07.

Self-Test 3

In questions 1 to 10 state the letter, or letters, corresponding to the correct answer or answers.

1) The number 0·028 57 correct to 3 places of decimals is

    a 0·028 **b** 0·029 **c** 0·286 **d** 0·0286

2) The sum of $5 + \dfrac{1}{100} + \dfrac{7}{1000}$ is

    a 5·17 **b** 5·017 **c** 5·0107 **d** 5·107

3) $13 \cdot 0063 \times 1000$ is equal to
 a $13 \cdot 063$ b $1300 \cdot 63$
 c $130 \cdot 063$ d $13 \, 006 \cdot 3$

4) $1 \cdot 5003 \div 100$ is equal to
 a $0 \cdot 015 \, 003$ b $0 \cdot 150 \, 03$
 c $0 \cdot 153$ d $1 \cdot 53$

5) $18 \cdot 2 \times 0 \cdot 013 \times 5 \cdot 21$ is equal to
 a $12 \cdot 326 \, 86$ b $123 \cdot 2686$
 c $1 \cdot 232 \, 686$ d $0 \cdot 123 \, 268 \, 6$

6) The number $158 \, 861$ correct to 2 significant figures is
 a 15 b $150 \, 000$
 c 16 d $160 \, 000$

7) The number $0 \cdot 081 \, 778$ correct to 3 significant figures is
 a $0 \cdot 082$ b $0 \cdot 081$ c $0 \cdot 0818$ d $0 \cdot 0817$

8) The number $0 \cdot 075 \, 538$ correct to 2 decimal places is
 a $0 \cdot 076$ b $0 \cdot 075$ c $0 \cdot 07$ d $0 \cdot 08$

9) The number $0 \cdot 1\dot{6}$ correct to 4 significant figures is
 a $0 \cdot 1616$ b $0 \cdot 1617$ c $0 \cdot 1667$ d $0 \cdot 1666$

10) $0 \cdot 017 \div 0 \cdot 027$ is equal to (correct to 2 significant figures)
 a $0 \cdot 63$ b $6 \cdot 3$ c $0 \cdot 063$ d 63

In questions 11 to 20 the answer is either true or false. State which.

11) $\dfrac{5}{100} + \dfrac{5}{10000} = 0 \cdot 0505$

12) $5 + \dfrac{1}{10} + \dfrac{3}{1000} = 5 \cdot 13$

13) $8 \cdot 26 - 1 \cdot 38 - 2 \cdot 44 = 4 \cdot 44$

14) $11 \cdot 011 \times 100 = 1111$

15) $0 \cdot 10101 \div 100 = 0 \cdot 010 \, 101$

16) $0 \cdot 0302 = \dfrac{3}{100} + \dfrac{2}{1000}$

17) $20 \, 963 = 21 \, 000$, correct to 2 significant figures

18) $0 \cdot 099 \, 83 = 0 \cdot 10$, correct to 2 significant figures

19) $0 \cdot 007 \, 891 = 0 \cdot 008$, correct to 3 decimal places

20) $0 \cdot 5 \div 0 \cdot 2 = 2 \cdot 5$

4. Squares, Square Roots, Reciprocals

Introduction

In the chapter we deal with the tables of squares, square roots and reciprocals. The methods of using the tables to find the square, square root and reciprocal of a number outside the range of the tables is also discussed.

Squares of Numbers

When a number is multiplied by itself the result is called the square of the number. The square of 9 is $9 \times 9 = 81$. Instead of writing 9×9 it is usual to write 9^2 which is read as the square of 9. Thus

$$12^2 = 12 \times 12 = 144$$

$$(1 \cdot 3)^2 = 1 \cdot 3 \times 1 \cdot 3 = 1 \cdot 69$$

The square of any number can be found by multiplication but a great deal of time and effort is saved by using printed tables. Either three or four figure tables may be used. In the three figure tables the squares of numbers are given correct to three significant figures, but in the four figure tables the squares are given correct to four significant figures. Hence the four figure tables are more accurate. Part of the tables of squares of numbers (four figure tables) is shown over.

How to Use the Tables of Squares of Numbers

1) **To find the square of a number having two significant figures.**

To find $(1 \cdot 6)^2$, find $1 \cdot 6$ in the first column (see sample table) and move along this row to the number under the column headed 0. We find the number $2 \cdot 560$. Hence $(1 \cdot 6)^2 = 2 \cdot 560$. Similarly, $(2 \cdot 3)^2 = 5 \cdot 290$.

2) **To find the square of a number having three significant figures.**

To find $(2 \cdot 15)^2$ find $2 \cdot 1$ in the first column (see sample table) and move along this row to the number under the column headed 5. We find the number $4 \cdot 623$. Hence $(2 \cdot 15)^2 = 4 \cdot 623$. The procedure is exactly the same when using three figure tables.

3) **To find the square of a number having four significant figures.**

To find $(2 \cdot 018)^2$, find $2 \cdot 0$ in the first column (see sample table) and move along this row to the number in the column headed 1. We find this number to be $4 \cdot 040$. Now move along the same row to the number in the column headed 8 of the proportional parts and read 33. Add this 33 (that is $0 \cdot 033$) to $4 \cdot 040$ giving $4 \cdot 073$. Hence $(2 \cdot 018)^2 = 4 \cdot 073$. Similarly $(1 \cdot 356)^2 = 1 \cdot 839$.

4) Squares of numbers outside the range of the tables.

Although the tables only give the squares of numbers from 1 to 10 they can be used to find the squares of numbers outside this range. The method is shown in the examples which follow.

Example 1   Find $(168{\cdot}8)^2$

$$(168{\cdot}8)^2 = 168{\cdot}8 \times 168{\cdot}8 = 1{\cdot}688 \times 100 \times 1{\cdot}688 \times 100 = (1{\cdot}688)^2 \times 100^2$$

From the tables of squares, $(1{\cdot}688)^2 = 2{\cdot}848$

Hence $(168{\cdot}8)^2 = 2{\cdot}848 \times 100^2 = 28480$

Example 2   Find $(0{\cdot}2388)^2$

$$(0{\cdot}2388)^2 = 2{\cdot}388 \times \frac{1}{10} \times 2{\cdot}388 \times \frac{1}{10} = (2{\cdot}388)^2 \times \frac{1}{100} = (2{\cdot}388)^2 \div 100$$

From the tables $(2{\cdot}388)^2 = 5{\cdot}702$

Hence $(0{\cdot}2388)^2 = 5{\cdot}702 \div 100 = 0{\cdot}057\,02$

| | | | | | | | | | | | | | ADD | | | | | |
x	0	1	2	3	4	5	6	7	8	9	1	2	3	4	5	6	7	8	9
1·0	1·000	1·020	1·040	1·061	1·082	1·103	1·124	1·145	1·166	1·188	2	4	6	8	10	13	15	17	19
1·1	1·210	1·232	1·254	1·277	1·300	1·323	1·346	1·369	1·392	1·416	2	5	7	9	11	14	16	18	21
1·2	1·440	1·464	1·488	1·513	1·538	1·563	1·588	1·613	1·638	1·664	2	5	7	10	12	15	17	20	22
1·3	1·690	1·716	1·742	1·769	1·796	1·823	1·850	1·877	1·904	1·932	3	5	8	11	13	16	19	22	24
1·4	1·960	1·988	2·016	2·045	2·074	2·103	2·132	2·161	2·190	2·220	3	6	9	12	14	17	20	23	26
1·5	2·250	2·280	2·310	2·341	2·372	2·403	2·434	2·465	2·496	2·528	3	6	9	12	15	19	22	25	28
1·6	2·560	2·592	2·624	2·657	2·690	2·723	2·756	2·789	2·822	2·856	3	7	10	13	16	20	23	26	30
1·7	2·890	2·924	2·958	2·993	3·028	3·063	3·098	3·133	3·168	3·204	3	7	10	14	17	21	24	28	31
1·8	3·240	3·276	3·312	3·349	3·386	3·423	3·460	3·497	3·534	3·572	4	7	11	15	18	22	26	30	33
1·9	3·610	3·648	3·686	3·725	3·764	3·803	3·842	3·881	3·920	3·960	4	8	12	16	19	23	27	31	35
2·0	4·000	4·040	4·080	4·121	4·162	4·203	4·244	4·285	4·326	4·368	4	8	12	16	20	25	29	33	37
2·1	4·410	4·452	4·494	4·537	4·580	4·623	4·666	4·709	4·752	4·796	4	9	13	17	21	26	30	34	39
2·2	4·840	4·884	4·928	4·973	5·018	5·063	5·108	5·153	5·198	5·244	4	9	13	18	22	27	31	36	40
2·3	5·290	5·336	5·382	5·429	5·476	5·523	5·507	5·617	5·664	5·712	5	9	14	19	23	28	33	38	42
2·4	5·760	5·808	5·856	5·905	5·954	6·003	6·052	6·101	6·150	6·200	5	10	15	20	24	29	34	39	44

Exercise 32

Find the square of the following numbers.

1) 1·5
2) 2·1
3) 8·6
4) 3·15
5) 7·68

6) 5·23
7) 4·263
8) 7·916
9) 8·017
10) 8·704

11) 23
12) 40·6
13) 3093
14) 112·3
15) 98·12

16) 0·019
17) 0·7292
18) 0·004 219
19) 0·2834
20) 0·000 578 4

Square Roots

The square root of a number is the number whose square equals the given number. Thus since $5^2 = 25$, the square root of $25 = 5$.

The sign $\sqrt{}$ is used to denote a square root and hence we write $\sqrt{25} = 5$.

Similarly, since $9^2 = 81$, $\sqrt{81} = 9$.

The square root of a number can usually be found with sufficient accuracy by using the printed tables of square roots. There are two of these tables. One gives the square roots of numbers 1 to 10 and the other gives the square roots of numbers from 10 to 100. The reason for having two tables is as follows:

$$\sqrt{2\cdot5} = 1\cdot581$$
$$\sqrt{25} = 5$$

Thus there are two square roots for the same figures, depending upon the position of the decimal point. The square root tables are used in the same way as the table of squares.

Examples 3

(i) $\sqrt{2\cdot748} = 1\cdot657$ (directly from the tables from 1 to 10)

(ii) $\sqrt{92\cdot65} = 9\cdot626$ (directly from the tables from 10 to 100)

(iii) To find $\sqrt{836\cdot3}$

Mark off the figures in pairs to the *left* of the decimal point. Each pair of figures is called a *period*. Thus 836·3 becomes 8′36·3. The first period is 8 so we use the table of square roots from 1 to 10 and look up $\sqrt{8\cdot363} = 2\cdot892$. To position the decimal point in the answer remember that for each period to the left of the decimal point in the original number there will be one figure to the left of the decimal point in the answer. Thus

$$\frac{2 \quad 8\cdot92}{8'36\cdot3}$$

$$\sqrt{836\cdot3} = 28\cdot92$$

(iv) To find $\sqrt{173\,900}$

Marking off in periods 173 900 becomes 17′39′00. The first period is 17 so we use the table of square roots from 10 to 100 and look up $\sqrt{17\cdot3900} = 4\cdot170$

$$\frac{4 \quad 1 \quad 7\cdot0}{17'39'00}$$

$$\sqrt{173\,900} = 417\cdot0$$

(v) To find $\sqrt{0\cdot000\,094\,31}$

In the case of numbers less than 1. mark off the periods to the right of the decimal point. 0·000 094 31 become 0·00′00′94′31. Apart from the zero pairs the first period is 94 so we use the tables from 10 to 100 to look up $\sqrt{94\cdot31} = 9\cdot712$. For each zero pair in the original number there will be one zero following the decimal point in the answer. Thus

$$\frac{0\cdot \ 0 \ \ 0 \ \ 9 \ \ 712}{0\cdot00'00'94'31}$$

$$\sqrt{0\cdot000\,094\,31} = 0\cdot009\,712$$

(vi) To find $\sqrt{0\cdot073\,65}$

Marking off in periods to the right of the decimal point 0·073 65 becomes 07'36'50. Since the first period is 07 we use the tables between 1 and 10 and look up $\sqrt{7 \cdot 365} = 2 \cdot 714$

$$0 \cdot \ 2 \ \ 7 \ \ 14$$
$$0'07'36'50'$$

$$\sqrt{0 \cdot 073\,65} = 0 \cdot 2714$$

Exercise 33

Find the square roots of the following numbers:

1) 3·4	7) 35	13) 900	19) 0·1537
2) 8·19	8) 89·2	14) 725·3	20) 0·001 698
3) 5·264	9) 53·17	15) 7142	21) 0·039 47
4) 9·239	10) 82·99	16) 89 000	22) 0·000 783 1
5) 7·015	11) 79·23	17) 3945	23) 0·001 978
6) 3·009	12) 50·01	18) 893 400 000	

The Square Root of a Product

The square root of a product is the product of the square roots. For example

$$\sqrt{4 \times 9} = \sqrt{4} \times \sqrt{9} = 2 \times 3 = 6$$

Also, $\sqrt{25 \times 16 \times 49} = \sqrt{25} \times \sqrt{16} \times \sqrt{49} = 5 \times 4 \times 7$

Exercise 34

Find the values of the following:

1) $\sqrt{4 \times 25}$	4) $\sqrt{16 \times 36}$	7) $\sqrt{36 \times 49 \times 64}$
2) $\sqrt{9 \times 25}$	5) $\sqrt{16 \times 25 \times 36}$	8) $\sqrt{4 \times 16 \times 25 \times 49 \times 81}$
3) $\sqrt{49 \times 49}$	6) $\sqrt{4 \times 9 \times 25}$	

The Square Root of a Fraction

To find the square root of a fraction, find the square roots of the numerator and denominator separately as shown in Example 4.

Example 4 Find the square root of $\frac{16}{25}$

$$\sqrt{\frac{16}{25}} = \frac{\sqrt{16}}{\sqrt{25}} = \frac{4}{5}$$

If the numbers under a square root sign are connected by a plus or a minus sign then we cannot find the square root by the methods used for products and quotients. We cannot say that $\sqrt{9 + 16} = \sqrt{9} + \sqrt{16} = 3 + 4 = 7$. We must add before finding the square root. Thus

$$\sqrt{9 + 16} = \sqrt{25} = 5$$
$$\text{and } \sqrt{25 - 9} = \sqrt{16} = 4$$

Exercise 35

Find the square roots of the following:

1) $\dfrac{4}{9}$ 5) $\dfrac{81}{100}$ 9) $\dfrac{48}{75}$ 14) $43+38$

2) $\dfrac{9}{16}$ 6) $\dfrac{12}{27}$ 10) $\dfrac{10}{360}$ 15) $65-29$

3) $\dfrac{25}{49}$ 7) $\dfrac{100}{256}$ 11) $25+144$

12) $169-25$

4) $\dfrac{36}{81}$ 8) $\dfrac{125}{245}$ 13) $25-16$

Reciprocals of Numbers

The reciprocal of a number is $\dfrac{1}{\text{number}}$. Thus the reciprocal of

$$5 = \frac{1}{5}$$

and the reciprocal of $21\cdot3$ is $\dfrac{1}{21\cdot3}$.

The table of reciprocals of numbers is used in much the same way as the table of squares of numbers, except that the proportional parts are subtracted and not added. The table gives the reciprocals of numbers from 1 to 10 in decimal form.

From the tables:

the reciprocal of $6 = 0\cdot1667$

the reciprocal of $3\cdot157 = 0\cdot3168$

The method of finding the reciprocals of numbers less than 1 or greater than 10 is shown in Example 5.

Examples 5   (i) To find the reciprocal of $639\cdot2$.

$$\frac{1}{639\cdot2} = \frac{1}{6\cdot392} \times \frac{1}{100}$$

From the table of reciprocals we find that the reciprocal of $6\cdot392$ is $0\cdot1565$

$$\frac{1}{639\cdot2} = 0\cdot1565 \times \frac{1}{100} = \frac{0\cdot1565}{100} = 0\cdot001\,565$$

(ii) To find the reciprocal of $0\cdot039\,82$

$$\frac{1}{0\cdot039\,82} = \frac{1}{3\cdot982} \times \frac{100}{1}$$

From the table of reciprocals we find the reciprocal of $3\cdot982$ to be $0\cdot2512$.

$$\frac{1}{0\cdot039\,82} = 0\cdot2512 \times 100 = 25\cdot12$$

Exercise 36

Find the reciprocals of the following numbers:

1) 3·4	5) 7·015	9) 900	13) 0·039 47
2) 8·19	6) 35	10) 7142	14) 0·000 783 1
3) 5·264	7) 89·2	11) 0·1537	15) 0·001 978
4) 9·239	8) 53·17	12) 0·001 698	

Use of Tables in Calculations

Calculations may often be speeded up by making use of the tables of squares, square roots and reciprocals.

Example 6   Find the value of $\sqrt{(8·135)^2+(12·36)^2}$

$$\sqrt{(8·135)^2+(12·36)^2} = \sqrt{66·18+152·8}\ldots \text{ (by using the table of squares)}$$

$$= \sqrt{218·98} = 14·80\ldots \text{ (by using the table of square roots)}$$

Example 7   Find the value of $\dfrac{1}{\sqrt{7·517}}+\dfrac{1}{(3·625)^2}$

$$\frac{1}{\sqrt{7·517}}+\frac{1}{(3·625)^2} = \frac{1}{2·741}+\frac{1}{13·14}\ldots \text{ (by using the square and square root tables)}$$

$$= 0·3649+0·0761. \text{ (by using the reciprocal table)}$$

$$= 0·4410$$

Exercise 37

Find the values of:

1) $\dfrac{1}{(15·28)^2}$

2) $\dfrac{1}{(0·1372)^2}$

3) $\dfrac{1}{(250)^2}$

4) $\dfrac{1}{\sqrt{8·406}}$

5) $\dfrac{1}{\sqrt{18·73}}$

6) $\dfrac{1}{\sqrt{0·01798}}$

7) $\dfrac{1}{(30·15)^2+(8·29)^2}$

8) $\dfrac{1}{(11·26)^2+(8·18)^2}$

9) $\sqrt{(2·65)^2+(5·16)^2}$

10) $\sqrt{(11·18)^2-(5·23)^2}$

11) $\dfrac{1}{8·2}+\dfrac{1}{9·9}$

12) $\dfrac{1}{0·7325}-\dfrac{1}{0·9817}$

13) $\dfrac{1}{\sqrt{7·517}}+\dfrac{1}{(8·209)^2}+\dfrac{1}{0·0749}$

14) $\dfrac{1}{71·36}+\dfrac{1}{\sqrt{863·5}}+\dfrac{1}{(7·589)^2}$

Mental Test 4

Try to write down the answers to the following without writing anything else.

1) The square of 13.

2) The square of 0·2.

3) The square of 30.

4) The square of 0·05.

5) The square of 400.

6) The square root of 1600.

7) The square root of 0·25.

8) The square root of 90 000.

9) The square root of 0·00 16.

10) The square root of 25+144.

11) The square root of 25−9.

12) The square root of 16×25.

13) The square root of 4×9×49.

14) The square root of $\frac{4}{9}$.

15) The reciprocal of 20.

16) The reciprocal of 0·2.

17) The reciprocal of 500.

18) The reciprocal of 0·05.

Self-Test 4

In the following state the letter (or letters) corresponding to the correct answer (or answers).

1) The square of 80 is
    a 64   **b** 640   **c** 6400

2) The square of 700 is
    a 490 000   **b** 49 000   **c** 4900

3) The square of 0·8 is
    a 6·4   **b** 0·64   **c** 0·064

4) The square of 0·09 is
    a 0·081   **b** 0·0081   **c** 0·81

5) The square root of 0·25 is
    a 0·5   **b** 0·05   **c** 0·158

6) The square root of 0·036 is
    a 0·6   **b** 0·06   **c** 0·1897

7) The square root of 0·0049 is
    a 0·7   **b** 0·07   **c** 0·2214

8) The square root of 1690 is
    a 130   **b** 13   **c** 41·11

9) The square root of 810 is
    a 28·46   **b** 90   **c** 9

10) The square root of 12 100 is
    a 1100   **b** 110   **c** 347·9

11) The reciprocal of 12·5 is
    a 8   **b** 0·08   **c** 0·8

12) The reciprocal of 0·25 is
    a 40   **b** 4   **c** 0·4

13 The reciprocal of 0·02 is
    a 5   **b** 50   **c** 500

14) The reciprocal of 250 is
    a 0·4   **b** 0·04   **c** 0·004

15) $(18·3)^2 − (8·3)^2$ is equal to
    a 100   **b** 266   **c** 26·6

16) An approximate value for $\sqrt{2563}$ is
    a 16·2   **b** 50·6   **c** 520

17) The reciprocal of 0·3128 is
    a 0·3197   **b** 3·197   **c** 31·97

18) $(30·16)^2 + \dfrac{1}{0·0478}$ is equal to
    a 93·06   **b** 111·89   **c** 930·5

5. Directed Numbers

Introduction

Directed numbers are numbers which have either a plus or a minus sign attached to them such as $+7$ and -5. In this chapter we shall study the rules for the addition, subtraction, multiplication and division of directed numbers. We need these rules in connection with logarithms which will be dealt with in Chapter 6.

Positive and Negative Numbers

Fig. 5.1 shows part of a Celcius (centigrade) thermometer. The freezing point of water is $0°C$ (nought degrees Celcius). Temperatures above freezing point may be read off the scale directly and so may those below freezing. We now have to decide on a method for showing whether a temperature is above or below zero. We may say that a temperature is 6 degrees above zero or 5 degrees below zero but these statements are not compact enough for calculations. Therefore we say that a temperature of $+6°$ is a temperature which is $6°$ above zero and a temperature of 5 degrees below zero would be written $-5°$. We have thus used the signs $+$ and $-$ to indicate a change of direction.

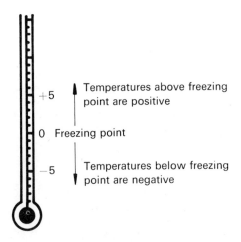

Fig. 5.1

Again if starting from a given point, distances measured to the right are regarded as being positive then distances measured to the left are regarded as being negative. As stated in the introduction, numbers which have a sign attached to them are called directed numbers. Thus $+7$ is a positive number and -7 is a negative number.

The Addition of Directed Numbers

In Fig. 5.2, a movement from left to right (i.e. in the direction 0A) is regarded as positive, whilst a movement from right to left (i.e. in the direction 0B) is regarded as negative.

To find the value of $+6+3$

Measure 6 units to the right of 0 (Fig. 5.2) and then measure a further 3 units to the right. The final position is 9 units to the right of 0. Hence,

$$+6+3 = +9$$

To find the value of $-5+(-4)$

Again in Fig. 5.2, measure 5 units to the left of 0 and then measure a further 4 units to the left. The final position is 9 units to the left of 0. Hence,

$$-5+(-4) = -9$$

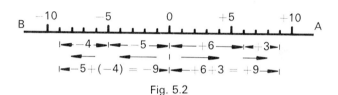

Fig. 5.2

From these results we obtain the rule:

To add several numbers together whose signs are the same add the numbers together. The sign of the sum is the same as the sign of each of the numbers.

Positive signs are frequently omitted as shown in the following examples.

1) $+5+9 = +14$

   More often this is written
   $5+9 = 14$

2) $-7+(-9) = -16$

   More often this is written
   $-7-9 = -16$

3) $-7-6-4 = -17$

Exercise 38

Find the values of the following:

1) $+8+7$
2) $-7-5$
3) $-15-17$
4) $8+6$
5) $-9-6-5-4$
6) $3+6+8+9$
7) $-2-5-8-3$
8) $9+6+5+3$

The Addition of Numbers Having Different Signs

To find the value of $-4+11$

Measure 4 units to the left of 0 (Fig. 5.3) and from this point measure

11 units to the right. The final position is 7 units to the right of 0. Hence,

$$-4+11 = 7$$

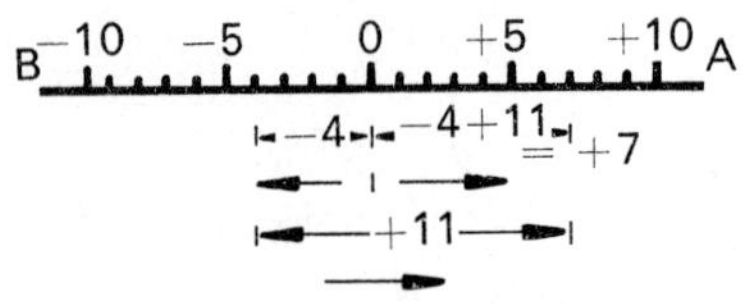

Fig. 5.3

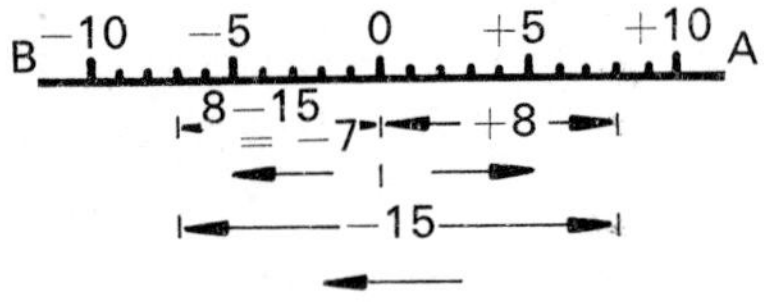

Fig. 5.4

To find the value of 8—15

Measure 8 units to the right of 0 (Fig. 5.4) and from this point measure 15 units to the left. The final position is 7 units to the left of 0. Hence,

$$8-15 = -7$$

From these results we obtain the rule:
To add two numbers together whose signs are different, subtract the numerically smaller from the larger. The sign of the result will be the same as the sign of the numerically larger number.

Examples

1) $-12+6 = -6$

2) $11-16 = -5$

When dealing with several numbers having mixed signs add the positive and negative numbers together separately. The set of numbers is then reduced to two numbers, one positive and the other negative, which are added in the way shown above.

Example

$$-16+11-7+3+8 = -23+22 = -1$$

Exercise 39

Find values for the following:

1) 6—11	4) 12—7	7) 23—21—8+2
2) 7—16	5) —8+9—2	8) —7+11—9—3+15
3) —5+10	6) 15—7—8	

Subtraction of Directed Numbers

To find the value of —4—(+7)

To represent +7 we measure 7 units to the right of 0 (Fig. 5.5). Therefore to represent —(+7) we must reverse direction and measure 7 units to the left of 0 and hence —(+7) is the same as —7. Hence,

$$-4-(+7) = -4-7 = -11$$

To find the value of +3—(—10)

To represent —10 we measure 10 units to the left of 0 (Fig. 5.5). Therefore to represent —(—10) we measure 10 units to the right of 0 and hence —(—10) is the same as +10. Hence,

$$+3-(-10) = 3+10 = 13$$

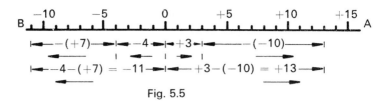

Fig. 5.5

The rule is:

To subtract a directed number change its sign and add the resulting number.

Examples

1) $-10-(-6) = -10+6 = -4$

2) $7-(+8) = 7-8 = -1$

3) $8-(-3) = 8+3 = 11$

Exercise 40

Find values for the following:

1) $8-(+6)$ 3) $8-(-6)$ 5) $-4-(-5)$ 7) $-10-(-5)$

2) $-5-(-8)$ 4) $-3-(-7)$ 6) $-2-(+3)$ 8) $7-(-9)$

Multiplication of Directed Numbers

$$\text{Now } 5+5+5 = 15$$

$$\text{That is, } 3\times5 = 15$$

Thus two positive numbers multiplied together give a positive product.

$$\text{Now } (-5)+(-5)+(-5) = -15$$

$$\text{That is, } 3\times(-5) = -15$$

Thus a positive number multiplied by a negative number gives a negative product. Suppose, now, that we wish to find the value of $(-3)\times(-5)$. We can write (-3) as $-(+3)$ and hence

$$(-3)\times(-5) = -(+3)\times(-5) = -(-15) = +15$$

Thus a negative number multiplied by a negative number gives a positive product.

We may summarise the above results as follows:

$$(+)\times(+) = (+) \qquad (-)\times(+) = (-)$$
$$(+)\times(-) = (-) \qquad (-)\times(-) = (+)$$

and the rule is:

The product of two numbers with like signs is positive whilst the product of two numbers with unlike signs is negative.

Examples

1) $7\times4 = 28$

2) $7\times(-4) = -28$

3) $(-7)\times4 = -28$

4) $(-7)\times(-4) = 28$

Exercise 41

Find the values of the following:

1) $7 \times (-6)$ 4) $(-7) \times (-6)$ 7) $3 \times (-4) \times (-2) \times 5$

2) $(-6) \times 7$ 5) $(-2) \times (-4) \times (-6)$ 8) $(-3)^2$

3) 7×6 6) $(-2)^2$

Division of Directed Numbers

The rules for division must be very similar to those used for multiplication, since if $3 \times (-5) = -15$, then $\frac{-15}{3} = -5$. Also $\frac{-15}{-5} = 3$

The rule is:

When dividing, numbers with like signs give a positive quotient and numbers with unlike signs give a negative quotient.

The rule may be summarised as follows:

$$(+) \div (+) = (+) \qquad (+) \div (-) = (-)$$
$$(-) \div (+) = (-) \qquad (-) \div (-) = (+)$$

Examples

1) $\frac{20}{4} = 5$

2) $\frac{20}{-4} = -5$

3) $\frac{-20}{4} = -5$

4) $\frac{-20}{-4} = 5$

5) $\frac{(-9) \times (-4) \times 5}{3 \times (-2)} = \frac{36 \times 5}{-6} = \frac{180}{-6} = -30$

Exercise 42

1) $6 \div (-2)$ 6) $1 \div (-1)$ 11) $\frac{(-8)}{(-4) \times (-2)}$

2) $(-6) \div 2$ 7) $(-4) \div (-2)$

       8) $(-3) \div 3$ 12) $\frac{(-3) \times (-4) \times (-2)}{3 \times 4}$

3) $(-6) \div (-2)$

       9) $8 \div (-4)$ 13) $\frac{4 \times (-6) \times (-8)}{(-3) \times (-2) \times (-4)}$

4) $6 \div 2$

       10) $\frac{(-6) \times 4}{(-2)}$ 14) $\frac{5 \times (-3) \times 6}{10 \times 3}$

5) $(-10) \div 5$

Summary

1) Directed numbers are numbers with a sign attached to them. $+7$ is a positive number and -3 is a negative number.

2) To add several numbers together whose signs are the same, add the numbers together. The sign of the sum is the same as the sign of each of the numbers.

3) To add two numbers together whose signs are different, subtract the numerically smaller number from the numerically larger. The sign of the result is the same as the sign of the numerically larger number.

4) To subtract a directed number change its sign and add the resulting number.

5) The product of two numbers having like signs is positive. The product of two numbers having unlike signs is negative.

6) The quotient of two numbers having like signs is positive. The quotient of two numbers having unlike signs is negative.

Mental Test 5

Try to write down the answers to the following without writing anything else. Find values for the following:

1) $7+5$

2) $-4+8$

3) $-13-12$

4) $-8-9$

5) $7-11$

6) $8-16$

7) $-5-12$

8) $-3+7$

9) $11-5$

10) $-8-10$

11) $-7-5-4$

12) $-6+8-5$

13) $17-8-5$

14) $20-19+8-3$

15) $8-(+5)$

16) $(-4)-(-7)$

17) $8-(-3)$

18) $-6-(-2)$

19) $-5-(+6)$

20) $-3-(-6)-(-4)$

21) 5×4

22) $(-5)\times4$

23) $5\times(-4)$

24) $(-5)\times(-4)$

25) $(-5)^2$

26) $(-8)^2$

27) $3\times(-4)+2\times(-3)$

28) $(-3)\times2-(-2)\times4$

29) $6\div3$

30) $6\div(-3)$

31) $(-6)\div(-2)$

32) $(-6)\div3$

33) $(-6)\div(-2)$

34) $2\div(-2)$

35) $(-1)\div1$

36) $\dfrac{(-3)\times(-4)}{(-2)}$

Self Test 5

The answers to the following are either true or false. Write down the appropriate word for each problem.

1) $-5-6=11$

2) $-8+3=-5$

3) $-7-(+5)=12$

4) $-5-(-8)=3$

5) $(-6)\times(-7)=42$

6) $(-8)\times5=40$

7) $3\times(-4)=12$

8) $8\div(-2)=-4$

9) $(-9)\div(-3)=3$

10) $(-6)^2=36$

6. Indices and Logarithms

Introduction

Many calculations require the multiplication and division of awkward numbers. The calculation is frequently laborious if ordinary multiplication and division is used and the processes may be greatly speeded up by using logarithms. Since the theory of logarithms depends upon the theory of indices we will first deal with the laws of indices.

Powers of Numbers

The quantity $2\times2\times2\times2$ is written 2^4 and it is called the fourth power of 2. The figure 4, which gives the number of 2's to be multiplied together is called the index (plural: indices).

$$5^6 = 5\times5\times5\times5\times5\times5$$
$$7^3 = 7\times7\times7$$

Laws of Indices

(i) Multiplication

Let us see what happens when we multiply powers of the same number together.

$$5^2\times5^4 = (5\times5)\times(5\times5\times5\times5) = 5^6$$
$$2^3\times2^5 = (2\times2\times2)\times(2\times2\times2\times2\times2) = 2^8$$

In both the examples above we see that we could have obtained the result by adding the indices together. Thus

$$5^2\times5^4 = 5^{2+4} = 5^6$$
$$2^3\times2^5 = 2^{3+5} = 2^8$$

The law is:

When multiplying powers of the same number together, add the indices.

Example 1   Simplify $7^2\times7^5\times7^9$

$$7^2\times7^5\times7^9 = 7^{2+5+9} = 7^{16}$$

(ii) Division

Now let us see what happens when we divide powers of the same number.

$$\frac{3^5}{3^2} = \frac{3\times3\times3\times3\times3}{3\times3} = 3\times3\times3 = 3^3$$

We see that the result could have been obtained by subtracting the indices. Thus,

$$\frac{3^5}{3^2} = 3^{5-2} = 3^3$$

The rule is:

When dividing powers of the same number subtract the index of the denominator from the index of the numerator.

Examples 2

1) $\dfrac{5^7}{5^3} = 5^{7-3} = 5^4$

2) $\dfrac{7^3 \times 7^4 \times 7^8}{7^5 \times 7^6} = \dfrac{7^{3+4+8}}{7^{5+6}} = \dfrac{7^{15}}{7^{11}} = 7^{15-11} = 7^4$

(iii) **Powers**

What is the value of $(2^3)^2$? One way of solving the problem is to proceed as follows:

$$(2^3)^2 = 2^3 \times 2^3 = 2^{3+3} = 2^6$$

We see that the same result would be produced if we multiplied the two indices together. Thus,

$$(2^3)^2 = 2^{3 \times 2} = 2^6$$

The rule is:

When raising the power of a number to a power, multiply the indices together.

Examples 3

1) $(5^4)^3 = 5^{4 \times 3} = 5^{12}$

2) $(3^2 \times 7^4)^3 = 3^{2 \times 3} \times 7^{4 \times 3} = 3^6 \times 7^{12}$

3) $\left(\dfrac{5^7}{3^5}\right)^6 = \dfrac{5^{7 \times 6}}{3^{5 \times 6}} = \dfrac{5^{42}}{3^{30}}$

(iv) **Negative indices**

Let us attempt to simplify $\dfrac{2^3}{2^6}$

$$\dfrac{2^3}{2^6} = \dfrac{2 \times 2 \times 2}{2 \times 2 \times 2 \times 2 \times 2 \times 2} = \dfrac{1}{2 \times 2 \times 2} = \dfrac{1}{2^3}$$

But by the rule for division,

$$\dfrac{2^3}{2^6} = 2^{3-6} = 2^{-3}$$

Hence, $\dfrac{1}{2^3} = 2^{-3}$

A negative index therefore indicates the reciprocal of the quantity.

Examples 4

1) $3^{-1} = \dfrac{1}{3}$

2) $5 \times 2^{-3} = \dfrac{5}{2^3}$

3) $(4 \times 7^2)^{-3} = \dfrac{1}{(4 \times 7^2)^3} = \dfrac{1}{4^3 \times 7^6}$

(Note that 4 is really 4^1 and $(4^1)^3 = 4^{1 \times 3} = 4^3$)

(v) Fractional indices

To find a meaning for $5^{\frac{1}{3}}$.

$$\sqrt[3]{5} \times \sqrt[3]{5} \times \sqrt[3]{5} = 5$$

$$5^{\frac{1}{3}} \times 5^{\frac{1}{3}} \times 5^{\frac{1}{3}} = 5^{\frac{1}{3} + \frac{1}{3} + \frac{1}{3}} = 5^1 = 5$$

Therefore $5^{\frac{1}{3}} = \sqrt[3]{5}$

($\sqrt[3]{5}$ is said to be the cube root of five. Similarly $\sqrt[5]{7}$ is described as the fifth root of seven.)

Therefore a fractional index represents the root of the quantity. The denominator of the fractional index denotes the root to be taken.

Examples 5   1) $2^{\frac{1}{2}} = \sqrt{2}$ (Note that for square roots the number 2 indicating the root is usually omitted.)

2) $\sqrt[5]{7} = 7^{\frac{1}{5}}$

3) To find the value of $\sqrt[4]{81}$.

$$81 = 3^4$$

$$\sqrt[4]{81} = 81^{\frac{1}{4}} = (3^4)^{\frac{1}{4}} \qquad 3^{4 \times \frac{1}{4}} = 3^1 = 3$$

(vi) Zero index

$$\frac{2^5}{2^5} = 2^{5-5} = 2^0$$

But $2^5 \div 2^5 = 1$ and hence $2^0 = 1$

Again, $\dfrac{3^4}{3^4} = 3^{4-4} = 3^0$

But, $3^4 \div 3^4 = 1$ and hence $3^0 = 1$

By doing several examples similar to those above we would discover that *any number raised to the power of zero is equal to 1.*

Examples 6   1) $25^0 = 1$

2) $(0 \cdot 56)^0 = 1$

3) $(\frac{1}{4})^0 = 1$

Exercise 43

Simplify each of the following:

Find the values of the following:

1) $2^5 \times 2^6$

2) $3^4 \times 3^7$

3) $5^3 \times 5^4 \times 5^6$

4) $3 \times 3^2 \times 3^5$

5) $7^5 \div 7^2$

6) $3^{12} \div 3^4$

7) $2^8 \div 2^4$

8) $10^5 \times 10^3 \div 10^4$

9) $3^7 \times 3^6 \div 3^5$

10) $\dfrac{2^5 \times 2^6}{2^2 \times 2^7}$

11) $(5^3)^4$

12) $(3 \times 5^4)^2$

13) $(10^3)^4$

14) $(2 \times 3^2 \times 5^3)^4$

15) $\left(\dfrac{3}{4}\right)^3$

16) $\left(\dfrac{5^2}{7^3}\right)^4$

17) 10^{-1}

18) 2^{-2}

19) 3^{-4}

20) 2^{-4}

21) 5^{-2}

22) $4^{\frac{1}{2}}$

23) $27^{\frac{1}{3}}$

24) $8^{\frac{1}{3}}$

25) $16^{\frac{1}{4}}$

26) 33^0

27) $\left(\dfrac{3}{4}\right)^0$

28) 125^0

29) $16^{-\frac{1}{2}}$

30) $125^{-\frac{1}{3}}$

Numbers in Standard Form

Any number can be expressed as a value between 1 and 10 multiplied by a power of 10. A number expressed in this way is said to be in standard form. The repeating of zeros in very large and very small numbers often leads to errors. Stating the number in standard form helps to avoid these errors.

Examples 7

1) $49 \cdot 4 = 4 \cdot 94 \times 10$

2) $385 \cdot 3 = 3 \cdot 853 \times 100 = 3 \cdot 853 \times 10^2$

3) $20\,000\,000 = 2 \times 10\,000\,000 = 2 \times 10^7$

4) $0 \cdot 596 = \dfrac{5 \cdot 96}{10} = 5 \cdot 96 \times 10^{-1}$

5) $0 \cdot 000\,478 = \dfrac{4 \cdot 78}{10\,000} = \dfrac{4 \cdot 78}{10^4} = 4 \cdot 78 \times 10^{-4}$

Exercise 44

1) Write the following in standard form:
   (a) 19·6
   (b) 385
   (c) 59 876
   (d) 1 500 000
   (e) 0·013
   (f) 0·003 85
   (g) 0·000 698
   (h) 0·023 85

2) Write down the values of the following:
   (a) $1 \cdot 5 \times 10^2$
   (b) $4 \cdot 7 \times 10^4$
   (c) $3 \cdot 6 \times 10^6$
   (d) $9 \cdot 45 \times 10^3$
   (e) $2 \cdot 5 \times 10^{-1}$
   (f) $4 \cdot 0 \times 10^{-3}$
   (g) $8 \cdot 0 \times 10^{-5}$
   (h) $4 \cdot 0 \times 10^{-2}$

3) State which of the following pairs of numbers is the larger:
   (a) $5 \cdot 8 \times 10^2$ and $2 \cdot 1 \times 10^3$
   (b) $9 \cdot 4 \times 10^3$ and $9 \cdot 95 \times 10^3$
   (c) $8 \cdot 58 \times 10^4$ and $9 \cdot 87 \times 10^3$

4) State which of the following pairs of numbers is the smaller:
   (a) $2 \cdot 1 \times 10^{-2}$ and $3 \cdot 8 \times 10^{-2}$
   (b) $8 \cdot 72 \times 10^{-3}$ and $9 \cdot 7 \times 10^{-2}$
   (c) $3 \cdot 83 \times 10^{-2}$ and $2 \cdot 11 \times 10^{-4}$

Logarithms

Any positive number can be expressed as a power of 10. For example $100 = 10^2$ and $86 = 10^{1 \cdot 9345}$. These powers of 10 are called logarithms to the base 10. That is,

$$\text{number} = 10^{\text{power}} = 10^{\text{logarithm}}$$

We have seen that $86 = 10^{1 \cdot 9345}$ and we write

$$\log_{10} 86 = 1 \cdot 9345$$

The base 10 is indicated as shown above, but it is frequently omitted and we write,

$$\log 86 = 1 \cdot 9345$$

The logarithm tables give the logarithms of numbers between 1 and 10, they are shown on pages 216 and 217. The figures in the first column of the complete table are the numbers from 10 to 99. The corresponding figures in the column headed 0 are the logarithms of these numbers. Thus

$$\log 2 \cdot 1 = 0 \cdot 3222$$

If the number has a third significant figure the logarithm is found in the appropriate column of the next 9 columns. Thus

$$\log 2 \cdot 13 = 0 \cdot 3284$$

When the number has a fourth significant figure we use the last 9 columns which give us, for every fourth significant figure, a number which must be added to the logarithm already found for the first three significant figures. Thus to find log 2·134 we find log 2·13 = 0·3284. Using the last 9 columns we find in the column headed 4, the number 8. This is added to 3284 to give 3292.

$$\log 2{\cdot}134 = 0{\cdot}3292$$

Exercise 45

Write down the logarithms of the following numbers:

1) 3·6	4) 8·39	7) 8·305	10) 5·698
2) 4·8	5) 9·17	8) 6·117	
3) 3·42	6) 4·186	9) 2·876	

To find the logarithms of numbers outside the range of 1 to 10, we make use of numbers in standard form. Then, by using the multiplication law of indices and the log tables we find the complete logarithm. For example

To find log 249·3

$$249{\cdot}3 = 2{\cdot}493 \times 10^2$$

From the log tables: $\log 2{\cdot}493 = 0{\cdot}3967$

$$249{\cdot}3 = 10^{0{\cdot}3967} \times 10^2 = 10^{2{\cdot}3967}$$

$$\log 249{\cdot}3 = 2{\cdot}3967$$

A logarithm therefore consists of two parts:

   (i) a whole number part called the *characteristic*.

   (ii) a decimal part called the *mantissa*.

As can be seen from the above example the characteristic depends upon the size of the number. It is found by subtracting 1 from the number of figures which occur to the left of the decimal point in the given number. The mantissa is found directly from the log tables.

Examples 8   1) In log 8293 the characteristic is 3 and hence log 8293 = 3·9188

2) In log 829·3 the characteristic is 2 and hence log 829·3 = 2·9188

3) In log 82·93 the characteristic is 1 and hence log 82·93 = 1·9188

4) In log 8·293 the characteristic is 0 and hence log 8·293 = 0·9188

Numbers which have the same set of significant figures have the same mantissa in their logarithms.

Exercise 46

1) Write down the characteristics for the following:

   (a) 23   (b) 23 000   (c) 17 970

   (d) 983   (e) 950 000 (f) 55·27

   (g) 1·794 (h) 333·4   (i) 2893

   (j) 390·1

2) Write down the logarithms of the following numbers:

   (a) 7, 70, 700, 7000, 70 000

   (b) 3·1, 31, 310, 3100, 3 100 000

   (c) 48·3, 483 000, 4·83, 483

   (d) 7895, 7·895, 78·95, 78 950

   (e) 1·003, 10·03, 1003, 100·3

Anti-Logarithms

The table of anti-logarithms contains the numbers which correspond to the given logarithm. The table is used in a similar way to the log tables but it must be remembered that:

(i) The mantissa (or decimal part) of the logarithm only is used in the table.

(ii) The number of figures to the left of the decimal point is found by *adding 1* to the characteristic of the logarithm.

Example 9 To find the number whose logarithm is 2·1825

Using the mantissa ·1825 we find from the anti-log tables that the number corresponding is 1523. Since the characteristic is 2, the number must have three figures to the left of the decimal point. The number is therefore 152·3 (note that log 152·3 = 2·1825).

Exercise 47

Write down the anti-logs of the following

Find the values of the following:

1) 0·32, 2·32, 4·32, 1·32

2) 3·275, 0·275, 4·275, 6·275

3) 0·5987, 1·5987, 4·5987, 2·5987

4) 3·8949, 0·8949, 2·8949, 4·8949

5) $10^{0.38}$

6) $10^{1.263}$

7) $10^{3.1683}$

8) $10^{2.563}$

Rules for the Use of Logarithms

It has been shown that logarithms are indices and hence when using logarithms the rules of indices must be observed.

(i) Multiplication

To find $39·27 \times 6·127$

$$\log 39·27 = 1·5941 \text{ and } \log 6·127 = 0·7873$$
$$39·27 \times 6·127 = 10^{1.5941} \times 10^{0.7873} = 10^{1.5941 + 0.7873} = 10^{2.3814}$$

By finding the anti-log of 2·3814 we find that

$$39·27 \times 6·127 = 240·6$$

From this example we see that the rule for multiplication using logs is:

Find the logs of the numbers to be multiplied and add them together. The required product is found by taking the anti-log of the sum.

The method shown above is not very convenient and it is better to use the tablular method shown below.

number	log
39·27	1·5941
6·127	0·7873
Answer = 240·6	2·3814

(ii) **Division**

To find $\dfrac{293 \cdot 6}{18 \cdot 78}$

Log $293 \cdot 6 = 2 \cdot 4678$ and **log** $18 \cdot 78 = 1 \cdot 2737$

$$\frac{293 \cdot 6}{18 \cdot 78} = \frac{10^{2 \cdot 4678}}{10^{1 \cdot 2737}} = 10^{2 \cdot 4678 - 1 \cdot 2737} = 10^{1 \cdot 1941}$$

By finding the antilog of $1 \cdot 1941$ we see that

$$\frac{293 \cdot 6}{18 \cdot 78} = 15 \cdot 63$$

From this example we see that the rule for division using logarithms is:

Find the logarithm of each number. Subtract the log of the denominator from the log of the numerator. The quotient is found by taking the antilog of the difference.

A better way of performing the process is the tabular method shown below.

number	log
293·6	2·4678
18·78	1·2737
Answer = 15·63	1·1941

Example 10   Find the value of $\dfrac{783 \cdot 9 \times 2 \cdot 023}{2 \cdot 168 \times 39 \cdot 47}$

number	log	number	log
783·9	2·8943	2·168	0·3361
2·023	0·3060	39·47	1·5963
numerator	3·2003	denominator	1·9324
denominator	1·9324		
Answer = 18·53	1·2679		

Exercise 48

Use logs to find the values of the following:

1) $17 \cdot 63 \times 20 \cdot 54$

2) $328 \cdot 4 \times 54 \cdot 7$

3) $6819 \times 1 \cdot 285 \times 17$

4) $305 \cdot 2 \times 1 \cdot 003 \times 12 \cdot 36$

5) $25 \cdot 14 \div 12 \cdot 95$

6) $8 \cdot 165 \div 3 \cdot 142$

7) $128 \cdot 3 \div 12 \cdot 95$

8) $1 \cdot 975 \div 1 \cdot 261$

9) $\dfrac{95 \cdot 83 \times 6 \cdot 138}{8 \cdot 179}$

10) $\dfrac{9 \cdot 125 \times 123}{120 \cdot 2}$

11) $\dfrac{42 \cdot 7 \times 16 \cdot 15 \times 3 \cdot 298}{11 \cdot 69 \times 7 \cdot 58}$

12) $\dfrac{16 \cdot 13 \times 270 \cdot 5 \times 1 \cdot 297}{15 \cdot 38 \times 139 \cdot 6 \times 1 \cdot 389}$

(iii) **Powers**

To find $(3 \cdot 968)^3$

$$\log 3 \cdot 968 = 0 \cdot 5986 \text{ and therefore } 3 \cdot 968 = 10^{0 \cdot 5986}$$
$$(3 \cdot 968)^3 = (10^{0 \cdot 5986})^3 = 10^{0 \cdot 5986 \times 3} = 10^{1 \cdot 7958}$$

By finding the antilog of $1 \cdot 7958$,

$$(3 \cdot 968)^3 = 62 \cdot 48$$

From this example we see that the rule for finding powers of numbers is: *Find the log of the number and multiply it by the index denoting the power. The value of the number raised to the given power is found by taking the antilog of the product.*

Example 11   Find the value of $(11 \cdot 63 \times 2 \cdot 87)^4$

number	log
11·63	1·0656
2·87	0·4579
11·63 × 2·87	1·5235
	×4
Answer = 1 242 000	6·0940

(iv) **Roots**

To find $\sqrt[4]{70 \cdot 35}$

$$\log 70 \cdot 35 = 1 \cdot 8473 \text{ and therefore } 70 \cdot 35 = 10^{1 \cdot 8473}$$
$$\sqrt[4]{70 \cdot 35} = (70 \cdot 35)^{\frac{1}{4}} = (10^{1 \cdot 8473})^{\frac{1}{4}} = 10^{1 \cdot 8473 \times \frac{1}{4}}$$
$$= 10^{1 \cdot 8473 \div 4} = 10^{0 \cdot 4618}$$

By finding the antilog of $0 \cdot 4618$,

$$\sqrt[4]{70 \cdot 35} = 2 \cdot 896$$

From this example we see that the rule for finding the root of a number is: *Find the log of the number and divide it by the number denoting the root. The result obtained by this division is the log of the required root and its antilog is the required root.*

Example 12   Find the value of $\sqrt[3]{(1 \cdot 832)^2 \times 6 \cdot 327}$

number	log
1·832	0·2630
	×2
(1·832)²	0·5260
6·327	0·8012
(1·832)² × 6·327	1·3272
	÷3
Answer = 2·770	0·4424

Exercise 49

Use logs to find the values of the following:

1) $(7\cdot326)^3$

2) $(29\cdot38)^2$

3) $(1\cdot098)^5$

4) $(2\cdot998)^2 \times 11\cdot35$

5) $(16\cdot29)^3 \div 86\cdot76$

6) $73\cdot25 \div (3\cdot924)^3$

7) $\dfrac{(7\cdot36)^2 \times (1\cdot088)^3}{42\cdot35}$

8) $\dfrac{45\,827}{(56\cdot3)^2 \times (1\cdot82)^3}$

9) $\sqrt[3]{15\cdot38}$

10) $\sqrt[3]{(2\cdot593)^2}$

11) $\sqrt{1\cdot637} \times 11\cdot87$

12) $\sqrt{61\cdot5} \times (19\cdot27)^3$

Logarithms of Numbers Between 0 and 1

$$0\cdot1 = \frac{1}{10} = 10^{-1} \qquad\qquad \text{Hence } \log 0\cdot1 = -1$$

$$0\cdot01 = \frac{1}{100} = \frac{1}{10^2} = 10^{-2} \qquad\qquad \text{Hence } \log 0\cdot01 = -2$$

$$0\cdot001 = \frac{1}{1000} = \frac{1}{10^3} = 10^{-3} \qquad \text{Hence } \log 0\cdot001 = -3$$

From these results we may deduce that:

The logarithms of numbers between 0 and 1 are negative.

Example 13   To find the logarithm of $0\cdot3783$

$$0\cdot3783 = \frac{3\cdot783}{10} = 3\cdot783 \times 10^{-1} = 10^{0\cdot5778} \times 10^{-1} = 10^{-1+0\cdot5778}$$

$$\log 0\cdot3783 = -1 + 0\cdot5778$$

The characteristic is therefore -1 and the mantissa is $0\cdot5778$. In the case of numbers greater than 1, the mantissa remains the same when the numbers are multiplied or divided by powers of 10. That is, with the same set of significant figures we have the same mantissa. It would be advantageous if we could do the same thing for the logs of numbers between 0 and 1. This can be done if we retain the negative characteristic as shown above. However to write $\log 0\cdot3783$ as $-1+0\cdot5778$ would be awkward so we adopt the notation $\bar{1}\cdot5778$. The minus sign is written above the characteristic but it must be clearly understood that

$$\bar{1}\cdot5778 = -1 + 0\cdot5778$$
$$\bar{2}\cdot6093 = -2 + 0\cdot6093$$

We refer to $\bar{1}\cdot5778$ as bar 1 point 5778 and $\bar{2}\cdot6093$ as bar 2 point 6093.

Using the bar notation:

$$\log 0\cdot4623 \quad = \bar{1}\cdot6649$$
$$\log 0\cdot04623 \quad = \bar{2}\cdot6649$$
$$\log 0\cdot004\,623 = \bar{3}\cdot6649$$

The negative characteristic is numerically one more than the number of zeros which follow the decimal point in the given number.

The Anti-Logs for Logs With Negative Characteristics

When using the anti-log tables only the mantissa is used. The number of zeros following the decimal point is 1 less than the numerical value of the negative characteristic.

Example 14   To find the number whose log is $2 \cdot 5231$.

Using the mantissa $\cdot 5231$ we find, in the antilog tables, that the corresponding number is 3335. Since the characteristic is $\bar{2}$, the number must have one zero following the decimal point. Hence the number is $0 \cdot 033\,35$. (Note that log $0 \cdot 033\,35 = \bar{2} \cdot 5231$.)

Exercise 50

Write down the logs of the following numbers:

Find the numbers whose logs are:

1) 2·817, 0·2817, 0·028 17, 0·002 817
2) 4·597, 0·4597, 0·004 597, 0·000 045 97
3) 0·097 68, 0·000 976 8, 0·9768
4) 0·000 058 75, 0·058 75, 0·000 587 5

5) $\bar{1} \cdot 4337$
6) $\bar{3} \cdot 8199$
7) $\bar{4} \cdot 5486$

8) $\bar{2} \cdot 4871$
9) $\bar{8} \cdot 5319$
10) $\bar{1} \cdot 0218$

Adding and Subtracting Negative Characteristics

The rules are the same as when adding or subtracting directed numbers.

Examples 15   1) Add $\bar{2}$ and $\bar{3}$.
$$\bar{2}+\bar{3} = -2+(-3) = -2-3 = -5 = \bar{5}$$
2) Add 3, 2 and 1.
$$\bar{3}+\bar{2}+\bar{1} = -3+(-2)+(-1) = -3-2-1 = -6 = \bar{6}$$
3) Find $\bar{3}-\bar{2}$.
$$\bar{3}-\bar{2} = -3-(-2) = -3+2 = -1 = \bar{1}$$
4) Find $2-\bar{3}$.
$$2-\bar{3} = 2-(-3) = 2+3 = 5$$

Exercise 51

Add the following:

Subtract the following:

1) $1+\bar{1}$
2) $3+\bar{2}$
3) $\bar{1}+\bar{3}$
4) $\bar{2}+\bar{2}$
5) $3+\bar{2}$

6) $0+\bar{2}$
7) $\bar{3}+0$
8) $\bar{5}+\bar{4}$
9) $\bar{6}+3$
10) $2+\bar{4}$

11) $2-3$
12) $2-5$
13) $0-3$
14) $\bar{2}-1$
15) $1-\bar{2}$

16) $3-\bar{2}$
17) $\bar{2}-\bar{2}$
18) $\bar{1}-\bar{4}$
19) $\bar{4}-\bar{1}$
20) $0-\bar{3}$

Example 16   Add together the following logarithms:

$\bar{1} \cdot 7318$ Adding the decimal parts together we get $2 \cdot 3018$. The
$\bar{1} \cdot 8042$ characteristic then becomes
$\underline{2 \cdot 7658}$
$$2+(-2)+(-1)+(-1) = -2 = \bar{2}$$
$\overline{\bar{2} \cdot 3018}$

Example 17   Subtract the following logarithms:

$\bar{3}\cdot5903$ The characteristic of the answer becomes (since there is no
$\bar{2}\cdot4061$ carry over) $-3-(-2) = -3+2 = -1 = \bar{1}$

$\overline{}$

$\bar{1}\cdot1842$

Example 18   Subtract the following logarithms:

$\bar{3}\cdot2584$ We cannot take $0\cdot5789$ from $0\cdot2584$ so we borrow 1 from $\bar{3}$
$1\cdot5789$ thereby making it $\bar{4}$. We now take $0\cdot5789$ from $1\cdot2584$. The
$\overline{}$ characteristic becomes $(-4)-1 = -5 = \bar{5}$
$\bar{5}\cdot6795$

Exercise 52

Add the following:

1) $\bar{2}\cdot7+1\cdot4$ 8) $\bar{2}\cdot4+\bar{1}\cdot6$
2) $\bar{1}\cdot2+3\cdot1$ 9) $\bar{2}\cdot4+\bar{1}\cdot8$
3) $0\cdot6+\bar{2}\cdot3$ 10) $1\cdot2+\bar{1}\cdot9$
4) $2\cdot7+\bar{3}\cdot4$ 11) $\bar{3}\cdot7+1\cdot5$
5) $2\cdot1+\bar{1}\cdot0$ 12) $\bar{2}\cdot8+\bar{3}\cdot7$
6) $\bar{1}\cdot3+\bar{1}\cdot4$ 13) $\bar{1}\cdot9+4\cdot5$
7) $\bar{2}\cdot0+\bar{2}\cdot1$ 14) $\bar{2}\cdot6+3\cdot7$

Subtract the following:

18) $3\cdot8-\bar{2}\cdot7$ 25) $2\cdot5-3\cdot6$
19) $\bar{2}\cdot6-1\cdot4$ 26) $1\cdot3-1\cdot8$
20) $\bar{1}\cdot7-\bar{1}\cdot3$ 27) $\bar{2}\cdot3-1\cdot8$
21) $\bar{1}\cdot8-\bar{3}\cdot5$ 28) $\bar{2}\cdot3-\bar{1}\cdot8$
22) $1\cdot7-3\cdot2$ 29) $\bar{1}\cdot5-\bar{1}\cdot7$
23) $2\cdot8-\bar{2}\cdot6$ 30) $\bar{1}\cdot3-\bar{3}\cdot5$
24) $\bar{3}\cdot5-\bar{1}\cdot4$

Add the following:

15) $1\cdot5176+1\cdot8973+\bar{5}\cdot4398+0\cdot0625$
16) $\bar{3}\cdot3785+2\cdot2778+1\cdot6879+\bar{2}\cdot8898$
17) $3\cdot1189+\bar{2}\cdot7615+\bar{5}\cdot2319+\bar{6}\cdot0527$

Subtract the following:

31) $3\cdot2973-\bar{4}\cdot3879$
32) $0\cdot4973-0\cdot8769$
33) $\bar{2}\cdot5321-1\cdot9897$
34) $\bar{3}\cdot0036-\bar{6}\cdot8798$

Multiplying and Dividing Negative Characteristics

Again the rules are exactly the same as those used with directed numbers.

Example 19   Multiply $\bar{2}\cdot6192$ by 4

$\bar{2}\cdot6192$ $0\cdot6192\times4 = 2\cdot4768$. Carrying the 2 we have the char-
$\times4$ acteristic $= 4\times(-2)+2 = -8+2 = -6 = \bar{6}$.

$\overline{}$

$\bar{6}\cdot4768$

Divide $\bar{5}\cdot8293$ by 3

We must make the negative characteristic exactly divisible by 3, so we write

$$\bar{5}\cdot8293\div3 = (\bar{6}+1\cdot8293)\div3 = \bar{2}\cdot6098$$

Example 20   The work is best set out as follows:

$$\frac{3)\bar{6}+1\cdot8293}{\bar{2}+0\cdot6098} = \bar{2}\cdot6098$$

Example 21   Find the value of $\sqrt[5]{0\cdot0139}$

To find the root of a number we find the log of the number and divide it by the number denoting the root. Thus,

$$\log 0\cdot0139 = \bar{2}\cdot1430$$

$$\frac{5)\bar{5}+3\cdot1430}{\bar{1}+0\cdot6286} = \bar{1}\cdot6286$$

By finding the antilog of $\bar{1}\cdot6286$, $\sqrt[5]{0\cdot0139} = 0\cdot4252$

(Note that $\bar{5}+3\cdot1430 = -5+3+0\cdot1430 = -2+0\cdot1430 = \bar{2}\cdot1430$)

Exercise 53

Simplify the following:

1) $\bar{1}\cdot4\times2$	9) $\bar{3}\cdot5\div5$	17) $\sqrt[5]{0\cdot6978}$
2) $\bar{3}\cdot1\times3$	10) $\bar{4}\cdot1\div3$	
3) $\bar{1}\cdot7\times2$	11) $(0\cdot3614)^3$	Find the value of the following:
4) $\bar{2}\cdot8\times3$	12) $(0\cdot7856)^5$	18) $\dfrac{0\cdot3786\times0\cdot039\,72}{31\cdot67}$
5) $\bar{1}\cdot8\times5$	13) $(0\cdot001\,347)^2$	
6) $\bar{2}\cdot6\div2$	14) $\sqrt{0\cdot2569}$	19) $\dfrac{97\cdot61\times0\cdot000\,46}{0\cdot091\,74}$
7) $\bar{3}\cdot9\div3$	15) $\sqrt[3]{0\cdot069\,87}$	
8) $\bar{1}\cdot2\div2$	16) $\sqrt[3]{0\cdot000\,781\,6}$	20) $\dfrac{0\cdot0146\times0\cdot798\times643}{33\,000\times11\cdot8}$

Summary

1) When multiplying powers of the same number together add the indices.

2) When dividing powers of the same number, subtract the index of the divisor from the index of the dividend.

3) When raising the power of a number to a power, multiply the indices together.

4) A negative index indicates the reciprocal of the quantity.

5) A fractional index represents the root of the quantity. The denominator of the fractional index denotes the root that is to be taken.

6) Any number raised to the power of zero equals 1.

7) Any number can be expressed as a number between 1 and 10 multiplied by a power of 10. A number expressed in this way is in standard form.

8) Any positive number can be expressed as a power of 10. These powers of 10 are called logarithms to the base 10. Thus number = $10^{\text{power}} = 10^{\text{logarithm}}$.

9) A logarithm consists of (i) a whole number part called the characteristic, (ii) a decimal part called the mantissa. The characteristic depends upon the size of the number—in the case of numbers greater than 1 it is found by subtracting 1 from the number of figures to the left of the decimal point. Numbers less than 1 have a negative characteristic and in this case the negative characteristic

is one more than the number of zeros which follow the decimal point in the given number. The mantissa is found directly from the log tables.

10) The antilog tables contain the numbers which correspond to the given log. The mantissa (decimal part) of the log only is used in the table.

11) To multiply a set of numbers together find the logs of the numbers and add them together. The required product is found by taking the antilog of the sum.

12) To divide one number by another find the logs of each of the numbers. Subtract the log of the divisor from the log of the dividend. The required quotient is found by taking the antilog of the difference.

13) To find the power of a number find the log of the number and multiply it by the index denoting the power. The value of the number raised to the given power is found by taking the antilog of the product.

14) To find the root of a number find the log of the number and divide it by the number denoting the root. The result obtained by this division is the log of the required root and its antilog is the required root.

15) When adding and subtracting negative characteristics the rules are exactly the same as those used for directed numbers.

16) When dividing a log with a negative characteristic, the negative characteristic must be made exactly divisible by the divisor.

Mental Test 6

Try to write down the answers to the following questions without writing down anything else.

1) Simplify $3^2 \times 3^4$

2) Simplify $5^7 \times 5^3$

3) Simplify $2^2 \times 2^3 \times 2^4 \times 2^5$

4) Simplify $4^8 \div 4^2$

5) Simplify $3^9 \div 3^3$

6) Remove the bracket: $(3^2 \times 5^3)^4$

7) Remove the bracket: $(7^5)^6$

8) Remove the bracket: $(\frac{3}{4})^2$

9) Find the value in decimals of 10^{-2}

10) Find the value in decimals of 2^{-2}

11) Find the value in decimals of 5^{-1}

12) What is the value of 18^0?

13) Find the value of $4^{\frac{1}{2}}$

14) Find the value of $27^{\frac{1}{3}}$

15) Find the value of $16^{\frac{1}{4}}$

16) What is the logarithm of 100?

17) What is the value of $\bar{2} - \bar{3}$?

18) Divide $\bar{1} \cdot 7$ by 3

19) Multiply $\bar{2} \cdot 6$ by 3

20) Add $\bar{1} \cdot 7$ and $\bar{2} \cdot 4$

Self-Test 6

1) What power of 2 gives 32?

    a 5   b 16   c 4   d $\frac{1}{16}$

2) The product of $2 \cdot 5 \times 10^4$ and 8×10^{-5} is

    a $1 \cdot 8$ b $2 \cdot 0$ c $5 \cdot 5$ d 105

3) The cube root of $0 \cdot 036\,03$ is equal to

    a $0 \cdot 3303$ b $0 \cdot 033\,03$

    c $0 \cdot 6002$ d $6 \cdot 002$

4) 0·097 63 when written in standard form is

   a $97·63 \times 10^3$ **b** $9·763 \times 10^2$

   c $9·763 \times 10^{-2}$ **d** $97·63 \times 10^{-3}$

5) The cube root of 27×10^{-6} is equal to

   a 3×10^{-3} **b** $5·20 \times 10^{-3}$

   c 3×10^{-2} **d** $5·20 \times 10^{-2}$

6) The expression $(3 \times 5^2 \times 7^3)^4$ with the bracket removed is equal to

   a $3^4 \times 5^2 \times 7^3$ **b** $3^4 \times 5^8 \times 7^{12}$

   c $3 \times 5^8 \times 7^{12}$ **d** $3 \times 5^2 \times 7^{12}$

7) What number has a logarithm of $\bar{2}$?

   a -100 **b** $-0·01$

   c 100 **d** $0·01$

8) The largest of the numbers $\frac{1}{7}$, $1·3 \times 10^{-1}$, $0·12$ and $1·4 \times 10^{-2}$ is

   a $\frac{1}{7}$ **b** $1·3 \times 10^{-1}$

   c $0·12$ **d** $1·4 \times 10^{-2}$

9) The value of $\left(\frac{1}{9}\right)^{\frac{1}{2}}$ is

   a 3 **b** $\frac{1}{3}$ **c** $4·5$ **d** $\frac{1}{4·5}$

10) The value of $10^{1·3243}$ is

   a $13·243$ **b** $0·134\,23$

   c $2·110$ **d** $21·10$

11) The value of $10^{0·3010} \times 10^{0·4771}$ is

   a 6 **b** 60 **c** $0·7781$ **d** $7·781$

12) $\bar{2}·8 \div 6$ is equal to

   a $\bar{2}·6$ **b** $-2·6$ **c** $\bar{1}·8$ **d** $-1·8$

Electronic Calculating Machines

A great deal of time and effort is often expended in arithmetic calculations even when logarithms are used. Much of this time and effort may be saved by using one of the electronic calculators. There are many types on the market but for most of us, a calculator which will add, subtract, multiply and divide is good enough.

The keyboard of a calculator has 10 number keys marked 0, 1, 2, 3, 4, 5, 6, 7, 8 and 9. There is also a decimal point. In the case of a simple calculator there are four function keys $+$, $-$, $\times$ and $\div$ and also an $=$ key. There is always a clear key, usually marked C, which is used to clear the display. Before each calculation it is safer to depress the C key.

Example 1   To find the value of $9·632 + 18·564 - 12·768$

Keyboard setting	Display
9 · 6 3 2	9·632
+ 1 8 · 5 6 4 =	28·196
− 1 2 · 7 6 8 =	15·428

Hence $9·632 + 18·564 - 12·768 = 15·428$

Note that when performing arithmetical operations the order of pressing the keys is always *FUNCTION* ($+$, $-$, $\times$ or $\div$) *NUMBER EQUALS*.

Example 2   Find the value of $19·56 \times 29·63 \div 11·98$

	Keyboard setting	**Display**
	$\boxed{1}\,\boxed{9}\,\boxed{\cdot}\,\boxed{5}\,\boxed{6}$	19·56
	$\boxed{\times}\,\boxed{2}\,\boxed{9}\,\boxed{\cdot}\,\boxed{6}\,\boxed{3}\,\boxed{=}$	579·5628
	$\boxed{\div}\,\boxed{1}\,\boxed{1}\,\boxed{\cdot}\,\boxed{9}\,\boxed{8}\,\boxed{=}$	48·377529

Hence $19·56 \times 29·63 \div 11·98 = 38·157\,899$

Most calculators have an 8 figure display but, of course, answers can be given to any number of significant figures up to 8.

If, as a result of a multiplication or addition the product or the sum contains more than 8 figures to the left of the decimal point then the machine will show the overflow indicator. To avoid this happening it pays to alternatively multiply and divide where this is possible or to express the numbers in standard form.

Example 3   Find the value of $\dfrac{289·53 \times 6548·79 \times 900·876}{87·63 \times 587·26}$

If we perform the operations

$\boxed{2}\,\boxed{8}\,\boxed{9}\,\boxed{\cdot}\,\boxed{5}\,\boxed{3}\,\boxed{\times}\,\boxed{6}\,\boxed{5}\,\boxed{4}\,\boxed{8}\,\boxed{\cdot}\,\boxed{7}\,\boxed{9}\,\boxed{=}$

$\boxed{\times}\,\boxed{9}\,\boxed{0}\,\boxed{0}\,\boxed{\cdot}\,\boxed{8}\,\boxed{7}\,\boxed{6}\,\boxed{=}$

the overflow is brought into action.

However if we perform the operations like this:

$\boxed{2}\,\boxed{8}\,\boxed{9}\,\boxed{\cdot}\,\boxed{5}\,\boxed{3}\,\boxed{\div}\,\boxed{8}\,\boxed{7}\,\boxed{\cdot}\,\boxed{6}\,\boxed{3}\,\boxed{=}$

$\boxed{\times}\,\boxed{6}\,\boxed{5}\,\boxed{4}\,\boxed{8}\,\boxed{\cdot}\,\boxed{7}\,\boxed{9}\,\boxed{=}\,\boxed{\div}\,\boxed{5}\,\boxed{8}\,\boxed{7}\,\boxed{\cdot}\,\boxed{2}\,\boxed{6}\,\boxed{=}$

$\boxed{\times}\,\boxed{9}\,\boxed{0}\,\boxed{0}\,\boxed{\cdot}\,\boxed{8}\,\boxed{7}\,\boxed{6}\,\boxed{=}$

we get the answer as $33\,192·226$

Example 4   What is the value of $6\,857\,000 \times 119\,000 \times 85$?

Clearly if we multiply out directly the machine will show the overflow indicator. Therefore express each of the numbers in standard form as follows:

$$6·857 \times 10^6 \times 1·19 \times 10^5 \times 8·5 \times 10^1$$

The operations are then:

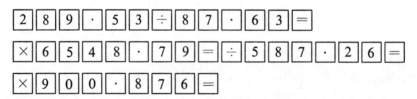

$\boxed{6}\,\boxed{\cdot}\,\boxed{8}\,\boxed{5}\,\boxed{7}\,\boxed{\times}\,\boxed{1}\,\boxed{\cdot}\,\boxed{1}\,\boxed{9}\,\boxed{=}\,\boxed{\times}\,\boxed{8}\,\boxed{\cdot}\,\boxed{5}\,\boxed{=}$

The product is $69·358\,555$

Hence $6\,857\,000 \times 119\,000 \times 85 = 69·358\,555 \times 10^{12}$

$$\text{or } 6·935\,855 \times 10^{13}$$

If we attempt to divide a very small number by a large number then all we shall get on the display is a series of zeros. However by expressing the numbers in standard form this difficulty is overcome.

Find the value of $\dfrac{0 \cdot 000\,632}{8\,000\,000}$

Expressing each number in standard form we have

$6 \cdot 32 \times 10^{-4} \div 8 \times 10^{6}$

Performing the operations:

| 6 | · | 3 | 2 | ÷ | 8 | = |

we get the answer to be 0·79. Hence:

$$\frac{0 \cdot 000\,632}{8\,000\,000} = 0 \cdot 79 \times 10^{-10} : \text{ or } 7 \cdot 9 \times 10^{-11}$$

Powers of numbers are very easy to obtain using some calculators.

Find $6 \cdot 358^{9}$

| 6 | · | 3 | 5 | 8 | × | = | = | = | = | = | = | = | = |

(The display is 16 977 927)

gives the required operations. Note that the number of equal signs is always one less than the power of the number. (This method does not apply to all calculators. If it does not work for yours then perform the operations $6 \cdot 358 \times 6 \cdot 358 = \times 6 \cdot 358 =$ until nine multiplications have been performed.)

Roots of numbers can only be found by using logarithms but, if desired, the division of the logarithm by the root can be performed on the calculator.

To give yourself practice on the calculator try exercises 48, 49 and 53 (numbers 11 to 20 inclusive).

Miscellaneous Exercise

Exercise 54

All the questions are of the type set in recent arithmetic examinations. The questions are of two types. Those in Section A are short answer type questions which should be answered fairly quickly. Those in section B are of the long answer type and should take about 20 minutes or so to answer.

Section A

1) Simplify $(2\frac{1}{2}-1\frac{1}{3})\div1\frac{5}{9}$

2) Simplify, without using tables, $\dfrac{2\cdot7\times0\cdot6}{0\cdot75}$

3) Simplify $2\frac{8}{9}\div(1\frac{2}{3}+\frac{1}{2})$

4) Find, without using tables, the exact value of $46\cdot002\div374$

5) Simplify $(2\frac{1}{2}-1\frac{3}{8})\times1\frac{1}{3}$

6) Simplify, without using tables, $\dfrac{0\cdot26\times14}{6\cdot5}$

7) When a number is divided by 73 the quotient is 11 and the remainder is 27; find the number.

8) Simplify $\dfrac{(3\frac{1}{2}\times1\frac{1}{2})-3}{9}$

9) Simplify $\dfrac{17\cdot6\times1\cdot5}{0\cdot33}$

10) Without using tables find the value of $2^{-1}\times8^{\frac{1}{3}}$

11) Use logarithms to find the fifth root of $0\cdot003\,148$

12) Evaluate $4^{-\frac{1}{2}}+\left(\dfrac{1}{27}\right)^{\frac{1}{3}}$

13) Write down using tables (a) $\dfrac{1}{0\cdot3057}$
(b) $(237\cdot5)^2$

14) Find the value of $\dfrac{5\cdot7\times10^5}{3\cdot8\times10^4}$

15) Find the value of $\sqrt{(12\cdot65)^2-(7\cdot35)^2}$

16) Find the value of $\left(\dfrac{1}{31\cdot25}\right)^2$

17) What is the value of $64^{\frac{1}{3}}$?

18) Find the value of $\sqrt{0\cdot327}$

19) Simplify $\dfrac{(10^2)^3\times10^5}{10^7}$

20) Using tables, find correct to three significant figures, the value of
$$\dfrac{1}{3\cdot65}+\dfrac{1}{0\cdot904}$$

21) Given that $\dfrac{1}{1\cdot684}=0\cdot5937$, write down the values of $\dfrac{1}{0\cdot016\,84}$ and $\dfrac{1}{5\cdot937}$

22) Multiply, without using tables, $23\cdot46$ by $0\cdot385$, giving your answer (i) exact, (ii) correct to 3 significant figures.

23) What is the fraction which is half way between $\frac{2}{7}$ and $\frac{6}{11}$?

24) Divide, without using tables, $873\cdot747$ by $2\cdot814$ exactly.

25) Given that $\dfrac{469\times564}{325\times329}=2\cdot4$, find the value of $\dfrac{4\cdot69\times0\cdot564}{3250\times0\cdot0329}$

26) Simplify $(6\frac{1}{3}-3\frac{1}{2}+2\frac{1}{6})\div3\frac{1}{3}$

27) Find the value of $\dfrac{7\times0\cdot3\times4\cdot8}{180\times3\cdot5}$ giving the answer as a decimal.

28) Express the number $35\cdot445\,49$ (i) correct to 3 signficant figures, (ii) correct to 3 decimal places, (iii) correct to the nearest 10.

29) Without using tables calculate the exact value of $3\cdot14\times(0\cdot5)^2$

30) Find the LCM of 16, 24 and 32.

31) Find the value of $\left(4\frac{1}{2}\right)^2$

32) Write down $\frac{5}{8}$ as a decimal.

33) Multiply 0·0405 by 24·8 giving the answer correct to 3 significant figures.

34) Find the difference between the largest and the smallest of $\frac{5}{8}$, $\frac{11}{18}$ and $\frac{17}{24}$.

35) Find the value of the product $1·25 \times 1·025 \times 1·0025$.

36) Express $4030 \div 401$ as a decimal correct to 3 decimal places.

37) Simplify $(\frac{1}{3}+\frac{1}{4}+\frac{1}{5})\times 1\frac{1}{5}$

38) Divide 52·26 by 7·8

39) Evaluate $\sqrt{(0·5)^2+(1·2)^2}$

40) Simplify $(2\frac{1}{4}+1\frac{5}{6})\times 3\frac{3}{7}$

Section B

41) $A = \frac{4}{5}, B = \frac{7}{8}, C = \frac{3}{4}$ and $D = \frac{8}{9}$

    (i) Arrange the above letters in order of size, the smallest first.
    (ii) Calculate $A+B-C$ as a decimal.
    (iii) Calculate $(A\times B)-(C\times D)$ as a fraction.

42) Calculate by logs:

    (a) $\dfrac{632·5\times 45·72}{(6·785)^2}$

    (b) $\sqrt{(9·563)^2-49·83}$

43) Use tables to find the value of:

    (a) $(0·5678)^2+(0·708)^3$
    (b) $\sqrt[3]{0·044\,67}$

44) Use tables to evaluate, correct to 3 significant figures:

    (a) $(0·0753)^3$

    (b) $\dfrac{1}{(0·0753)^3}$

    (c) $\dfrac{36·54}{0·9863}$

45) Use tables to evaluate:

    (i) $\sqrt{9\times 10^5}$

    (ii) $(0·7245)^3$

    (iii) $\dfrac{1}{1·577}+\dfrac{1}{0·853}$

46) Use tables to calculate
$$\frac{21·45\times 0·012\,97}{0·7128}$$

47) Use tables to find the value of
$$\frac{(6·962)^2\times 0·073\,25}{50·58}$$

48) Use logs to evaluate:

    (a) $\sqrt[3]{0·0822}$

    (b) $\dfrac{47·28\times (0·8129)^2}{723·9}$

49) Find the product of $4·47\times 10^7$ and $5·27\times 10^{-3}$. Give your answer in the form $A\times 10^n$, where A is a number between 1 and 10 and n is a positive integer.

50) Use logs to find the value of:

    (a) $\sqrt[3]{(0·6025)^2+0·3}$

    (b) $\sqrt{\dfrac{4·796}{24·86}}$

7. The Metric System

Introduction

In this chapter we shall first deal with the metric system as applied to mass and length. Then the addition, subtraction, multiplication and division of metric quantities are discussed. Finally domestic problems involving the metric system are discussed.

The Metric System of Length

The metric system is essentially a decimal system. The standard unit of length is the metre but for some purposes the metre is too large a unit and it is therefore split up into smaller units as follows:

$$1 \text{ metre (m)} = 10 \text{ decimetres (dm)}$$
$$= 100 \text{ centimetres (cm)}$$
$$= 1000 \text{ millimetres (mm)}$$

When dealing with large distances the metre is too small a unit and large distances are measured in kilometres.

$$1 \text{ kilometre (km)} = 1000 \text{ metres}$$

Since the metric system is essentially a decimal system we can easily convert from one unit to another by simply moving the decimal point the required number of places.

Example 1 Convert 3·792 m into centimetres.

$$1 \text{ m} = 100 \text{ cm}$$
$$3{\cdot}792 \text{ m} = 100 \times 3{\cdot}792 \text{ cm} = 379{\cdot}2 \text{ cm}$$

Example 2 Convert 98 375 mm into metres.

$$1000 \text{ mm} = 1 \text{ m}$$
$$1 \text{ mm} = \frac{1}{1000} \text{ m}$$
$$98\,375 \text{ mm} = \frac{98\,375}{1000} \text{ m} = 98{\cdot}375 \text{ m}$$

Sometimes you may have difficulty in deciding whether to multiply or divide when converting from one unit to another. If you remember that when converting to a smaller unit you multiply and when converting to a larger unit you divide, this difficulty will disappear.

The Metric System for Mass

The standard unit of mass is the kilogramme which is suitable for most purposes connected with weights and measures. However for some purposes the kilogramme is too large a unit and the gramme is then used. For very small masses the milligramme is used.

$$1 \text{ kilogramme (kg)} = 1000 \text{ grammes (g)}$$
$$1 \text{ gramme} = 1000 \text{ milligrammes (mg)}$$

Example 3   Convert 5397 mg into grammes

$$1000 \text{ mg} = 1 \text{ g}$$
$$1 \text{ mg} = \frac{1}{1000} \text{ g}$$
$$5397 \text{ mg} = \frac{5397}{1000} \text{ g} = 5\cdot397 \text{ g}$$

Example 4   Convert 2·56 kg into grammes.

$$1 \text{ kg} = 1000 \text{ g}$$
$$2\cdot56 \text{ kg} = 1000 \times 2\cdot56 \text{ g} = 2560 \text{ g}$$

Exercise 55

1) Convert to metres:
   (a) 5·63 km   (b) 0·68 km
   (c) 17·698 km   (d) 592 cm
   (e) 68 cm   (f) 6895 mm
   (g) 73 mm   (h) 4597 cm
   (i) 798 mm   (j) 5 mm

2) Convert to kilometres:
   (a) 9753 m   (b) 259 m
   (c) 58 m   (d) 2985 cm
   (e) 790 685 mm

3) Convert to centimetres:
   (a) 4·68 m   (b) 0·782 m
   (c) 5·16 km   (d) 3897 mm
   (e) 88 mm

4) Convert to millimetres:
   (a) 1·234 m   (b) 0·58 km
   (c) 25·8 cm   (d) 389 cm
   (e) 0·052 m

5) Convert to kilogrammes:
   (a) 530 g   (b) 35 000 g
   (c) 2473 mg   (d) 597 600 mg

6) Convert into grammes:
   (a) 56 000 mg   (b) 96 mg
   (c) 8·63 kg   (d) 0·081 kg
   (e) 584 mg

The Addition and Subtraction of Metric Quantities

When adding or subtracting lengths or masses it is important that all the quantities be converted to a common unit.

Example 5   Add together 36·1 m, 39·2 cm and 532 mm and express the answer in metres.

$$39\cdot2 \text{ cm} = \frac{39\cdot2}{100} \text{ m} = 0\cdot392 \text{ m}$$

$$532 \text{ mm} = \frac{532}{1000} \text{ m} = 0\cdot532 \text{ m}$$

We now have to add the lengths 36·1 m, 0·392 m and 0·532 m. We write the numbers down in the same way as when adding decimal numbers, that is, with the decimal points directly underneath each other. Thus

$$36 \cdot 1$$
$$0 \cdot 392$$
$$0 \cdot 532$$
$$\overline{}$$
$$37 \cdot 024$$

The answer is therefore, 37·024 m.

Example 6   From a length of cloth 120 m long, the following lengths are cut: $3\frac{1}{2}$ m, $30\frac{1}{4}$ m, 18 m 36 cm and 8 m 27 cm. What length of cloth remains?

Converting all the lengths to metres and decimals of a metre we have:

Lengths cut off = 3·5 m, 30·25 m, 18·36 m and 8·27 m

Adding these lengths together

$$3 \cdot 5$$
$$30 \cdot 25$$
$$18 \cdot 36$$
$$8 \cdot 27$$
$$\overline{}$$
$$60 \cdot 38$$

Hence the total length cut off the cloth is 60·38 m. To find the length remaining we have to subtract 60·38 m from 120 m. Thus

$$120 \cdot 00$$
$$60 \cdot 38$$
$$\overline{}$$
$$59 \cdot 62$$

Hence 59·62 m of cloth remains.

Exercise 56

1) Add together 39 cm, 3·62 m and 497 mm and express the answer in millimetres.

2) Add together 26·3 cm, 347 mm and 0·783 m and express the answer in metres.

3) A piece of cord 1·3 m long has the following lengths cut from it: 26 cm, $\frac{1}{2}$ m, 358 mm and 12 cm. How much cord remains?

4) Add together the following masses and express the answer in kilogrammes: 583 g, 19·164 kg and 20 500 mg.

5) A housewife buys the following items of food: 500 g tomatoes, 3 kg potatoes, 250 g butter and $\frac{1}{2}$ kg of sugar. What is the total mass of her purchases?

6) A greengrocer starts the day with 85 kg of apples. He sells $2\frac{1}{2}$ kg, 500 g, 2500 g, $3\frac{1}{4}$ kg and 2 kg 250 g. What mass of apples has he left?

7) A motorist drives 5·8 km to work, but on the way he has to make a detour of 750 m. He drives to an hotel for lunch which is a distance of 830 m from his office. He drives home without having to make a detour. How far, in kilometres, has he driven during the day?

8) Calculate the amount of ribbon left on a reel containing 50 m when the following lengths are cut: 50 cm, $\frac{1}{2}$ m, 2 m 30 cm and $4\frac{1}{4}$ m.

Multiplying and Dividing Metric Quantities

Multiplying and dividing metric quantities are done in the same way as the multiplication and division of decimal numbers.

Example 7

28 lengths of cloth each 3·8 m long are required for the manufacture of dresses. What total length of cloth is required?

Length required $= 28 \times 3\cdot 8$ m

$$
\begin{array}{r}
28 \\
38 \\
\hline
84 \\
224 \\
\hline
1064
\end{array}
$$

Placing the decimal point, we see that

total length of cloth required $= 106\cdot 4$ m.

Alternatively we can perform the multiplication by using logs.

number	log
28	1·4472
3·8	0·5798
Answer = 106·4	2·0270

Hence, as before, the total length of cloth required $= 106\cdot 4$ m.

Example 8

How many lengths of string each 79 cm long can be cut from a ball containing 54 m and what length remains?

To do this problem we can either bring 79 cm to metres or we can convert 54 m into centimetres. Adopting the latter course we have

$$54 \text{ m} = 54 \times 100 \text{ cm} = 5400 \text{ cm}$$

We now have to divide 5400 by 79. This is best done by taking logs. Thus

number	log
5400	3·7324
79	1·8976
Answer = 68·36	1·8348

Hence we can cut 68 lengths of string and a piece 0·36 of a length remains.

Length remaining $= 0\cdot 36 \times 79$ cm $= 28\cdot 4$ cm

Therefore we can cut 68 lengths of string and a piece 28·4 cm long remains.

Exercise 57

1) 47 pieces of wood each 85 cm long are required. What total length of wood, in metres, is needed?

2) 158 lengths of cloth each 3·2 m long are required. Find the total length of cloth needed.

3) 27 lengths of cloth each 2 m 26 cm are to be cut from a roll containing 80 m. What length of cloth remains?

4) How many lengths of string each 58 cm long can be cut from a ball containing 30 m and how much string remains?

5) How many lengths of wood 18 cm long can be cut from a plank $6\frac{1}{2}$ m long?

6) Frozen peas are packed in boxes which contain 450 g. What mass of peas are needed to fill 2340 boxes?

7) Calculate the number of pieces of wallpaper each 2·7 m long that can be cut from a roll 17 m long.

8) 6 curtains are required each 2 m long. Allowing 5 cm for turnover at the top and 5 cm at the bottom of each curtain, how much material is needed?

Domestic Problems

The examples which follow illustrate the type of problems which most householders will experience from time to time.

Example 9   A room 12 m long and 7·2 m wide is to be carpeted with strips of carpet 90 cm wide running parallel to the length of the room. How many metres of carpet 90 cm wide are required?

It is a good idea to draw a diagram (Fig. 7.1) so that we have a picture of the room in front of us.

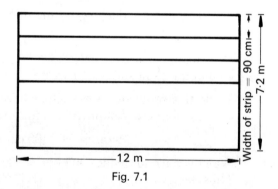

Fig. 7.1

$$\text{Since } 7\cdot2 \text{ m} = 7\cdot2 \times 100 \text{ cm} = 720 \text{ cm}$$
$$\text{number of strips required} = \frac{720}{90} = 8$$
$$\text{Total length of carpet 90 cm wide} = 8 \times 12 \text{ m} = 96 \text{ m}$$

Example 10   A room 6·2 m long, 8·3 m wide and 2·8 m high is to be papered. The width of the wallpaper is 80 cm and 7 pieces each 2·8 m long can be cut from each roll. Calculate the number of rolls of paper required. Neglect the allowance for doors and windows.

First make a drawing of the walls opened out as shown in Fig. 7.2. The total length of the walls is then seen to be $6\cdot2 + 8\cdot3 + 6\cdot2 + 8\cdot3 = 29$ m.

The problem now is to find how many times 80 cm will divide into 29 m. Converting 29 m into centimetres we have

$$\text{Number of pieces of wallpaper required} = \frac{2900}{80} = 36\cdot25$$

Hence we need 37 strips of paper and

$$\text{number of rolls required} = \frac{37}{7} = 5\cdot3$$

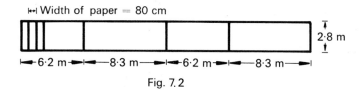

Fig. 7.2

Since we cannot buy 0·3 of a roll of wallpaper we must buy 6 rolls.

Example 11   Find the length of carpet required for a flight of 5 stairs having treads 21 cm wide and risers 19 cm high. Allow $1\frac{1}{4}$ m of carpet at the top and at the bottom.

First draw a diagram of the stairs (Fig. 7.3). Note that with the additional lengths at the top and bottom there are 5 risers but only 4 treads. Working in metres,

length of carpet required: 5 risers at 0.19 m = 0·95 m
4 treads at 0·21 m = 0·84 m
Top and bottom = 2·50 m

4·29 m

say $4\frac{1}{2}$ m

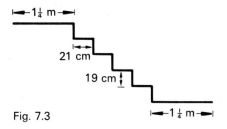

Fig. 7.3

Exercise 58

1) A customer wishes to cover a room 8 m by 7·2 m with vinyl strips 120 cm wide. If the strips are to be 8 m long find the length of vinyl needed.

2) A housewife wishes to carpet a room measuring 10·8 m long by 12·4 m wide. She chooses carpet which is 90 cm wide. If the strips are laid to run parallel to the width of the room, what length of carpet is required?

3) A hall measuring 9 m by 1·8 m is to be carpeted with strips 60 cm wide. What length of carpet is required?

4) A staircase having 9 steps is to be carpeted. The treads are 21·5 cm wide and the risers are 20 cm high. Allowing 2 m at the top and ½ m at the bottom, how much carpet is required?

5) A room is 8 m long, 6 m wide and 2·5 m high. The width of wallpaper is 80 cm and 7 strips each 2·5 m long can be cut from a roll. Calculate the number of rolls needed.

6) A certain wallpaper is available in rolls 17 m long and 75 cm wide. A room 6·3 m long and 5·8 m wide is to be papered with this wallpaper. If the room is 2·8 m high, how many rolls of paper are needed?

7) Calculate the length of stair carpet needed to cover a flight of 7 stairs if the treads are 32 cm wide and the risers 23 cm high. A length of 1½ m is to be allowed at the top and at the bottom.

Mental Test 7

Try to answer the following questions without writing anything down except the answer.

1) Add 15·2 m and 25 cm.

2) Convert 579 mm into centimetres.

3) How many metres are there in 9·7 km?

4) How many centimetres are there in 3·76 m?

5) Add 5½ m and 480 mm.

6) Multiply 9 cm by 20 and express the answer in metres.

7) 25 packets each having a mass of 360 mg are made up. What is their total mass in grammes?

8) A length of 9 m and one of 6 m are cut from a roll of cloth 29 m long. How much cloth remains?

9) From a stock of 2000 kg of sugar the following amounts were sold: 200 kg, 150 kg and 90 kg. How much sugar remains?

10) 100 kg of flour were made up into 500 g bags. How many bags were there?

11) What is the total mass of sugar required to fill 800 cartons each containing 250 g. Answer in kilogrammes.

12) How many lengths of cord each 20 cm long can be cut from a length of 5 m?

Self-Test 7

The answers to the following are either true or false. Write down the appropriate word.

1) 25 cm = 0·25 m

2) 4 cm = 0·4 m

3) 5 m = 500 mm

4) 2 km = 20000 cm

5) 8000 mm = 80 m

6) 5 × 80 cm = 4 m

7) 20 × 200 g = 4 kg

8) 1·5 m ÷ 30 = 50 mm

9) 1000 m = 0·01 km

10) 13·5 kg = 13 500 g

11) 18 g = 18 000 mg

12) 12 × 50 g = 0·6 kg

13) 3·5 kg ÷ 50 = 7 g

14) 50 mm × 9 = 4·5 cm

15) 80 mg × 15 = 1·2 g

8. Money and Simple Accounts

The British System

The British system of decimal currency uses the pound as the basic unit. The only sub-unit used is the penny such that

$$100 \text{ pence} = 1 \text{ pound}$$

The abbreviation p is used for pence and the abbreviation £ is used for pounds. A decimal point is used to separate the pounds from the pence, for example

£3·58 meaning three pounds and fifty-eight pence

There are two ways of expressing amounts less than £1. For example 74 pence may be written as £0·74 or 74 p; 5 pence may be written as £0·05 or as 5 p.

The smallest unit used is the half-penny which is always written as a fraction i.e. as $\frac{1}{2}$. Thus £5·17$\frac{1}{2}$ means 5 pounds and 17$\frac{1}{2}$ pence. 53$\frac{1}{2}$ pence is written as either 53$\frac{1}{2}$ p or as £0·53$\frac{1}{2}$. Note carefully that $\frac{1}{2}$ p = £0·005, a fact which is useful when solving some problems with decimal currency.

Addition and Subtraction

The addition of sums of money is done in almost the same way as the addition of decimals. The exception occurs with the half-pence piece.

Example 1

Add together £3·78, £5·23 and £8·19

£3·78 Write down the amounts with the decimal points directly
£5·23 beneath one another. First add the pence which total 120.
£8·19 This is equal to £1·20 so we write 20 in the pence columns
———— and carry the £1. Now add the pounds $1+8+5+3 = 17$.
£17·20

Example 2

Add together £2·58$\frac{1}{2}$, £3·27$\frac{1}{2}$ and £5·73$\frac{1}{2}$

£2·58$\frac{1}{2}$ First add the half-pence and we get 1$\frac{1}{2}$ p. Write $\frac{1}{2}$ in the
£3·27$\frac{1}{2}$ answer and carry 1 p. Now add the whole pence: $1+73+$
£5·73$\frac{1}{2}$ $27+58 = 159$ p. This is equal to £1·59 so write 59 in the
———— answer and carry £1. Finally add the pounds thus:
£11·59$\frac{1}{2}$ $1+2+3+5 = £11$.

Example 3

Add together 39 p, 84$\frac{1}{2}$ p and £1·73

£0·39 When amounts are given in pence it is best to write these as
£0·84$\frac{1}{2}$ pounds. Thus 39 p is written £0·39, etc. The addition is
£1·73 then performed as previously described.
————
£2·96$\frac{1}{2}$

Example 4   Subtract £2·36½ from £3·08

£3·08   We cannot take 36½ p from 8 p so we borrow £1 = 100 p
£2·36½   from the £3 on the top line. Then 108−36½ = 71½. The £3
———   becomes £2 and we have 2−2 = 0 thus giving an answer of
£0·71½   £0·71½ or 71½ p

Exercise 59

1) Express the following amounts as pence: £0·68, £0·63, £0·58½.

2) Express the following as pence: £2·16, £3·59½, £17·68.

3) Express the following as pounds: 35 p, 78½ p, 6 p, 3 p.

4) Express the following as pounds: 246 p, 983½ p, 26 532 p.

5) Add the following sums of money together:
   (a) £2·15, £3·28, £4·63
   (b) £8·28, £109·17, £27·98, £70·15
   (c) £0·17½, £1·63½, £1·71, £1·90½
   (d) 82 p, 71 p, 82 p
   (e) 17½ p, 27 p, 81½ p, 74½ p

6) Subtract the following:
   (a) £7·60 from £9·84
   (b) £3·49 from £11·42
   (c) £18·73½ from £87·35
   (d) £0·54½ from £1·32½
   (e) 54 p from £2·63½

Balancing

When dealing with the addition and subtraction of sums of money it is impossible to be too careful. Whenever possible checks should be made and one way of doing this is the method of balancing.

Example 5   The following table shows the amounts of money taken by various departments of a large store during six successive weeks.

	Grocery	Toys	Childs wear	Womens wear	Mens wear
Week 1	£2087·58	£976·43	£875·34	£1794·69	£1068·89
Week 2	£2165·42	£758·58	£918·89	£1689·73	£1265·98
Week 3	£2200·31	£834·67	£812·89	£2178·98	£1358·90
Week 4	£2178·95	£768·50	£805·12	£2334·42	£1234·56
Week 5	£2317·78	£812·34	£798·03	£3217·87	£1178·92
Week 6	£2412·67	£913·42	£821·76	£2816·33	£1245·89

Add separately each column and each row and check by obtaining the overall totals for each.

	Grocery	Toys	Childs wear	Womens wear	Mens wear	Totals
Week 1	£2087·58	£976·43	£875·34	£1794·69	£1068·89	£6802·93
Week 2	£2165·42	£758·58	£918·89	£1689·73	£1265·98	£6798·60
Week 3	£2200·31	£834·67	£812·89	£2178·98	£1358·90	£7385·75
Week 4	£2178·95	£768·50	£805·12	£2334·42	£1234·56	£7321·55
Week 5	£2317·78	£812·34	£798·03	£3217·87	£1178·92	£8324·94
Week 6	£2412·67	£913·42	£821·76	£2816·33	£1245·89	£8210·07
Totals	£13 362·71	£5063·94	£5032·03	£14 032·02	£7353·14	£44 843·84

The overall total is shown within the box. All the additions are correct if the overall total obtained by adding the vertical total column equals the overall total obtained by adding the horizontal total row.

Exercise 60

1) The table below shows the weekly expenditure of a household for four successive weeks. Find the total expenditure for each week and also the total expenditure for each item for the four weeks. Finally add together the vertical and horizontal totals to obtain the final total for the four weeks.

	Food	Clothing	Heating	Rent	Sundries	Totals
Week 1	£8·90	£3·16	£3·20	£6·00	£1·35	
Week 2	£7·85	£2·53	£4·16	£6·00	£0·78	
Week 3	£9·36	£4·98	£3·78	£6·00	£0·56	
Week 4	£8·63	£2·13	£5·06	£6·00	£1·25	
Totals						

2) The following table shows the earnings of 5 men during the month of July. Work out the vertical and horizontal totals as shown and by finding the overall total perform a balance.

	Man A	Man B	Man C	Man D	Man E	Totals
Week 1	£45·76	£39·88	£51·63	£87·62	£49·88	
Week 2	£42·89	£43·67	£54·68	£78·90	£51·27	
Week 3	£52·78	£64·68	£53·22	£80·81	£48·69	
Week 4	£77·83	£49·73	£50·00	£71·42	£36·25	
Totals						

3) The table below shows income tax deductions made from a women's earnings during six months of a tax year. Calculate the weekly and monthly totals and perform a balance.

	Week 1	Week 2	Week 3	Week 4	Week 5	Totals
April	—	£4·75	£4·28	£3·98	—	
May	£4·03	£4·16	£4·08	£4·27	—	
June	£3·79	£3·89	£4·33	£3·78	—	
July	£4·16	£4·12	£4·13	£4·33	£3·88	
August	£3·77	£6·23	£4·08	£3·77	—	
September	£3·99	£4·43	£4·00	£3·79	—	
Totals						

Financial Statements

It is important that you should be able to understand a financial statement. The one which is shown below is a statement for a Club dance.

	Income				*Expenditure*	
Date	**Particulars**	**Receipts**	**Date**	**Particulars**	**Payments**
8/6	Sale of 400 tickets @ £2	800·00	11/6	Hire of hall	75·00
			17/6	Printing of tickets	33·50
20/6	Sale of 250 tickets @ £2	500·00	23/6	Cost of band	180·00
23/6	Sale of tickets at door. 120 @ £2·50	300·00	23/6	Cost of buffet @ £1 per head	770·00
					1058·50
				Balance carried down	541·50
	Total	**£1600·00**			**£1600·00**

The statement shows clearly how much money has been received and how much has been spent. The balance carried down is the profit made on the dance and it is found by subtracting the total payments (£1058·50) from the total receipts (£1600·00). This balance is added to the total payments and both sides of the book i.e. income and expenditure should be the same.

The accounts for business transactions are kept in a book called the ledger which is usually ruled as shown in Example 6. The general rule for entering up ledger accounts is:

debit—the amounts of money placed in the account
credit—the amounts of money flowing out of the account

Example 6   Enter the following transactions in a Cash Account. Balance the account and bring down the balance.

1/5   Cash in hand £58·73
8/5   Paid telephone bill £33·40
10/5   Received cash from L. Thomas £29·00
12/5   Bought goods for cash £15·74
15/5   Cash sales £89·70
18/5   Paid into bank £75·00

Dr			Cash a/c		Cr
		£			£
May 1	To balance b/d	58·73	May 8	By telephone	33·40
May 10	" L. Thomas	29·00	May 12	" purchases	15·74
May 15	" sales	89·70	May 18	" bank	75·00
		177·43	May 20	" balance c/d	53·29
May 22	To balance	53·29			177·43

The following points should be carefully noted:

(1) The name of the account is Cash a/c (a/c stands for account).

(2) Left hand side: Dr = debit. Right hand side: Cr = credit.

(3) c/d stands for carried down. b/d stands for brought down.

(4) For the entries receipts are entered under Dr and payments are entered under Cr.

(5) On the debit side all entries are prefixed 'to' and the name of the account from which the money is received is stated.

(6) On the credit side all entries are prefixed 'by' and the name of the account into which the money is paid is stated.

(7) The opening balance is the amount left in the account from the previous period.

(8) The closing balance is the amount necessary for the account to balance. On the credit side the payments made amount to £33·40 + £15·74 + £75·00 = £124·14. The closing balance is found by subtracting this from the total receipts of £177·43 giving a closing balance of £53·29. Thus the account shows that we have a balance of £53·29 in our cash account on May 22nd.

Exercise 61

Draw up financial statements to show the following transactions taking care to balance the receipts and payments columns.

1) Hockey club accounts:

1/9 Annual subscriptions 32 members @ £1·50 each

10/9 Match fees for game v Old Manorians £5·50

10/9 Cost of teas for game v Old Manorians £4·20

10/9 Umpires expenses £0·75

17/9 Match fees for mixed game v Moorpark £4·20

17/9 Cost of teas £4·60

17/9 Umpires expenses £0·55

2) Annual outing of Youth Club:

5/7 Received £0·80 from each of 70 members

7/7 Received subsidy of £25 from General Committee

9/7 Hire of 2 coaches and drivers £36

9/7 Cost of 72 teas at 60 p each

3) Firm's annual sports day:

3/6 Received subsidy from directors £50·00

5/6 Received £31 from competitors

8/6 Hire of tents £29

8/6 Competitors prizes £73

8/6 Cost of raffle tickets and prizes £8·60

8/6 Sale of raffle tickets £27·30

4) Enter the following transactions in the Cash account. Balance the account and bring down the balance.

1st Jan   Cash in hand £39·47
5th Jan   Paid telephone account £17·89
8th Jan   Received cash from P. Smith £42·00
12th Jan   Bought goods for cash £53·25
29th Jan   Cash sales £108·75
31st Jan   Paid into bank £105·00

5) Enter the following transactions in a Cash account. Balance the account and bring down the balance.

3rd March   Cash in hand £97·57
9th March   Bought goods for cash £73·78
16th March Cash sales £128·97
18th March Received from T. Barnes £54·00
28th March Banked £175·00
30th March Bought postage stamps £3·40

Petty Cash Book

Most offices keep a small amount of cash available for day to day running expenses such as cost of postage stamps, stationery, etc. This cash is called petty cash and it is important that an account be kept of how the money is spent. The account is kept in the petty cash book and it is prepared in much the same way as the financial statements previously discussed.

Example 7   Enter the following transactions in a petty cash book.

1st Jan   Petty cash in hand £8·00
3rd Jan   Parcel post 75 p
4th Jan   Letter postage 84 p
5th Jan   Window cleaner £1·20
6th Jan   Purchase of stationery £1·35
7th Jan   Received reimbursement for the week's expenditure to keep balance in hand at £8·00

Receipts	Date	Particulars	Payments
8·00	1st Jan	Cash in hand	
	3rd Jan	Parcel post	0·75
	4th Jan	Letter Post	0·84
	5th Jan	Window cleaner	1·20
	6th Jan	Stationery	1·35
		Total	4·14
4·14	7th Jan	Reimbursement	
		Balance carried down	8·00
12·14			12·14

Sometimes it is desirable to know how much petty cash has been spent on the various items for a given period. For instance we might want to know how much has been spent on postage or on cleaning, etc. The method of entering the items shown in Example 7 is not very satisfactory in this respect because to obtain the information required means adding together several different entries. It is therefore better to set out the petty cash book in analysis columns as shown in Example 8.

Example 8

A petty cash book has analysis columns for postage, stationery, travelling expenses, office expenses and cleaning. Enter the following transactions:

2nd July Received from cashier £10
3rd July Bus fares 28 p, postage 49 p
4th July Envelopes 65 p, string 24 p
5th July Parcel post 76 p, office teas 70 p
6th July Window cleaning £2·30, railway fares £1·25
7th July Pencils 40 p, Cleaners wages £2·50
9th July Received reimbursement for the week's expenditure to keep balance in hand at £10

Receipts	Date	Particulars	Payments	Postage	Stationery	Travelling Expenses	Office Expenses	Cleaning
10·00	2nd July	Balance in hand						
	3rd July	Bus fares	0·28			0·28		
	3rd July	Postage	0·49	0·49				
	4th July	Envelopes	0·65		0·65			
	4th July	String	0·24		0·24			
	5th July	Parcel post	0·76	0·76				
	5th July	Office teas	0·70				0·70	
	6th July	Window cleaning	2·30					2·30
	6th July	Railway fares	1·25			1·25		
	7th July	Pencils	0·40		0·40			
	7th July	Cleaners wages	2·50					2·50
		Totals	9·57	1·25	1·29	1·53	0·70	4·80
9·57	9th July	Reimbursement						
		Balance carried down	10·00					
19·57			19·57					

Exercise 62

1) Enter the following transactions in a suitably ruled petty cash book:

8th Jan Petty cash balance in hand £9·00
9th Jan Postage 21 p, telegram 55 p
10th Jan Parcel post 93 p, window cleaner £1, bus fares 32 p
11th Jan Ball point pens 35 p, envelopes 64 p, Xerox copying 32 p
12th Jan Taxi fare 87 p, string 28 p
13th Jan Cleaners wages £3
15th Jan Reimbursement to keep balance in hand at £9

2) Enter the following transactions in a petty cash book which has analysis columns for postage, stationery, travelling expenses, cleaning and office expenses:

3rd Jan Petty cash balance in hand £12

4th Jan Postage 94 p, telegram 55 p, Xerox copying 64 p

5th Jan Pencils 48 p, train fare 78 p, office teas 68 p

6th Jan Window cleaning £1·35, typewriter ribbons 75 p

7th Jan Parcel postage 87 p, note-paper 80 p

8th Jan Office teas 75 p, Cleaners wages £3·50

10th Jan Reimbursement to keep cash in hand at £12

3) Enter the following transactions in a petty cash book which has three analysis columns for postage, stationery and travelling expenses.

5th June Balance in hand £16, postage stamps £2

6th June Telegram 75 p, envelopes 63 p, bus fares 28 p

7th June Note-paper 45 p, parcel post 98 p

8th June Erasers 35 p, railway fares 46 p, pencils 45 p

9th June Envelopes 54 p, string 36 p

12th June Reimbursement to keep cash in hand (or *float*) at £16

Multiplication and Division

The multiplication and division of decimal currency are very similar to the methods used with decimal numbers.

Example 9 Find the cost of 23 articles if each costs 27 p.

	number	log
Now 27 p = £0·27	23	1·3617
Cost of 23 articles @ £0·27 =	0·27	$\bar{1}$·4314
23 × £0·27 = £6·21	6·21	0·7931

Example 10 Find the cost of 19 articles costing $21\frac{1}{2}$ p each.

	number	log
Now $21\frac{1}{2}$ p = £0·215	19	1·2788
Cost of 19 articles @ £0·215 each = £4·08$\frac{1}{2}$	0·215	$\bar{1}$·3324
(Note that $\frac{1}{2}$ p = £0·005 and hence £4·085 = £4·08$\frac{1}{2}$)	4·085	0·6112

Example 11 If 127 articles cost £14·60$\frac{1}{2}$ find the cost of each article.

Now £14·60$\frac{1}{2}$ is a mixture of decimals and fractions and the first step is to make it into a wholly decimal number by remembering that $\frac{1}{2}$ p = £0·005. Hence
£14·60$\frac{1}{2}$ = £14·605.

£14·605 ÷ 127 = £0·11$\frac{1}{2}$ or 11$\frac{1}{2}$ p

	number	log
	14·605	1·1647
	127	2·1038
	0·1150	$\bar{1}$·0609

Exercise 63

1) Find the cost of 12 articles costing 15 p each.

2) Find the cost of 85 articles costing 7$\frac{1}{2}$ p each.

3) How much does 43 articles @ $39\frac{1}{2}$ p each cost?

4) What is the cost of 24 articles costing £7·03$\frac{1}{2}$ each?

5) If 12 identical articles cost £1·56, how much does each cost?

6) If 241 identical articles cost £51·81$\frac{1}{2}$, how much does each cost?

7) If 5000 articles cost £6525, find the cost of each article.

8) If 125 articles cost £270·62$\frac{1}{2}$, what is the cost of each article?

Invoices

An invoice is a record of the goods supplied by a manufacturer or wholesaler to a retailer. It looks rather like a bill but it is not a demand for payment. A copy of the invoice is usually sent by post to the purchaser when the goods are dispatched. At this stage only simple invoices are discussed; no attempt is made to deal with discounts etc., and the discount arrangements have been left out on the typical sample invoice shown below.

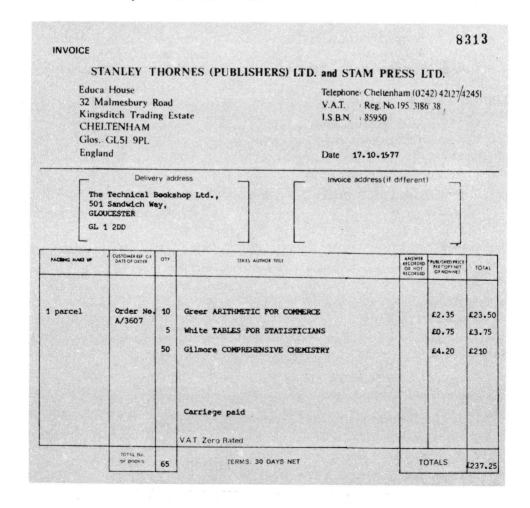

The last column is found by multiplying the quantity by the unit price. The total amount owed by the purchaser is £237·25, which is the total of the last column.

Exercise 64

Complete the following invoices:

1)

Quantity	Description	Unit cost	£
10	Single sheets	£2·25	
25	Double sheets	£4·05	
20	Bedspreads	£7·95	
5	Quilts	£12·80	

2)

Quantity	Description	Unit cost	£
20	Bath towels	£6·20	
15	Hand towels	£2·10	
30	Small towels	£1·36	
50	Flannels	£0·25	

Make out invoices for the following goods:

3) 50 m of rayon taffeta at $58\frac{1}{2}$ p per metre
   40 m nylon taffeta at £1·53 per metre
   35 m of rayon brocade at £1·47 per metre
   30 m nylon chiffon at £1·56 per metre

4) 4 bookshelves at £3·48 each
   5 wardrobes at £27·30 each
   6 beds at £19·55 each
   10 sideboards at £22·50 each
   20 dining room chairs at £5·45 each

5) 10 dolls at £1·98 each
   20 dolls' dresses at 45 p each
   5 dolls' prams at £12·35 each
   3 dolls' cots at £7·48 each
   4 dolls' beds at £3·48 each

Mental Test 8

Try to answer the following questions without writing down anything except the answer.

1) Add £1·36, £2·33 and £3·54.

2) Find the cost of 10 articles if they cost 6 p each.

3) Find the cost of 100 articles if they cost £1·20 each.

4) Find the cost of one article if 10 cost 75 p.

5) 100 similar articles cost £1·50. How much does each cost?

6) Find the cost of 20 articles at 15 p each.

7) 25 articles cost £5. How much does each cost?

8) Find the cost of 5 articles at 99 p each.

9) Find the cost of 8 articles at 99 p each.

10) Find the cost of 50 articles at 30 p each.

Self-Test 8

In the following questions decide if the given answer is true or false.

1) In the British system of decimal currency, 100 p = £1.

2) £1·78 means one pound and 78 pence.

3) 36 pence may be written as £.36.

4) One half-penny is equal to £0·005.

5) $58\frac{1}{2}$ p + 27 p is equal to £0·85$\frac{1}{2}$.

6) $73\frac{1}{2}$ p may be written as £0·735.

7) The cost of 5 articles each costing $7\frac{1}{2}$ p is £0·37$\frac{1}{2}$.

8) If 10 articles cost £3·75 the cost of each article is 37$\frac{1}{2}$ p.

9) If 25 articles cost £19 each article costs £0·76.

10) Sheets cost £2·75 each. The cost of 20 sheets is £55.

9. Ratio and Proportion

A ratio is a comparison between two similar quantities. If the length of a certain ship is 120 metres and a model of it is 1 metre long then the length of the model is $\frac{1}{120}$th of the length of the ship. In making the model the dimensions of the ship are all reduced in the ratio of 1 to 120. The ratio 1 to 120 is usually written $1:120$.

As indicated above a ratio may be expressed as a fraction and all ratios may be looked upon as fractions. Thus the ratio $2:5 = \frac{2}{5}$. The two terms of a ratio may be multiplied or divided without altering the value of the ratio. Hence $6:36 = 1:6 = \frac{1}{6}$. Again, $1:5 = 4:20$.

Before a ratio can be stated the units must be the same. We can state the ratio between 7 pence and £2 provided both sums of money are brought to the same units. Thus if we convert £2 to 200 p the ratio between the two amounts of money is $7:200$.

Example 1

Express the ratio 20 p to £4 in its simplest form.

$$£4 = 4 \times 100\,p = 400\,p$$

$$20:400 = \frac{20}{400} = \frac{1}{20}$$

Example 2

Express the ratio $4:\frac{1}{4}$ in is lowest terms.

$$4:\frac{1}{4} = 4 \div \frac{1}{4} = 4 \times \frac{4}{1} = \frac{16}{1}$$

$$4:\frac{1}{4} = 16:1$$

Example 3

Two lengths are in the ratio $8:5$. If the first length is 120 metres, what is the second length?

The second length $= \frac{5}{8}$ of the first length $= \frac{5}{8} \times 120 = 75$ metres.

Example 4

Two amounts of money are in the ratio of $12:7$. If the second amount is £21 what is the first amount?

First amount $= \frac{12}{7} \times £21 = £36$

Exercise 65

Express the following ratios as fractions in their lowest terms:

1) $8:3$

2) $4:6$

3) $12:4$

4) $9:15$

5) $8:12$

6) Express the ratio of 30 p to £2 as a fraction in its lowest terms.

7) Express the ratio £5 : 80 p as a fraction in its lowest terms.

8) Two lengths are in the ratio $7:5$. If the first length is 210 metres, what is the second length?

9) Two amounts of money are in the ratio $8:5$. If the second amount is £120, what is the first amount?

10) Express $3:\frac{1}{2}$ in its lowest terms.

Proportional Parts

The diagram (Fig. 9.1) shows a line AB whose length is 16 centimetres divided into two parts in the ratio 3:5. As can be seen in the diagram the line has been divided into a total of 8 parts. The length AC contains 3 parts and the length BC contains 5 parts. Each part is $\frac{16}{8} = 2$ centimetres long; hence AC is $3 \times 2 = 6$ centimetres long and BC is $5 \times 2 = 10$ centimetres long. We could tackle this problem in this way:

Total number of parts $= 3+5 = 8$ parts
Length of each part $\quad= \frac{16}{8} = 2$ centimetres
Length of AC $\quad\quad\quad= 3 \times 2 = 6$ centimetres
Length of BC $\quad\quad\quad= 5 \times 2 = 10$ centimetres

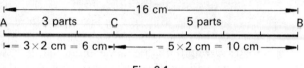

Fig. 9.1

Example 5   Divide £1100 into two parts in the ratio 7:3.

Total number of parts $\;= 7+3 = 10$
Amount of each part $= \frac{1100}{10} = £110$
Amount of first part $\quad= 7 \times 110 = £770$
Amount of second part $= 3 \times 110 = £330$

Example 6   An aircraft carries 2880 litres of fuel distributed in three tanks in the ratio 3:5:4. Find the quantity in each tank.

Total number of parts $= 3+5+4 = 12$
Amount of each part $\;= \frac{2880}{12} = 240$ litres
Amount of 3 parts $\quad= 3 \times 240 = 720$ litres
Amount of 4 parts $\quad= 4 \times 240 = 960$ litres
Amount of 5 parts $\quad= 5 \times 240 = 1200$ litres

The three tanks contain 720, 1200 and 960 litres.

Exercise 66

1) Divide £800 in the ratio 5:3.

2) Divide £80 in the ratio 4:1.

3) Divide £120 in the ratio 5:4:3.

4) A sum of money is divided into two parts in the ratio 5:7. If the smaller amount is £200, find the larger amount.

5) An alloy consists of copper, zinc and tin in the ratios 2:3:5. Find the amount of each metal in 75 kilogrammes of the alloy.

6) A line is to be divided into three parts in the ratios 2:7:11. If the line is 840 millimetres long, calculate the length of each part.

7) Two villages have populations of 336 and 240 respectively. The two villages are to share a grant of £10 728 in proportion to their populations. Calculate how much each village receives.

8) Four friends contribute sums of money to a charitable organisation in the ratio of 2:4:5:7. If the largest amount contributed is £1·40, calculate the total amount contributed by the four people.

Direct Proportion

Two quantities are said to vary directly, or be in direct proportion, if they increase or decrease at the same rate. Thus the quantity of petrol used and the distance travelled by a motor car are in direct proportion. Again if we buy potatoes at 20 pence for 2 kilogrammes then we expect to pay 40 p for 4 kilogrammes and 10 p for 1 kilogramme. That is if we double the amount bought then we double the cost; if we halve the amount bought we halve the cost.

In solving problems on direct proportion we can use either the unitary method or the fractional method. They are illustrated in Example 7.

Example 7
If 25 kilogrammes of butter cost £17 how much does 8 kilogrammes cost?

(1) Using the unitary method:

25 kilogrammes cost £17 or 1700 pence
1 kilogramme costs $\frac{1700}{25}$ = 68 pence
8 kilogrammes cost 8×68 = 544 pence or £5·44

(2) Using the fractional method:

Cost of 8 kilogrammes =
$$\frac{8}{25} \times 1700 = \frac{8 \times 1700}{25} = 544 \text{ pence or £5·44}$$

Example 8
A recipe for Boeuf Stroganoff quotes the following amounts to serve four people: 450 grammes of rump steak, 3 tablespoons flour, 4 tablespoons butter, 50 grammes of onion, 75 grammes of mushrooms, 140 grammes of sour cream. What amounts should be used for six people?

The quantities required and the number of people are in direct proportion. Hence the amounts must be increased in the ratio of 6:4 or 3:2.

Amount of rump steak $= \frac{3}{2} \times 450 = 675$ grammes
Amount of flour $\qquad = \frac{3}{2} \times 3 = 4\frac{1}{2}$ tablespoons
Amount of butter $\qquad = \frac{3}{2} \times 4 = 6$ tablespoons
Amount of onion $\qquad = \frac{3}{2} \times 50 = 75$ grammes
Amount of mushrooms $= \frac{3}{2} \times 75 = 112\frac{1}{2}$ grammes
Amount of sour cream $= \frac{3}{2} \times 140 = 210$ grammes

Exercise 67

1) If 7 kilogrammes of apples cost £2·80, how much does 12 kilogrammes cost?

2) If 74 exercise books cost £5·92, how much do 53 cost?

3) If 40 articles cost £35, how much does 1 article cost? What is the cost of 55 articles?

4) Eggs cost 70 p per 10. How much will 25 eggs cost?

5) A car travels 205 kilometres on 20 litres of petrol. How much petrol is needed for a journey of 340 kilometres?

6) The ingredients for a cake which will serve 12 people are as follows: 55 grammes of butter, 110 grammes of castor sugar, 6 egg yolks, 120 grammes plain flour and 3 tablespoons of milk. What quantities are needed to serve 4 people?

7) If 9 metres of carpet cost £21, how much will 96 metres cost?

8) A train travels 200 kilometres in 4 hours. How long will it take to complete a journey of 350 kilometres?

Inverse Proportion

Suppose that 8 men working on a certain job take 10 days to complete it. If we double the number of men then we should halve the time taken. If we halve the number of men then the job will probably take twice as long. This is an example of inverse proportion.

Example 9

20 men working in a factory produce 3000 articles in 12 working days. How long will it take 15 men to produce the 3000 articles?

The number of men is reduced in the ratio $\frac{15}{20} = \frac{3}{4}$
Since this is an example of inverse proportion the number of days required must be increased in the ratio $\frac{4}{3}$.

Number of days required $= \frac{4}{3} \times 12 = 16$ days

Exercise 68

1) A farmer employs 12 men to harvest his potato crop. They take 9 days to do the job. If he had employed 8 men how long would it have taken them?

2) 10 men produce 500 articles in 5 working days. How long would it take 15 men to produce the same amount?

3) Two gear wheels mesh together. One has 40 teeth and the other has 25 teeth. If the larger wheel makes 100 revolutions per minute how many revolutions per minute does the smaller wheel make?

4) A bag contains sweets. When divided amongst 8 children each child receives 9 sweets. If the sweets were divided amongst 12 children how many sweets would each receive?

5) 4 men can do a piece of work in 30 hours. How many men would be required to do the work in 6 hours?

Foreign Exchange

Every country has its own monetary system. If there is to be trade and travel between any two countries there must be a rate at which the money of one country can be converted into money of the other country. This rate is called the rate of exchange.

FOREIGN MONETARY SYSTEMS & EXCHANGE RATE JANUARY 1976

Country	Monetary unit	Rate of exchange
Belgium	100 centimes = 1 franc	BF 80·05 = £1
France	100 centimes = 1 franc	F 9·05 = £1
Germany	100 pfennig = 1 mark	DM 5·29 = £1
Greece	100 lepta = 1 drachma	DR 71 = £1
Italy	100 centesimi = 1 lira	Lit 1386 = £1
Spain	100 centimos = 1 peseta	Ptas 121 = £1
Switzerland	100 centimes = 1 franc	SWF 5·30 = £1
United States	100 cents = 1 dollar	$2·03 = £1

The methods used for direct proportion are applicable to problems in foreign exchange.

Example 10   If £1 = 120 Spanish pesetas, find to the nearest half-penny the value in British money of 1000 pesetas.

(1) Using the unitary method:

120 pesetas = £1

$$1 \text{ peseta} = £\frac{1}{120}$$

$$1000 \text{ pesetas} = £\frac{1}{120} \times 1000 = £\frac{1000}{120} = £8 \cdot 33\frac{1}{2}$$

(2) Using the fractional method:

$$1000 \text{ pesetas} = £\frac{1000}{120} = £8 \cdot 33\frac{1}{2}$$

Example 11   A tourist changes travellers cheques for £40 into French francs at 9·12 francs to the pound. How many francs does he get?

$$£40 = 40 \times 9 \cdot 12 \text{ francs} = 364 \cdot 8 \text{ francs}$$

Exercise 69

Where necessary give the answers to 2 places of decimals.
Using the exchange rates given above find:

1) The number of German marks equivalent to £15.

2) The number of Spanish pesetas equivalent to £25.

3) The number of United States dollars equivalent to £32.

4) The number of pounds equivalent to 223 United States dollars.

5) The number of pounds equivalent to 8960 Italian lire.

6) The number of Belgian francs equivalent to £98·50.

7) A transistor set costs £26·30 in the United Kingdom. An American visitor wants to purchase a set but wishes to pay in United States dollars. What is the equivalent price in dollars?

8) A tourist changes travellers cheques for £50 into Greek currency at 67 drachma to the £1. He spends 3120 drachma and changes the remainder back into sterling at the same rate. How much did the tourist receive?

9) Calculate the rate of exchange if a bank exchanges 810 Swedish krona for £90.

10) A person on holiday in France changed £80 into francs at a rate of 9·20 francs to the £1. His hotel expenses were 62 francs per day for eight days and his other expenses were 204 francs. On returning home he changed what francs he had left into sterling at a rate of 9·12 francs to the £1. How much did he receive to the nearest penny?

Partnerships

A partnership consists of two or more people who are carrying on a business or enterprise with a view to making a profit. Sometimes profits and losses are shared equally but often profits are shared in proportion to the amount of money that each partner has invested in the business.

Example 12   The profits of a business are to be shared in proportion to the amount of capital invested by each partner. A invests £6400 and B invests

£9600. How much should each partner receive if the profits are £5500?

$$\text{The total capital invested} \quad = £6400 + £9600 = £16\,000$$

$$\text{First partner's share of profits} = \frac{6400}{16\,000} \times £5500 = £2200$$

$$\text{Second partner's share} \quad = \frac{9600}{16\,000} \times £5500 = £3300$$

Alternatively we can proceed as follows:

Ratio of capital $= 6400 : 9600 = 2 : 3$
Total number of parts $= 2 + 3 = 5$
First partner's share $= \frac{2}{5} \times £5500 = £2200$
Second partner's share $= \frac{3}{5} \times £5500 = £3300$

Exercise 70

1) Two partners invest £3500 and £7000 respectively in an enterprise. The profits are to be shared in proportion to the capital invested. If the profits for a certain year are £6000, how much does each receive?

2) The profits of a business are shared in proportion to capital invested. A and B invest £5000 and £6000 respectively. How much will each receive from a profit of £22 000?

3) A, B and C invest £9000, £10 000 and £12 000 respectively in a business. The profits are to be shared in propor-tion to the capital invested. How much does each receive from a profit of £93 000?

4) A and B are in partnership in an enterprise and share profits in propor-tion to the amount of capital invested. Their capitals are £2500 and £3500 respectively. If A receives £1000 as his share of the profits, what were the total profits of the enterprise?

5) A, B and C invest, respectively, £6000, £8000 and £12 000 in a business venture. If C received £4500 as his share, how much did the other two receive?

Summary

1) A ratio is a comparison between two similar quantities. A ratio may be expressed as a fraction. Thus the ratio $5 : 7 = \frac{5}{7}$.

2) Before a ratio can be stated the units must be the same.

3) If a quantity is divided in the ratio of $3 : 4 : 5$ then it has been divided into $3 + 4 + 5 = 12$ parts altogether. The first part is $\frac{3}{12}$th of the total, the second part is $\frac{4}{12}$th of the total and the third part is $\frac{5}{12}$th of the total.

4) Two quantities are in direct proportion if they increase or decrease at the same rate. In solving problems on direct proportion either the unitary method or the fractional method may be used.

5) Two quantities vary inversely if when one is doubled the other is halved.

6) The rate at which the money of one country can be converted into the money of another country is called the *rate of exchange*. Prob-lems in exchange rates may be treated as problems in direct pro-portion.

7) The profits made by a partnership are usually shared in proportion to the amount of capital invested by each partner. Problems on partnerships are solved by using proportional parts.

Mental Test 9

Try to answer the following without writing down anything except the answer.

1) Express 3 : 6 as a fraction in its lowest terms.

2) Express 32 : 12 as a fraction in its lowest terms.

3) Express the ratio £4 : 50 p as a fraction in its lowest terms.

4) Two lengths are in the ratio 3 : 2. If the first length is 150 cm, what is the second length?

5) Two amounts of money are in the ratio 7 : 3. If the second amount is £45, what is the first?

6) Divide £600 in the ratio 7 : 3.

7) A sum of money is divided in the ratio 2 : 3. If the smaller amount is £20, what is the larger amount?

8) An alloy consists of copper, lead and zinc in the ratios 2 : 3 : 5. How much copper is there in 500 kg.

9) If 5 kg apples cost £2 how much do 7 kg cost?

10) If 20 articles cost £1 how much do 10 articles cost?

11) A train travels a distance of 200 km in 4 hours. How long will it take to complete a journey of 250 km?

12) 12 men take 10 days to complete a job. How long will it take 6 men?

13) A bag of sweets is divided between 4 children. Each receives 5 sweets. If the sweets were divided between 2 children how many would each receive?

14) If the rate of exchange is 120 pesetas = £1, how many pesetas does a traveller receive for £5?

15) A traveller gets 15 000 lira for £10. What is the rate of exchange?

Self-Test 9

In questions 1 to 15 the answer is either true or false. State which.

1) The ratio 6 : 3 is the same as the ratio 2 : 1.

2) The ratio 5 : 10 is the same as the ratio 2 : 1.

3) The ratios 20 : 100 : 300 are the same as the ratios 1 : 5 : 15.

4) The fraction $\frac{2}{3}$ means the same as the ratio 2 : 3.

5) The ratio 18 : 24 is the same as $\frac{3}{4}$.

6) The ratio 18 : 30 is the same as $\frac{5}{2}$.

7) The ratio 9 : 2 may be written $4\frac{1}{2}$: 1.

8) The ratio 8 pence : £4 is the same as $\frac{2}{1}$.

9) The ratio 70 pence : £1·40 is the same as $\frac{1}{2}$.

10) When £600 is divided in the ratio 3 : 2 the two amounts are £360 and £240.

11) When £900 is divided in the ratios 2 : 3 : 5 the three amounts are £200, £300 and £400.

12) If 120 Belgian francs are worth £1·50 then the exchange rate is 80 Belgian francs to the £1.

13) The exchange rate for the French franc is 9·12 francs = £1. The franc is therefore worth about 11 pence.

14) In Italy 100 centesimi = 1 lira and 1500 lira = £1. The centesimi is therefore worth about 0·07 pence.

15) Two partners invest £500 and £1000 in a business. If the profits are shared in proportion to the amount invested then if the profits are £1200 each receives £600.

In questions 16 to 22 state the letter corresponding to the correct answer.

16) When £1200 is divided in the ratio 7 : 5 the smallest amount is:
    a £700 **b** £500 **c** £240 **d** £480

17) When £360 is divided in the ratio 5 : 4 : 3 the smallest amount is:
    a £30   **b** £150 **c** £120 **d** £90

18) A, B and C share a sum of money in the ratio $7:5:14$. If B receives £18 less than C, then C receives:

   a £28 **b** £14 **c** £10 **d** £52

19) An alloy contains copper, lead and tin in the ratios of $15:3:2$. The amount of lead in 400 kg of the alloy is:

   a 300 kg **b** 60 kg **c** 40 kg **d** 200 kg

20) A line 920 cm long is divided into four parts in the ratios $15:13:10:8$. The longest part is:

   a 260 cm   **b** 200 cm

   c 300 cm   **d** 160 cm

21) X, Y and Z share a sum of money in the ratios $7:8:16$. Z receives £27 more than X. The sum of money that is shared is:

   a £279 **b** £558 **c** £93 **d** £48

22) 40 men working in a factory produce 6000 articles in 12 working days. The length of time required for 15 men to produce the 6000 articles is.

   a 32 days   **b** $4\frac{1}{2}$ days

   c 64 days   **d** 9 days

10. Percentages

When comparing fractions it is often convenient to express them with a denominator of a hundred. Thus:

$$\frac{1}{2} = \frac{50}{100}$$

$$\frac{2}{5} = \frac{40}{100}$$

Fractions expressed with a denominator of 100 are called *percentages*. Thus:

$$\frac{1}{4} = \frac{25}{100} = 25 \text{ per cent}$$

$$\frac{3}{10} = \frac{30}{100} = 30 \text{ per cent}$$

The sign % is usually used instead of the words per cent.

To convert a fraction into a percentage we multiply it by 100.

Examples 1

$$\frac{3}{4} = \frac{3}{4} \times 100\% = 75\%$$

$$\frac{17}{20} = \frac{17}{20} \times 100\% = 85\%$$

Exercise 71

Convert the following fractions to percentages:

1) $\frac{7}{10}$

2) $\frac{11}{20}$

3) $\frac{9}{25}$

4) $\frac{4}{5}$

5) $\frac{31}{50}$

6) $\frac{1}{4}$

7) $\frac{9}{10}$

8) $\frac{19}{20}$

Decimal numbers may be converted into percentages by using the same rule. Thus:

$$0{\cdot}3 = \frac{3}{10} = \frac{3}{10} \times 100 = 30\%$$

The same result is produced if we omit the intermediate step of turning $0{\cdot}3$ into a vulgar fraction and just multiply $0{\cdot}3$ by 100. Thus:

$$0{\cdot}3 = 0{\cdot}3 \times 100\% = 30\%$$

Examples 2

$$0{\cdot}56 = 0{\cdot}56 \times 100\% = 56\%$$
$$0{\cdot}683 = 0{\cdot}683 \times 100\% = 68{\cdot}3\%$$

Exercise 72

Convert the following decimal numbers into percentages:

1) 0·7

2) 0·73

3) 0·68

4) 0·813

5) 0·927

6) 0·333

7) 0·819

To convert a percentage into a fraction we divide by 100.

Examples 3

$$45\% = \frac{45}{100} = 0{\cdot}45$$

$$3{\cdot}9\% = \frac{3{\cdot}9}{100} = 0{\cdot}039$$

Note that all we have done is to move the decimal point 2 places to the left.

Exercise 73

Convert the following percentages into decimal fractions:

1) 32%   4) 24%   7) 2·5%   10) 20·1%
2) 78%   5) 31·5%   8) 1·25%
3) 6%   6) 48·2%   9) 3·95%

Percentage of a Quantity

It is easy to find the percentage of a quantity if we first express the percentage as a fraction.

Examples 4

1) What is 10% of 40?

Expressing 10% as a fraction it is $\frac{10}{100}$ and the problem then becomes: what is $\frac{10}{100}$ of 40?

$$10\% \text{ of } 40 = \frac{10}{100} \times 40 = 4$$

2) What is 25% of £50?

$$25\% \text{ of } £50 = \frac{25}{100} \times £50 = £12{\cdot}50$$

3) 22% of a certain length is 55 cm. What is the complete length?

We have that 22% of the length = 55 cm

$$1\% \text{ of the length} = \frac{55}{22} \text{ cm} = 2{\cdot}5 \text{ cm}$$

Now the complete length will be 100%, hence:

$$\text{Complete length} = 100 \times 2{\cdot}5 \text{ cm} = 250 \text{ cm}$$

Alternatively

$$22\% \text{ of the length} = 55 \text{ cm}$$

$$\text{Complete length} = \frac{100}{22} \times 55 = \frac{100 \times 55}{22} = 250 \text{ cm}$$

4) What percentage is 37 of 264? Give the answer correct to 5 significant figures.

$$\text{Percentage} = \frac{37}{264} \times 100 = \frac{37 \times 100}{264} = 14{\cdot}015\%$$

Exercise 74

1) What is:
  (a) 20% of 50   (b) 30% of 80   (c) 5% of 120   (d) 12% of 20

(e) 20·3% of 105   (f) 3·7% of 68?

2) What percentage is:
    (a) 25 of 200   (b) 30 of 150
    (c) 24 of 150   (d) 29 of 178
    (e) 15 of 33?

Where necessary give the answer correct to 3 significant figures.

3) A girl scores 36 marks out of 60 in an examination. What is her percentage mark? If the percentage needed to pass the examination is 45% how many marks are needed to pass?

4) If 20% of a length is 23 cm what is the complete length?

5) Given that 13·3 cm is 15% of a certain length, what is the complete length?

6) What is:
    (a) 9% of £80   (b) 12% of £110
    (c) 75% of £250?

7) Express the following statements in the form of a percentage:
    (a) 3 eggs are bad in a box containing 144 eggs.
    (b) In a school of 650 pupils, 20 are absent.
    (c) In a school of 980 pupils, 860 eat school lunches.

8) In a certain county the average number of children eating lunches at school was 29 336 which represents 74% of the total number of children attending school. Calculate the total number of children attending school in that county.

9) 23% of a consignment of bananas is bad. There are 34·5 kg of bad bananas. How many kilograms were there in the consignment?

10) A retailer accepts a consignment of 5000 ball point pens. He finds that 12% are faulty. How many faulty pens were there?

Percentage Profit and Loss

When a dealer buys or sells goods, the cost price is the price at which he buys the goods and the selling price is the price at which he sells the goods. If the selling price is greater than the cost price then a profit is made. The amount of profit is the difference between the selling price and the cost price. That is:

$$\text{Profit} = \text{selling price} - \text{cost price}$$

The profit per cent is always calculated on the cost price. That is:

$$\text{Profit \%} = \frac{\text{selling price} - \text{cost price}}{\text{cost price}} \times 100$$

If a loss is made the cost price is greater than the selling price. The loss is the difference between the cost price and the selling price. That is:

$$\text{Loss} = \text{cost price} - \text{selling price}$$

$$\text{Loss \%} = \frac{\text{cost price} - \text{selling price}}{\text{cost price}} \times 100$$

Examples 5

1) A shopkeeper buys an article for £5·00 and sells it for £6·00. What is his profit per cent?

We are given: cost price = £5 and selling price = £6

$$\text{Profit \%} = \frac{6-5}{5} \times 100 = \frac{1}{5} \times 100 = 20\%$$

2) A dealer buys 20 articles at a total cost of £5. He sells them for 30 p each. What is his profit per cent?

$$\text{Since } £5 = 500\,\text{p, cost price per article} = \frac{500}{20} = 25\,\text{p}$$

$$\text{Profit } \% = \frac{30-25}{25} \times 100 = \frac{5}{25} \times 100 = 20\%$$

3) A man buys a car for £1600 and sells it for £1200. Calculate his percentage loss.

$$\text{Loss} = \text{cost price} - \text{selling price} = £1600 - £1200 = £400$$

$$\text{Loss} \% = \frac{400}{1600} \times 100 = 25\%$$

Exercise 75

1) A shopkeeper buys an article for 80 p and sells it for £1. Calculate the percentage profit.

2) Calculate the profit per cent when:
(a) Cost price is £1·50 and selling price is £1·80.
(b) Cost price is 30 p and selling price is 35 p.

3) Calculate the loss per cent when:
(a) Cost price is 75 p and selling price is 65 p.
(b) Cost price is £6·53 and selling price is £5·88.

4) A greengrocer buys a box of 200 oranges for £5. He sells them for 3 p each. Calculate his percentage profit.

5) A dealer buys 100 similar articles for £60 and sells them for 80 p each. Find his profit per cent.

6) A retailer buys 30 articles at 8 p each. Three are damaged and unsaleable but he sells the others at 10 p each. What is the profit per cent?

7) A car is bought for £1700 and sold for £1400. What is the loss per cent?

8) The price of coal has increased from £20 to £22 per 1000 kilogrammes. What is the percentage increase in the price of coal?

Mark Up

The mark up is the same as the percentage profit calculated on the cost price. That is:

$$\text{Mark up} = \frac{\text{selling price} - \text{cost price}}{\text{cost price}} \times 100$$

Examples 6

1) A butcher buys a 15 kilogramme lamb for £7·50. He sells it at 65 p per kilogramme. Calculate the mark up.

$$\text{Cost price} \quad = \frac{750}{15} = 50\,\text{p per kilogramme}$$

$$\text{Selling price} = 65\,\text{p per kilogramme}$$

$$\text{Mark up} \quad = \frac{65-50}{50} \times 100 = 30\%$$

2) Calculate the selling price of potatoes if they are bought for £5 per 50 kg bag and the mark up is 25 %.

In questions of this type it is a good idea to set out the information in the form of a table, as shown below:

	Cost price	Profit	Selling price
%	100	25	125
p	10	$2\frac{1}{2}$	$12\frac{1}{2}$

Note that in problems on mark up the cost price is always 100% and that the selling price is the cost price plus the profit, in this case 100%+25% = 125%. In the second row the cost price is $\frac{500}{50}$ = 10 p per kilogramme. The profit is $10 \times \frac{25}{100} = 2\frac{1}{2}$ p per kg whilst the selling price is $10p + 2\frac{1}{2}p = 12\frac{1}{2}$ p per kg.

3) A retailer sells a dining table for £156. If his mark up is 30% find how much he paid for the table.

Drawing up a table as before, we have:

	Cost price	Profit	Selling price
%	100	30	130
£			156

So we have that 130% = £156. We now have to find 100%. We can use the unitary method. Thus:

$$130\% = £156$$

$$1\% = £\frac{156}{130}$$

$$100\% = £\frac{156}{130} \times 100 = £120$$

Hence the cost price is £120.

Exercise 76

1) A carpet shop buys carpet at £3 per metre length and sells it for £3·60 per metre. What is the mark up?

2) A greengrocer buys grapefruit at £16 for a box of 200. He sells them for 10 p each. Calculate his mark up.

3) A store buys dress material at £1.20 per metre length. If the mark up is to be 25% calculate the selling price of the material.

4) A department store buys washing machines for £45 each. Calculate the selling price of the machines if the mark up is 30%.

5) A dealer buys 20 secondhand electric fires for £50. His mark up is 50%. How much is his selling price for each fire?

6) A furniture shops sells dining chairs at £20 each. If the mark up is 25% what is the cost price of the chairs?

7) A carpet is sold to a customer for £98. If the mark up is 40%, find the cost price of the carpet.

8) A greengrocer sells oranges at 8 p each. If his mark up is $33\frac{1}{3}$% find how much was paid for a box of 100 oranges.

9) A baker has weekly takings of £1350. If his mark up is 20%, calculate his weekly profit.

10) A book shop has monthly sales of £6000. If the mark up is 30% calculate the monthly profit.

Margin

Although it is usual to calculate the profit as a percentage of the cost price it is much simpler for a retailer to calculate his profit as a percentage of the selling price. This is because his till shows the amount of his takings per day or per week and if his profit is calculated on the selling price it is easy to calculate his percentage profit. When the profit is stated as a percentage of the selling price it is called the *margin*.

Example 7   A retailer finds that a week's takings amount to £1200. His margin is 20%. Calculate his weekly profit, the mark up and the cost price of the goods sold.

Setting the information out in the form of a table we have:

	Cost price	Profit	Selling price
%	80	20	100
£			1200

Note that in problems dealing with margin we make the selling price equal to 100%.

$$100\% = £1200$$
$$1\% = \frac{£1200}{100} = £12$$
$$20\% = £12 \times 20 = £240$$
$$80\% = £12 \times 80 = £960$$

Hence the profit is £240 and the cost price if £960. Hence:

$$\text{Mark up} = \frac{240}{960} \times 100 = 25\%$$

Relation Between Margin and Mark Up

The method of dealing with margins and mark up is best illustrated by means of an example.

Example 8   A grocer marks up his goods by 30%. What is his margin?

The easiest way is to assume that he sells goods which cost him £100. Then:

Profit $= 30\%$ of £100 $= £30$
Selling price $= £100 + £30 = £130$
Margin $= \dfrac{\text{profit}}{\text{selling price}} \times 100 = \dfrac{30}{130} \times 100 = 23 \cdot 08\%$

Exercise 77

1) A dealer finds that his weekly takings are £1500. If his margin is 20% calculate his weekly profit.

2) A retailer has daily takings of £250. If his margin is 25% calculate his profit, mark up, and the cost price of the goods sold.

3) A grocer works on a mark up of 40%. What is his margin?

4) A furniture store works on a margin of 20%. What is the mark up?

5) A firm has a profit margin of 40% on the goods it sells. If the firm makes a profit during one month of £9600 calculate the value of the goods sold.

6) A carpet shop works on a margin of 35%. What is the mark-up? If its sales during one week are £530, what profit has it made?

7) A grocer marks up the cost of butter which he sells by 30%. Calculate his margin as a percentage of the selling price.

8) A butcher buys a 15 kg lamb for £9 and he sells it for 75 p per kg. Calculate his margin as a percentage of the selling price.

Gross and Net Profits

We have seen that the profit is found by subtracting the cost price from the selling price. This gives us the *gross profit*. However trades people usually have to take other expenses into account in calculating their *net profit*. For instance there will be wages to pay to assistants, running expenses for vans and other transport, rates, etc. These extra expenses are called *overheads*. In order to calculate the net profit these overheads must be subtracted from the gross profit. The total sales or takings are usually called the *turnover*.

$$\text{Gross profit} = \text{turnover} - \text{cost price}$$
$$\text{Net profit} = \text{gross profit} - \text{overheads}$$

Example 9

The sales of a store during a certain year were £35 000. The cost price of the goods sold was £22 000 and the overheads were £7000. Calculate:
(a) the gross profit and the net profit,
(b) the gross profit and net profit as a percentage of the turnover,
(c) the gross profit and the net profit as a percentage of the cost price.

(a) Gross profit = £35 000 − £22 000 = £13 000
    Net profit   = £13 000 − £7000 = £6000

(b) Gross profit % = $\dfrac{13\,000}{35\,000} \times 100 = 37 \cdot 1 \%$

    Net profit %   = $\dfrac{6000}{35\,000} \times 100 = 17 \cdot 1 \%$

(c) Gross profit % = $\dfrac{13\,000}{22\,000} \times 100 = 59 \cdot 1 \%$

    Net profit %   = $\dfrac{6000}{22\,000} \times 100 = 27 \cdot 3 \%$

Exercise 78

1) The sales of a small business totalled £38 000 during a certain year. If the cost price of the goods sold was £23 000 and the overheads were £7000, find:
(a) the net profit and the gross profit,
(b) the net and gross profit expressed as a percentage of the turnover,
(c) the net profit and gross profit expressed as a percentage of the cost price.

2) A grocer sells goods to the value of £250 per week and in doing so makes a gross profit of 25%. If his overheads amount to £20 per week find:
(a) the net profit per week,
(b) the net profit per week expressed as a percentage of weekly sales.

3) A small shopkeeper expects to make a net profit of £4200 in a year's trading. During the year the cost price of the goods he sells amount to £18 000 and his overheads amount to £4000. Calculate his annual sales so that he can make the expected profit and express this profit as a percentage of his annual sales.

4) The weekly sales of a confectioner amount to £350 per week and the cost price of his goods average out to £220 per week. He rents his shop at £28 per week and he pays an assistant £32 per week. Calculate:
(a) the net profit per week,
(b) the net profit expressed as a percentage of sales,
(c) the net profit expressed as a percentage of the cost price of the goods sold.

5) A chemist has total sales of £45 000

per year and the cost price of the goods he sells amount to £30 000 per year. His overheads consist of rates £450 per year, salaries £3000 per year, heating £530 per year and lighting £250 per year. Calculate:

(a) the gross profit,

(b) the overheads,

(c) the net profit,

(d) the net profit expressed as a percentage of the turnover,

(e) the net profit expressed as a percentage of the cost price.

Discount

When a customer buys an article from a retailer for cash he will often ask the retailer for a discount. This discount, which is usually a percentage of the selling price, is the amount which the retailer will take off his selling price thus reducing his profit.

Example 10 A radiogram is offered for sale at £60. A customer is offered a 10% discount for cash. How much does the customer actually pay?

$$\text{Discount} \quad = 10\% \text{ of } £60 = \frac{10}{100} \times £60 = £6$$

Amount paid by customer = £60−£6 = £54

(*Alternatively:* since only 90% of the selling price is paid,

$$\text{Amount customer pays} = 90\% \text{ of } £60 = \frac{90}{100} \times £60 = £54)$$

Sometimes discounts are quoted as so much in the pound, for instance 5 p in the £1. If we remember that 5 p in the £1 is the same as 5% then the calculation of discounts is the same as that shown in Example 10.

Example 11 How much will a girl pay for goods priced at £12·50 if a discount of 8 p in the £1 is offered for cash?

8 p in £1 is the same as 8%

$$\text{Discount} = \frac{8}{100} \times £12·50 = £1·00$$

Amount paid by the girl = £12·50−£1·00 = £11·50

Exercise 79

1) A chair marked for sale at £14 is sold for cash at a discount of 10%. What price did the customer pay?

2) A tailor charges £30 for a suit of clothes but allows a discount of 5% for cash. What is the cash price?

3) A grocer offers a discount of $2\frac{1}{2}$% to his customers provided their bills are paid within one week. If a bill of £7·25 is paid within one week, how much discount will the grocer allow?

4) A shop offers a discount of 5 p in the £1. How much discount will be allowed on a washing machine costing £85?

5) A furniture store offers a discount of 7 p in the £1 for cash sales. A customer buys a three piece suite priced at £285. How much will she actually pay?

Trade Discount

Trade discounts are discounts offered by a manufacturer, or a wholesaler to a retailer. The list price quoted by the manufacturer is the price at which the retailer is expected to sell the article. Trade discounts are usually of the order of 20%, 25% or $33\frac{1}{3}$%.

Example 12

A manufacturer offers a trade discount of 25% to retailers. Calculate the price a retailer will pay for an article if it is listed by the manufacturer at £160.

$$\text{Trade discount} = 25\% \text{ of } £160 = \frac{25}{100} \times £160 = £40$$

$$\text{Price to retailer} = £160 - £40 = £120$$

Sometimes a manufacturer will offer an additional discount for an early settlement by the retailer.

Example 13

A manufacturer invoices his goods to a retailer less a trade discount of $33\frac{1}{3}$% and a further discount of 5% if the account is settled within 28 days. How much will the retailer actually pay for goods invoiced at £270 if he gets the benefit of both discounts?

First note that $33\frac{1}{3}$% is the same as $\frac{1}{3}$.

Trade discount $= 33\frac{1}{3}$% of £270 $= \frac{1}{3}$ of £270 $= £90$

Price to retailer $= £270 - £90 = £180$

Cash discount $= 5\%$ of £180 $= \frac{5}{100} \times £180 = £9$

Amount retailer actually pays $= £180 - £9 = £171$

(Note carefully that it is wrong to add the two discount percentages together thus saying that the total discount is $38\frac{1}{3}$%. The actual total discount is $36\frac{2}{3}$%.)

Sometimes problems occur in which we are told the discounts and the price the retailer pays. We are then asked to find the list or wholesale price.

Example 14

A housewife's grocery bill, after a deduction of a discount of 5%, amounts to £4·75. What is the gross amount of the bill?

Since the discount is 5% the amount paid is 95% of the gross amount. That is:

$$95\% = £4\cdot75$$

The gross amount is represented by 100%. Hence:

$$\text{Gross amount of bill} = \frac{100}{95} \times £4\cdot75 = £5$$

Example 15

A wholesaler allows a retailer a trade discount of 25% and a cash discount of 5% for immediate settlement. What is the wholesale price of goods for which the retailer pays £14·25.

Let wholesale price $= £100$

Less trade discount of 25% $= 75\%$ of £100 $= £75$

Less cash discount of 5% $= 95\%$ of £75 $= £71\cdot25$

Hence the ratio:

wholesalers price : retailers price $= 100 : 71 \cdot 25$

wholesalers price $= \dfrac{100}{71 \cdot 25} \times £14 \cdot 25 = £20$

Invoices with Discount

We have already dealt with invoices without discount on page 81. An invoice is a document which states the quantity, description and price of goods sold. It also gives details of any discounts and it is sent to the purchaser when the goods are despatched.

The following is a typical invoice:

INVOICE

No. 93   25 Great St
                                                                                London W1

N. Green, Esq.,
17 South St,
Cheltenham

Bought of S. Brown

Terms $2\frac{1}{2}\%$ one month

30 pairs shoes at £5·75 per pair	£172·50
20 pairs slippers at £2·20 per pair	44·00
40 pairs plimsolls at £1·80 per pair	72·00
	288·00
Less 20% discount	57·60
	£230·40

N. Green now owes S. Brown £230·40 but if he pays the account within one month he will be allowed a further $2\frac{1}{2}\%$ discount. Hence the amount he will actually pay is $97\frac{1}{2}\%$ of £230·40 or £224·64.

Exercise 80

1) A manufacturer offers a discount of 25% of an article which is listed at £224. How much will a retailer pay for it?

2) A wholesaler's list price for an article is £15. If he offers a trade discount of $33\frac{1}{3}\%$, how much will a retailer pay for the article?

3) A manufacturer offers a trade discount of 25%. A retailer pays £150 for a certain item. What is the manufacturer's price?

4) A car is listed by a manufacturer at £850. A garage owner buys it from the manufacturer for £595. What is the trade discount per cent?

5) A retailer pays £203 to a wholesaler for goods on which the wholesaler allows a discount of $33\frac{1}{3}\%$. What is the wholesaler's price?

6) A manufacturer allows a retailer a trade discount of 20% and a cash discount of 5% if payment is made within seven days. If the manufacturer's list price is £240, how much does the retailer pay if he gains the benefit of both discounts.

7) A wholesaler gives a trade discount of 25% to retailers and a cash discount of $2\frac{1}{2}\%$ provided settlement is made within one month. If a retailer pays

£146·25, how much is the wholesaler's list price?

8) A car is listed at £1600 by the manufacturer. A retailer in buying the car is offered a trade discount of 25% together with a cash discount of 3% for settlement within 28 days. If the retailer is entitled to both discounts, how much does he pay the manufacturer?

9) A wholesaler allows a retailer a 20% trade discount and a 5% discount for prompt payment. What is the wholesale price for goods for which the retailer paid £7·60?

10) Prepare an invoice for the following:
  50 pairs of double sheets at £8 per pair
  30 pairs of single sheets at £6 per pair

80 pillowcases at 75 p each
20 bedspreads at £7·55 each
The terms are 25% trade discount. If a cash discount of $2\frac{1}{2}$% is allowed for prompt payment, how much does a retailer pay for the goods?

11) Make out an invoice for the following. The terms are: a trade discount of 20% and a cash discount of 3% for payment within 7 days.
  250 pairs of socks at 45 p per pair
  150 pullovers at £4·35 each
  40 cricket sweaters at £8·70 each
  50 assorted ties at 90 p each

12) A retailer pays £8·64 for goods after a trade discount of 25% and a cash discount of 4% have been deducted. Calculate the list price of the goods.

Summary

1) Percentages are fractions with a denominator of 100.

2) To convert a fraction into a percentage multiply it by 100.

3) To convert a percentage into a fraction divide it by 100.

4) To find the percentage of a quantity first convert the percentage into a fraction and then multiply the quantity by the fraction.

5) Profit % $= \dfrac{\text{selling price} - \text{cost price}}{\text{cost price}} \times 100$

Loss % $= \dfrac{\text{cost price} - \text{selling price}}{\text{cost price}} \times 100$

6) Mark up $= \dfrac{\text{selling price} - \text{cost price}}{\text{cost price}} \times 100$

7) Margin $= \dfrac{\text{selling price} - \text{cost price}}{\text{selling price}} \times 100$

8) Gross profit = turnover − cost price
Net profit = gross profit − overheads

9) Discount, which is usually a percentage of the selling price, is the amount a retailer will take off his selling price thus reducing the profit. Thus:

Discount $= \text{selling price} \times \dfrac{\text{percentage discount}}{100}$

Mental Test 10

Try to answer the following without writing anything down except the answer.

1) Express $\frac{4}{5}$ as a percentage.

2) What is 30% as a decimal fraction?

3) Express $33\frac{1}{3}$% as a vulgar fraction.

4) Convert 0·89 into a percentage.

5) What is 30% of 80?

6) What is 7% of 50?

7) What is 8% of £40?

8) If the selling price of an article is £28 and the cost price is £22, what is the profit?

9) Find the profit per cent if selling price = £25 and cost price = £20.

10) If the selling price is £30 and cost price is £40, what is the loss?

11) A car is bought for £1000 and sold for £800. What is the loss per cent?

12) An article is bought for £30. If the mark up is 20% what is the selling price?

13) Cost price = £80. Mark up = 25%. Find selling price.

14) If the selling price of an article is £50 and the cost price is £40, calculate the margin.

15) Selling price = £120. Cost price = £90. Find the margin.

16) Turnover = £40000. Cost price = £25000. What is the gross profit?

17) Gross profit = £22000. Overheads = £12000. What is the net profit?

18) Turnover = £150000. Cost price = £100000. Overheads = £30000. What is the net profit?

19) A chair is offered for sale at £30. A cash discount of 5% is offered. How much is the discount?

20) A customer is offered a cash discount of 10% for prompt payment. How much will he pay for an article whose selling price is £30?

Self-Test 10

In questions 1 to 15 the answer is either true or false. State which.

1) A fraction expressed with a denominator of 100 is called a percentage.

2) $\frac{13}{25}$ is the same as 42%.

3) 0·725 is the same as 72·5%.

4) 3·5% is the same as $\frac{7}{20}$.

5) 20·45% is the same as 2·045.

6) 20% of 80 is 16.

7) If 15% of a complete length is 45 mm the complete length is 300 mm.

8) The total electorate for a certain constituency is 53000. If 30% did not vote in an election then 37100 did vote.

9) When a shopkeeper buys an article for £4 and sells it for £5 his percentage profit is 20%.

10) A dealer buys an article for £8 and sells it for £5. His percentage loss is 37·5%.

11) A man's salary is increased by 20% and he now gets £72 per week. Hence his salary before the increase was £60.

12) By selling an article for £9 a dealer made a profit of $33\frac{1}{3}$%. He therefore paid £6 for the article.

13) A shopkeeper marks up an article at £20 and by selling it for this price he makes a profit of 30%. On a cash sale he allows a discount of 20%. His profit on the cash sale is therefore 10%.

14) A wholesaler sells goods to a retailer at a profit of 20%. The retailer sells them to a customer at a profit of 10%. The overall profit is therefore 30%.

15) A manufacturer allows a trade discount of 25% of his list price to a retailer. In addition he allows a 5% discount for prompt payment. If the list price is £120 the retailer pays £84.

In questions 16 to 25 state the letter (or letters) which correspond to the correct answer (or answers).

16) 35% is the same as:

   a $\frac{35}{100}$ **b** $\frac{7}{20}$ **c** $\frac{35}{10}$ **d** 0·35

17) $\frac{11}{25}$ is the same as:

   a 4·4% **b** 44% **c** 22% **d** 440%

18) When a dealer sells an article for £18 he makes a profit of £3. His percentage profit is therefore:

   a 20% **b** $16\frac{2}{3}$% **c** $14\frac{2}{7}$% **d** 25%

19) When a shopkeeper buys an article

for £20 and sells it for £25 his percentage profit is:

   a 20%   **b** 30%   **c** 25%   **d** 80%

20) A dealer buys 40 articles at a total cost of £10. He sells them at 30 p each. His percentage profit is:

   a $16\frac{2}{3}$%   **b** 20%   **c** 30%   **d** 25%

21) An article was sold for £60 which was a loss on the cost price of 10%. The cost price was therefore:

   a £54   **b** £66

   c £66·66   **d** £70·50

22) The duty on an article is 25% of its value. If the duty paid is 80 p the value of the article is:

   a £8   **b** £3·20   **c** £1·80   **d** £1

23) An article is offered for sale at £120 which represents a mark up of 20%. On a cash sale he allows a discount of 10%. His profit on the sale is therefore:

   a 10%   **b** 8%   **c** 30%   **d** 18%

24) 30% of a certain length is 600 mm. The complete length is:

   a 20 mm   **b** 200 mm

   c 2000 mm   **d** 2 m

25) When a shopkeeper sells articles for £37·80 each he makes a profit of 26% on the cost price. During a sale the articles are marked at £31·20 each. He therefore makes a profit of:

   a 31%   **b** 3·8%   **c** 5%   **d** 4%

11. Symbolic Notation

The methods of algebra are an extension of those used in arithmetic. In algebra we use letters and symbols as well as numbers to represent quantities. When we write that a sum of money is £50 we are making a particular statement but if we write that a sum of money is £P we are making a general statement. This general statement will cover any number we care to substitute for P.

We shall need to do a little algebra in some of the chapters which follow.

Use of Symbols

The following examples will show how verbal statements can be translated into algebraic symbols. Notice that we can choose any symbols we like to represent the quantities concerned.

1) The sum of two numbers.
   Let the two numbers be x and y.
   Sum of the two numbers $= x+y$

2) Three times a number.
   Let the number be N.
   Three times the number $= 3 \times N$

3) One number divided by another number.
   Let one number be a and the other number be b.
   One number divided by another number $= \dfrac{a}{b}$

4) Five times the product of two numbers.
   Let the two numbers be m and n.
   5 times the product of the two numbers $= 5 \times m \times n$

Exercise 81

Translate the following into algebraic symbols:

1) Seven times a number.

2) Four times a number minus three.

3) Five times a number plus a second number.

4) The sum of two numbers divided by a third number.

5) Half of a number.

6) Eight times the product of three numbers.

7) Product of two numbers divided by a third number.

8) Three times a number minus four times a second number.

Substitution

The process of finding the numerical value of an algebraic expression for given values of the symbols that appear in it is called substitution.

Example 1   If $x = 3$, $y = 4$ and $z = 5$ find the values of:

(a) $2y+4$

(b) $3y+5z$

(c) $8-x$

(d) $\dfrac{y}{x}$

(e) $\dfrac{3y+2z}{x+z}$

Note that multiplication signs are often missed out when writing algebraic expressions so that, for instance, $2y$ means $2\times y$. These missed multiplication signs must reappear when the numbers are substituted for the symbols.

(a) $2y+4 = 2\times4+4 = 8+4 = 12$

(b) $3y+5z = 3\times4+5\times5 = 12+25 = 37$

(c) $8-x = 8-3 = 5$

(d) $\dfrac{y}{x} = \dfrac{4}{3} = 1\dfrac{1}{3}$

(e) $\dfrac{3y+2z}{x+z} = \dfrac{3\times4+2\times5}{3+5} = \dfrac{12+10}{8} = \dfrac{22}{8} = 2\dfrac{3}{4}$

Exercise 82

If $a = 2$, $b = 3$ and $c = 5$ find the values of the following:

1) $a+7$

2) $c-2$

3) $6-b$

4) $6b$

5) $9c$

6) ab

7) $3bc$

8) abc

9) $5c-2$

10) $4a+6b$

11) $8c-7$

12) $a+2b+5c$

13) $8c-4b$

14) $\frac{1}{2}a$

15) $\dfrac{ab}{8}$

16) $\dfrac{abc}{6}$

17) $\dfrac{2c}{a}$

18) $\dfrac{5a+9b+8c}{a+b+c}$

Powers

The quantity $a\times a\times a$ or aaa is usually written as a^3. a^3 is called the third power of a. The number 3 which indicates the number of threes to be multiplied together is called the index (plural: *indices*).

$$2^4 = 2\times2\times2\times2 = 16$$
$$y^5 = y\times y\times y\times y\times y$$

Example 2   Find the value of b^3 when $b = 5$.

$$b^3 = 5^3 = 5\times5\times5 = 125$$

When dealing with expressions like $8mn^4$ note that it is only the symbol n which is raised to the fourth power. Thus:

$$8mn^4 = 8\times m\times n\times n\times n\times n$$

Example 3   Find the value of $7p^2q^3$ when $p = 5$ and $q = 4$.

$$7p^2q^3 = 7\times5^2\times4^3 = 7\times25\times64 = 11\,200$$

Exercise 83

If $a = 2, b = 3$ and $c = 4$ find the values
of the following:

1) a^2 4) $2a^2c$ 7) a^2+c^2 10) $\dfrac{c^5}{ab^3}$

2) b^4 5) ab^2c^3 8) $7b^3c^2$

3) ab^3 6) $5a^2+6b^2$ 9) $\dfrac{3a^4}{c^2}$

Equations

Fig 11.1 shows a pair of scales which are in balance. That is each
scale pan contains exactly the same number of grammes. Therefore

$$x+2 = 7$$

This is an example of an equation. To solve the equation we have
to find a value for x such that the scales remain in balance. Now the
only way to keep the scales in balance is to add or subtract the same
amount from each pan. If we take 2 kilogrammes from the left hand
pan then we are left with x kilogrammes in this pan, but we must also
take 2 kilogrammes from the right hand pan to maintain balance.
That is,

$$x+2-2 = 7-2$$
$$x = 5$$

Therefore x is 5 kilogrammes.

We now take a second example as shown in Fig. 11.2. In the left hand
pan we have three packets exactly the same, whilst in the right hand
pan there is 6 kg. How many kilogrammes are there in each packet?

If we let there be x kilogrammes in each packet then there are $3x$
kilogrammes in the three packets. Therefore we have the equation:

$$3x = 6$$

We can maintain the balance of the scales if we multiply or divide
the quantities in each scale by the same amount. In our equation if we
divide each side by three we have

$$\frac{3x}{3} = \frac{6}{3}$$

Cancelling the threes on the left hand side we have

$$x = 2$$

and hence each packet contains 2 kilogrammes.

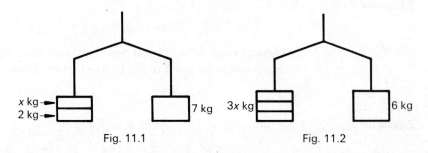

Fig. 11.1   Fig. 11.2

From these two examples we can say:

1) An equation expresses balance between two sets of quantities.

2) We can add or subtract the same amount from each side of the equation without destroying the balance.

3) We can multiply or divide each side of the equation by the same amount without destroying the balance.

These rules will become clearer if you study the following examples.

1) If $2y = 6$

$\qquad y = 3$ (dividing each side by 2)

2) If $\dfrac{a}{4} = 5$

$\qquad a = 20$ (multiplying each side by 4)

3) If $\dfrac{2m}{3} = 4$

$\qquad 2m = 12$ (multiplying each side by 3)
$\qquad m = 6$ (dividing each side by 2)

4) If $x + 4 = 7$

$\qquad x = 3$ (subtract 4 from each side)

5) If $2p + 7 = 19$

$\qquad 2p = 12$ (subtract 7 from each side)
$\qquad p = 6$ (divide each side by 2)

6) $x - 7 = 5$

$\qquad x = 12$ (add 7 to each side)

7) $3a - 4 = 8$

$\qquad 3a = 12$ (add 4 to each side)
$\qquad a = 4$ (divide each side by 3)

8) $\dfrac{4}{m} = 2$

$\qquad 4 = 2m$ (multiply each side by m)
$\qquad 2m = 4$ (transfer $2m$ to the left hand side and 4 to the right hand side)
$\qquad m = 2$ (divide each side by 2)

Exercise 84

Solve the following equations:

1) $x + 2 = 8$

2) $a + 7 = 12$

3) $m + 3 = 9$

4) $x - 2 = 5$

5) $y - 4 = 6$

6) $t - 5 = 8$

7) $3a = 12$

8) $2p = 10$

9) $7q = 28$

10) $\dfrac{a}{3} = 2$

11) $\dfrac{c}{5} = 4$

12) $\dfrac{x}{3} = 6$

13) $\dfrac{y}{4} = 8$

14) $2a + 5 = 13$

15) $3a + 7 = 25$

16) $4x - 3 = 9$

17) $2x - 6 = 12$

18) $5q - 1 = 9$

19) $\dfrac{6}{q} = 3$

20) $\dfrac{12}{y} = 6$

21) $\dfrac{1}{p} = 3$

22) $\dfrac{3}{r} = 2$

Formulae

A formula is an equation which describes the relationship between two or more quantities. The statement that $E = IR$ is a formula for E

in terms of I and R. The value of E may be found by simple arithmetic after substituting the given values of I and R.

Example 4   If $E = IR$ find the value of E when $I = 6$ and $R = 4$.

Substituting the given values of I and R and remembering that multiplication signs are omitted in formulae, we have:

$$E = IR = 6 \times 4 = 24$$

Example 5   The formula for the surface area of a sphere is $A = 4\pi r^2$ where $\pi = 3 \cdot 142$ and r is the radius of the sphere. Find the surface area of a sphere whose radius is 8.
Substituting the given values

$$A = 4 \times 3 \cdot 142 \times 8^2 = 804 \cdot 4$$

Exercise 85

1) If $v = u \mid at$ find v when $u = 5$, $a = 3$ and $t = 4$.

2) If $P = \dfrac{RT}{V}$ find P when $R = 48$, $T = 20$ and $V = 6$.

3) If $C = \pi D$ find C when $\pi = 3 \cdot 142$ and $D = 6$.

4) If $I = \dfrac{PRT}{100}$ find I when $P = 700$, $R = 12$ and $T = 3$.

5) If $P = \dfrac{1}{n}$ find P when $n = 5$.

6) If $K = \dfrac{WV^2}{2g}$ find K when $W = 64$, $V = 20$ and $g = 32$.

7) If $A = \frac{1}{2}BH$ find A when $B = 6$ and $H = 7$.

8) If $S = 90(n-4)$ find S when $n = 6$.

9) If $P = 3r^4$ find P when $r = 5$.

10) If $y = \dfrac{3t}{c}$ find y when $t = 12$ and $c = 6$.

Formulae and Equations

Suppose that we are given the formula $M = \dfrac{P}{Q}$ and that we have to find the value of Q given the values of M and P. We can do this by substituting the given values and solving the resulting equation for Q.

Example 6   Find Q from the equation $M = \dfrac{P}{Q}$ if $M = 3$ and $P = 6$.

Substituting the given values we have:

$$3 = \frac{6}{Q}$$

$$3Q = 6 \text{ (multiplying each side by } Q)$$
$$Q = 2 \text{ (dividing each side by 3)}$$

Example 7   Find T from the formula $D = \dfrac{T+2}{P}$ when $D = 5$ and $P = 3$.

Substituting the given values:

$$5 = \frac{T+2}{3}$$

$$15 = T+2 \text{ (multiplying each side by 3)}$$

$$13 = T \text{ (subtracting 2 from each side)}$$

Hence $T = 13$

Exercise 86

1) Find n from the formula $P = \dfrac{1}{n}$ when $P = 2$.

2) Find R from the formula $E = IR$ when $E = 20$ and $I = 4$.

3) Find B from the formula $A = BH$ when $A = 12$ and $H = 4$.

4) Find c from the formula $H = abc$ when $H = 40$, $a = 2$ and $b = 5$.

5) Find P from the formula $I = \dfrac{PRT}{100}$ when $I = 20$, $R = 5$ and $T = 4$.

6) Find D from the formula $C = \pi D$ when $\pi = 3 \cdot 142$ and $C = 27$.

7) Find r from the formula $A = \pi rl$ when $\pi = 3 \cdot 142$, $A = 96$ and $l = 12$.

8) Find W from the formula $K = Wa + b$ when $K = 30$, $b = 6$ and $a = 4$.

Summary

1) To find the value of an algebraic expression substitute the given values in the expression.

2) Multiplication signs are often missed out when writing algebraic expressions but they must reappear when numbers are substituted for the symbols.

3) The quantity b^4 is said to be the fourth power of b. The number 4 indicates the number of b's to be multiplied together and it is called an index.

4) To solve an equation we must do the same operation to both sides. Thus we can add or subtract the same amount from each side or we can multiply or divide both sides by the same amount.

5) A formula is an equation which describes the relationship between two or more quantities. To evaluate a formula substitute the given values for the symbols in the formula.

Mental Test 11

Try to answer the following questions without writing down anything except the answer.

Solve the following equations for x:

1) $3x = 12$

2) $5x = 10$

3) $7x = 21$

4) $x + 4 = 7$

5) $x + 5 = 8$

6) $x + 8 = 12$

7) $x - 2 = 8$

8) $x - 5 = 10$

9) $x - 7 = 12$

10) $\dfrac{4}{x} = 2$

11) $\dfrac{10}{x} = 5$

12) $\dfrac{9}{x} = 3$

Find the values of the following:

13) $A = 3D$ when $D = 2$

14) $I = PT$ when $P = 3$ and $T = 4$

15) $A = bh$ when $b = 3$ and $h = 4$

16) $E = \dfrac{I}{R}$ when $I = 12$ and $R = 3$

17) $K = 5q^2$ when $q = 2$

18) $Q = sn + 2$ when $s = 3$ and $n = 4$

19) $S = 3(n - 5)$ when $n = 8$

20) $R = q(5 - m)$ when $q = 2$ and $m = 3$.

Self-Test 11

In questions 1 to 20 the answer is either true or false. State which.

1) If $\frac{x}{7} = 3$ then $x = 21$

2) If $\frac{x}{5} = 10$ then $x = 2$

3) If $\frac{x}{4} = 16$ then $x = 64$

4) If $5x = 20$ then $x = 4$

5) If $3x = 6$ then $x = 18$

6) If $x - 5 = 10$ then $x = 5$

7) If $x + 8 = 16$ then $x = 2$

8) If $x + 7 = 14$ then $x = 21$

9) If $x + 3 = 6$ then $x = 3$

10) If $x - 7 = 14$ then $x = 21$

11) If $3x + 5 = 32$ then $x = 9$

12) If $2x - 8 = 16$ then $x = 4$

13) If $A = mf$ then $A = 30$ when $m = 5$ and $f = 6$

14) The value of $x^2 + y^2$ is 14 when $x = 4$ and $y = 3$

15) The value of $8ab$ is 48 when $a = 2$ and $b = 3$

16) If $P = \frac{RT}{Q}$ the value of P is 12 when $R = 6$, $T = 4$ and $Q = 2$

17) If $a = \frac{v-u}{t}$ then a has the value of 3 when $v = 17$, $u = 8$ and $t = 3$

18) If $m = \frac{n}{p}$ then $p = \frac{1}{2}$ when $n = 8$ and $m = 4$

19) If $x = \frac{u}{a}$ then $a = 2$ when $u = 8$ and $x = 4$

20) If $a = b - cx$ then $a = 12$ when $b = 24$, $c = 3$ and $x = 4$

12. Simple and Compound Interest

Simple Interest

Interest is the profit return on investment. If money is invested then interest is paid to the investor. If money is borrowed then the person who borrows the money will have to pay interest to the lender. The money which is invested or lent is called the *principal*. The percentage return is called the *rate per cent*. Thus interest at a rate of 12% means that the interest on a principal of £100 will be £12 per annum. The total formed by adding the principal and the interest is called the *amount*. The amount is therefore the total sum of money which remains invested after a period of time.

With simple interest the principal always stays the same no matter how many years the investment (or the loan) lasts.

Example 1

How much interest does a man pay if he borrows £400 for one year at an interest rate of 12%?

$$\text{Interest} = 12\% \text{ of } £400 = \frac{12}{100} \times £400 = £48$$

If money is borrowed for two years the amount of interest payable will be doubled; for three years three times as much interest is payable; and so on.

The interest payable (or earned) depends upon:

(i) The amount borrowed or lent i.e. the PRINCIPAL.
(ii) The rate of interest charged i.e. the RATE %.
(iii) The period of the loan i.e. the TIME (in years).

To calculate the SIMPLE INTEREST use the formula below:

$$I = \frac{PRT}{100}$$

where P stands for the principal
R stands for the rate per cent
T stands for the time in years

Example 2

Find the simple interest on £500 borrowed for 4 years at 11%.

Here we have $P = £500$, $R = 11\%$ and $T = 4$ years. Substituting these values in the simple interest formula gives:

$$I = \frac{500 \times 11 \times 4}{100} = 220$$

Thus the simple interest is £220.

Example 3

£700 is invested at 4% per annum. How long will it take for the amount to reach £784?

The interest = £784 − £700 = £84

We therefore have $I = 84$, $R = 4$ and $P = 700$ and we have to find T. Substituting these values in the simple interest formula gives:

$$84 = \frac{700 \times 4 \times T}{100}$$

$$84 \times 100 = 700 \times 4 \times T$$

$$T = \frac{84 \times 100}{700 \times 4} = 3$$

Hence the time taken is 3 years.

Simple interest tables (see page 228) are sometimes used to find the amount of interest due at the end of a given period of time. The table shows the appreciation (the increase in value) of £1. For instance:

£1 invested for 8 years at 11% per annum will become £1·88

£1 invested for 15 years at 8% per annum will become £2·20

Example 4   Using the simple interest tables calculate the simple interest earned by £850 invested for 9 years at 10% per annum.

From the simple interest table, in 9 years at 10% p.a. £1 becomes £1·90. To find the amount accruing from £850 multiply 1·90 by £850.

Amount accruing $= 1{\cdot}90 \times £850 = £1615$

Interest earned $= £1615 - £850 = £765$

Exercise 87

1) Find the simple interest on £700 invested for 3 years at 6% per annum.

2) Find the simple interest on £500 invested for 6 months at 8% per annum.

3) In what length of time will £500 be the interest on £2500 which is invested at 5% per annum?

4) In what length of time will £16 be the simple interest on £480 invested at 8% per annum?

5) In what length of time will £75 be the simple interest on £500 invested at 6% per annum?

6) The interest on £600 invested for 5 years is £210. What is the rate per cent?

7) The interest on £200 invested for 4 months is £6. What is the rate per cent?

8) What principal is needed so that the interest will be £48 if it is invested at 3% per annum for 5 years?

9) Which receives the more interest per annum:

£150 invested at 4% or £180 invested at $3\frac{1}{2}$%?

What is the annual difference?

10) A man invests £700 at 6% per annum and £300 at 8% per annum. What is his total annual interest on these investments?

11) A man deposited £350 in a bank and £14 interest was added at the end of the first year. The whole amount was left in the bank for a second year at the same rate of interest. Find the amount of interest on the £364 paid in the second year.

12) Using the simple interest table calculate the simple interest earned in each of the following cases:

(a) £350 invested at 6% p.a. for 9 years.

(b) £500 invested at 11% p.a. for 5 years.

(c) £2500 invested at 8% p.a. for 16 years.

(d) £7000 invested at 13% p.a. for 11 years

(e) £900 invested at 9% p.a. for 21 years.

Compound Interest

Compound interest is different from simple interest in that the interest which is added to the principal also attracts interest. If money is invested at compound interest, the interest due at the end of each year is added to the principal for the next year.

Example 5

Find the amount of money gained from an investment of £800 for 3 years at 10% per annum compound interest.

Interest on £800 for 1 year at 10% = 10% of £800 = £80
Add this interest to the original principal of £800
New principal = £880
Interest on £880 for 1 year at 10% = 10% of £880 = £88
Add this interest to the principal of £880
New principal = £968
Interest on £968 for 1 year at 10% = 10% of £968 = £96·80
Amount accruing at the end of 3 years = £968+£96·80 = £1064·80

Although all problems on compound interest can be worked out by the method of Example 5, the work is tedious and time consuming particularly if the period is lengthy. Here is a formula which will allow you to calculate the compound interest:

$$A = P\left(1+\frac{R}{100}\right)^n$$

where A stands for the amount of money accruing after n years
        P stands for the principal
        R stands for the rate per cent per annum
        n stands for the number of years for which the money is invested
You will have to make use of logarithms when using this formula.

Example 6

Calculate the interest earned on £750 invested at 12% per annum for 8 years.

Here we have $P = £750$, $R = 12\%$ and $n = 8$ years. Substituting these values in the compound interest formula we have

$$A = 750\times\left(1+\frac{12}{100}\right)^8 = 750\times(1\cdot12)^8$$

number	log
1·12	0·0492
	×8
	0·3936
750	2·8751
	3·2687

Antilog of 3·2687 = 1857

Hence the amount accruing after 8 years is £1857
The interest earned is £1857−£750 = £1107

Exercise 88

Use the compound interest formula and the log tables to calculate the compound interest earned in each of the following:

1) £250 invested for 5 years at 8% per annum.

2) £400 invested for 7 years at 9% per annum.

3) £1200 invested for 12 years at 10% per annum.

4) £2500 invested for 15 years at 11% per annum.

5) £5000 invested for 6 years at 7% per annum.

6) How much interest is earned when £800 is invested at 9% per annum simple interest for 6 years? How much would have been earned if the money had been invested at compound interest?

7) A man borrowed £1200 for 8 years at 11% compound interest. How much will he have to repay?

8) Find to the nearest dollar the amount accruing when $970 is invested for 10 years at 12% compound interest.

Compound Interest Tables

In business, compound interest tables are used to find the amount of interest due at the end of a given period of time. Part of such a table is shown below.

Year	5%	6%	7%	8%	9%	10%	11%	12%	13%	14%
1	1·050	1·060	1·070	1·080	1·090	1·100	1·110	1·120	1·130	1·140
2	1·103	1·124	1·145	1·166	1·188	1·210	1·232	1·254	1·277	1·300
3	1·158	1·191	1·225	1·260	1·295	1·331	1·368	1·405	1·443	1·482
4	1·216	1·262	1·311	1·360	1·412	1·464	1·518	1·574	1·603	1·689
5	1·276	1·338	1·403	1·469	1·539	1·611	1·685	1·762	1·842	1·925
6	1·340	1·419	1·501	1·587	1·677	1·772	1·870	1·974	2·082	2·195
7	1·407	1·504	1·606	1·714	1·828	1·949	2·076	2·211	2·353	2·502
8	1·477	1·594	1·718	1·851	1·993	2·144	2·304	2·476	2·658	2·853
9	1·551	1·689	1·838	1·999	2·172	2·358	2·558	2·773	3·004	3·252
10	1·629	1·791	1·967	2·159	2·367	2·594	2·839	3·106	3·395	3·707

The table shows the appreciation (the increase in value) of £1. For instance £1 invested for 5 years at 9% interest will become £1·539. Example 7 shows how the table is used in compound interest calculations.

Example 7

Using the compound interest table find the amount of compound interest earned by £750 invested for 6 years at 5% per annum.

From the table in 6 years at 5% £1 becomes £1·340
To find the amount accruing from £750 we multiply 1·340 by £750

$$\text{Amount accruing} = 1·340 \times £750 = £1005$$
$$\text{Interest earned} = £1005 - £750 = £255$$

Exercise 89

Using the compound interest table calculate the compound interest earned in each of the following:

1) £350 invested for 6 years at 7% per annum.

2) £500 invested for 5 years at 11% per annum.

3) £2500 invested at 5% per annum for 13 years.

4) £7000 invested for 7 years at 13% per annum.

5) £900 invested for 12 years at 9% per annum.

Depreciation

A business will own a number of assets such as machinery, type-writers, motor transport, etc. These assets reduce in value, i.e. depreciate, all the time. Each year the depreciation has to be calculated and charged as a business expense. A number of ways exist for calculating the depreciation. The commonest way is to use the reducing balance method in which the depreciation is calculated as a percentage of the book value of the assets at the beginning of the year.

Example 8

A small business buys a centre lathe costing £2000. It decides to calculate the depreciation each year as 20% of its value at the beginning of the year. Calculate the book value after three complete years.

Cost of lathe	= £2000
Depreciation first year (20%)	= £400 (20% of £2000)
Book value at start of second year	= £1600
Depreciation second year (20%)	= £320 (20% of £1600)
Book value at start of third year	= £1280
Depreciation third year (20%)	= £256 (20% of £1280)
Book value at end of third year	= £1024

Hence the lathe is reckoned to be worth £1024 at the end of the third year.

Although all problems with the reducing balance method of depreciation can be worked out by using the method of Example 8, it is much quicker to use the depreciation formula, which is very similar to the compound interest formula. It is:

$$A = P\left(1 - \frac{R}{100}\right)^n$$

where A stands for the book value after n years
P stands for the initial cost of the asset
R stands for the rate of depreciation
n stands for the number of years

Example 9

A business buys new machinery costing £12000. It decides to calculate the depreciation each year at 25% of its value at the beginning of the year. Calculate the book value at the end of 4 years.

We are given that $P = £12\,000$, $R = 25\%$ and $n = 4$ years. Substituting these values in the formula we have:

$$A = 12\,000 \times \left(1 - \frac{25}{100}\right)^4 = 12\,000 \times 0.75^4$$

We must use logarithms for this calculation.

number	log
0.75^4	$\overline{1}.8751$
	$\times 4$
	$\overline{1}.5004$
12 000	4.0792
	3.5796

The antilog of 3.5796 is 3798 and hence the book value of the machinery at the end of 4 years is £3798.

Exercise 90

1) A firm buys office machinery at a cost of £15 000. It is decided to calculate the depreciation each year as 15% of the book value at the beginning of the year. Calculate the book value at the end of 5 years.

2) The value of a machine depreciates each year by 12% of its value at the beginning of the year. If it cost £8000 when new calculate its value at the end of 7 years.

3) It is estimated that a machine costing £20 000 has a life of 10 years. It is decided to calculate the depreciation each year as $12\frac{1}{2}\%$ of the book value at the beginning of the year. Find the value of the machine at the end of the 10 years.

4) A machine which cost £5500 depreciates by 15% of the reducing balance. How much is the machine worth at the end of 5 years?

5) A lorry cost £6000 when new. 20% is written off its book value at the end of each year. Find its book value after 8 years.

Summary

1) With simple interest the principal stays the same no matter how long the loan or investment lasts. The formula is $I = \dfrac{PRT}{100}$.

2) With compound interest the principal increases (or decreases in the case of a loan) each year because the interest which is earned, is added to it. The formula is $A = P\left(1 + \dfrac{R}{100}\right)^n$.

3) Depreciation is usually calculated by using the reducing balance method. The formula is $A = P\left(1 - \dfrac{R}{100}\right)^n$.

Mental Test 12

Try to answer the following without writing anything down except the answer.

1) Find the interest on £200 invested at 5% for 1 year.

2) What is the simple interest on £100 invested for 3 years at 6% per annum?

3) Find the simple interest on £500 invested at 4% for 3 years.

4) What is the simple interest on £200 for $1\frac{1}{2}$ years at 4%?

5) What is the amount of compound interest if £100 is invested for 2 years at 10%?

6) Using the compound interest table on

page 228, calculate the amount accruing when £200 is invested for 3 years at 7% per annum.

7) How much does £500 become when it is invested at 5% simple interest for 2 years?

8) A machine depreciates at 10% per annum. If it cost £200 when new how much is it worth at the end of 2 years?

Self-Test 12

In each of the following questions state the letter corresponding to the correct answer.

1) The simple interest on £500 for 4 years at 7% per annum is:
    a £1400   **b** £14000
    c £20   **d** £140

2) The simple interest on £800 invested at 8% per annum for six months is:
    a £48   **b** £32   **c** £64   **d** £60

3) The simple interest on £800 invested for 5 years was £240. The rate of interest per annum is therefore:
    a 6%   **b** 5%   **c** 3%   **d** 7%

4) The simple interest on £800 invested at 5% per annum over a number of years amounted to £160. The cash was therefore invested for:
    a 7 years   **b** 5 years
    c 4 years   **d** 6 years

5) The simple interest on £400 invested for 4 months was £12. The rate of interest per annum is:
    a 36%   **b** 4·8%   **c** 7%   **d** 9%

6) A man invests £700 at 5% per annum and £300 at 6% per annum. The entire investment has an interest rate of:
    a 5½%   **b** 5·3%   **c** 11%   **d** 53%

7) A man invests £9000 at 10% per annum and £1000 at 8% per annum. His return on the complete investment is:
    a 18%   **b** 2%   **c** 10%   **d** 9·8%

8) What sum of money must be invested to give £30 simple interest if the rate is 6% per annum and the time is two years.
    a £250   **b** £300   **c** £400   **d** £360

9) A sum of money is invested at 8% per annum for 4 years and the simple interest is £160. The amount invested is:
    a £500   **b** £640   **c** £320   **d** £1280

10) A sum of money was invested at 5% per annum for 4 years. The total amount lying to the account of the investor at the end of the four years was £600. The amount originally invested was:
    a £800   **b** £600   **c** £500   **d** £1200

11) £500 invested for two years at 10% compound interest becomes:
    a £600   **b** £700
    c £605   **d** £665·50

12) £200 is invested at 12% compound interest for 5 years. The interest accruing at the end of the 5 years is:
    a £352·47   **b** £320
    c £152·47   **d** £120

13) A machine costing originally £2000 is depreciated by 20% of the book value at the beginning of each year. The value of the machine at the end of 5 years is:
    a nil   **b** £800   **c** £4976 **d** £655

14) A van costs £3500 when new. 25% is written off its value at the end of each year. Find its book value at the end of 10 years.
    a £197 **b** £5250 **c** nil   **d** £875

Miscellaneous Exercise

Exercise 91

All these questions are of the type set in examinations. The questions in section A are intended to take only a minute or two to solve but those in section B are intended to take up to 20 minutes to solve.

Section A

1) Find the cost of 12·7 kg of butter at 8·50 francs per kilogramme.

2) Taking £1 as 9·12 francs express 8·50 francs as pence correct to the nearest whole one pence.

3) Find the number of years in which a sum of £225 will yield £27 simple interest at the rate of 4% per annum.

4) Find the simple interest on a sum of £350 for 10 months at $4\frac{1}{2}$% per annum.

5) Find in francs, the price of 100 kg coal when 850 kg of this coal costs 199·75 francs.

6) The annual rent of a field amounts to £93·50 and it is shared by two farmers in the ratio 15 : 7. Find the difference in their shares.

7) A trainee's salary of £1575 is increased by 15%. Calculate the new salary.

8) Find the sum which was lent for 4 years at $4\frac{1}{2}$% per annum simple interest if it yielded £81 in interest in that time.

9) If £1 is equivalent to 2·06 dollars find how much 46 cents is worth correct to the nearest whole pence.

10) When the rate of exchange is 9·72 francs to the £1, how many francs does a traveller receive for £13·75.

11) A sum of £144·50 is divided between two people in the ratio 10 : 7. How much does each receive?

12) The price of a coat was £68·25 and this is reduced by 5%. Calculate the new price of the coat correct to the nearest whole pence.

13) 12 bottles of claret cost £16·20. How many bottles can be bought for £9·45?

14) A car runs for 4 km on a litre of petrol which costs 8 p. What would be the cost for a journey of 392 km?

15) Calculate correct to the nearest whole pence how much British money a man would receive for 75 francs when the rate of exchange is 9·34 francs to the £1.

16) For how many months would the simple interest on £60 at 4% per annum be £1·40?

17) A shopkeeper buys eggs at £0·18 for ten and sells them at 2 p each. What is his percentage profit?

18) If 24 arithmetic books and 3 answer books are bought for £47·52 and each arithmetic book costs £1·70 find the cost of each answer book.

19) A grocer buys 100 melons at 20 p each. If his mark up is 40% and he sells 95 of them how much profit does he make?

20) A dealer buys articles for £20 each and prices them at 25% above the cost price. When selling them he allows a discount of 5 p in the £1. How much does he get for each article?

21) Calculate the total cost of the following items:

    2000 envelopes at 90 p per hundred
        80 pencils at 7 p each
        10 reams of typing paper at £1·65 per ream
        11 packets of carbon paper at 85 p per packet

22) Calculate $34\frac{1}{2}$% of £298·76 to the nearest whole pence.

23) On returning from a business trip abroad an executive has remaining, 245

marks and 378 francs. How much sterling would he receive for this currency if the exchange rate is £1 = 9·12 francs and £1 = 5·37 marks?

24) Prepare an invoice for the following items:

    5 tennis racquets at £11·85 each
    8 tennis racquets at £9·76 each
    15 boxes of tennis balls at £3·08 per box
    25 pairs of tennis shoes at £2·27 per pair.

25) By booking independently at a Belgian hotel for a week's holiday a person is charged 560 francs per night. The same booking made through a travel agency would have cost £8·75 per night. How much in English currency did the man save on his holiday if the rate of exchange was 82 francs to the £1?

26) Express 45 cm as a percentage of 9 metres.

27) A man travels 2736 kilometres in his car for a total cost of £86·40. Find the consumption of petrol in kilometres per litre if petrol costs 16 p per litre. Give the answer to the nearest kilometre.

28) A shopkeeper purchased ties at 82 p each. He sells them at a profit of 25%. How many ties must he sell to make a profit of £10·25?

29) If £1 = $2·10 and £1 = 1460 lira; find the number of lira which are equivalent to 1 dollar.

30) The simple interest charged on a loan of £240 for 7 years was £184·80. Calculate the rate per cent per annum at which interest was charged.

Section B

31) Some new machinery in a factory was purchased for £16 920. In the firm's books the value of the machinery is depreciated at 20% per year, the depreciation being based on the book value of the machinery at the beginning of the year. Calculate, to the nearest £1, the value of the machinery at the end of 4 years.

32) The expenses of running a car for one year were as follows:

    (i) Tax £40
    (ii) Insurance £38·50
    (iii) Depreciation £180
    (iv) maintenance £31

During the year the owner travelled 18 400 km with an average petrol consumption of 13 km per litre. If the cost of petrol was 17 p per litre calculate the cost per kilometre correct to the nearest 0·1 of a pence.

33) A shopkeeper wishes to price an article so that he will make a profit of 25% on his cost price after allowing a discount of 5% for cash. At what will he price an article which costs him £84?

34) Two men A and B enter into a partnership. A provides £30 000 capital and B £18 000. From the profits B is to receive a salary of £4000 per year for managing the business. If the total profits in one year amount to £13 600, how much does each partner receive if the profits are to be divided in the ratio of the partners' capital.

35) A manufacturer issues a price list of his goods. A retailer when buying from the manufacturer receives a discount of 20% off the list price. A customer buying for cash is allowed a discount of 5% by the retailer. Calculate the percentage gross profit that the retailer will make when he sells goods for cash.

36) A washing machine is advertised for sale at £120. For hire purchase a customer can either:

    (i) pay a deposit of 25% and then 24 monthly payments of £5·40
  or (ii) pay 12 monthly instalments of £12·20

How much is paid by each method?

37) A man's property is valued in 1975 at £10 160 which is an increase of 27% over its value in 1973. What was its value in 1973?

38) Three men A, B and C share the profits of a business in the ratios of $1 : 3 : 7$. Find the total profit in a certain year if B's share was £5700. The next year the profits increase by 12%. Calculate the amount received by C in that year.

39) A machine which cost £5000 is depreciated at a rate of 5% based upon the book value at the beginning of the year. How much will it have depreciated in 5 years?

40) A man travels to France and exchanges £150 into francs at an exchange rate of 9·12 francs to the £1. He spends 800 francs. He then goes to Germany and exchanges the remainder of his francs into marks at an exchange rate of 100 francs = 58·9 marks. He spends 300 marks and converts his remaining marks into sterling upon his return home. How much will he get if the exchange rate is 5·37 marks = £1?

41) Calculate the compound interest due on a loan of £78000 for 3 years the interest being 8% per annum.

42) Three men A, B and C form a company. A invests £10000, B invests £8000 and C invests £7000. It is agreed that from the profits A will be paid £1000 for acting as managing director and the remaining profits divided amongst them in the ratio of the capital they have invested.

In the first year of the business they make a profit of £17400. How much does each receive?

At the end of the year A increases his investment by £2000. Calculate the increase in total income which A makes during the second year if they make £18000 profit in that year.

13. Wages and Salaries

Everyone who works for an employer receives a wage or salary in return for their labours. However the payment can be made in several different ways.

Payment by the Hour

Many people who work in factories, in the transport industry and in the building and construction industry are paid a certain amount of money for each hour that they work. Most employees work a basic week of so many hours and it is this basic week which fixes the hourly (or basic) rate of wages. The basic rate and the basic week are usually fixed by negotiation between the employer and the trades union which represents the workers.

Example 1

A man works a basic week of 38 hours and his basic rate is £1·25 per hour. Calculate his total wage for the week.

38 hours at £1·25 per hour $= 38 \times £1·25 = £47·50$

Hence the total wage for the week is £47·50.

Example 2

A factory worker is paid £52 for a basic week of 40 hours. What is his hourly rate?

$$\text{Hourly rate} = \frac{£52}{40} = £1·30$$

Exercise 92

Calculate the total pay in each of the following cases:

1) Basic rate = 80 p per hour.
 Basic week = 42 hours.

2) Basic rate = £1·15 per hour.
 Basic week = 39 hours.

3) Basic rate = 78 p per hour.
 Basic week = 37 hours.

4) Basic rate = £1·38 per hour.
 Basic week = 40 hours.

Calculate the hourly rate in each of the following cases:

5) Basic week = 42 hours.
 Weekly wage = £47·04.

6) Basic week = 39 hours.
 Weekly wage = £29·25.

7) Basic week = 40 hours.
 Weekly wage = £32·00.

8) Basic week = 44 hours.
 Weekly wage = £40·48.

Overtime

Hourly paid workers are usually paid extra money for working more hours than the basic week demands. These extra hours of work are called *overtime*.

Overtime is usually paid at one of the following rates:

(i) Time and a quarter – $1\frac{1}{4}$ times the basic rate.

(ii) Time and a half – $1\frac{1}{2}$ times the basic rate.

(iii) Double time – twice the basic rate.

Example 3   A girl is paid a basic rate of 72 p per hour. Find the rates of pay for overtime in the following cases: (a) time and a quarter; (b) time and a half; (c) double time.

(a) Overtime rate at time and a quarter $= 1\frac{1}{4} \times 72\,p$
$$= 1{\cdot}25 \times 72\,p = 90\,p$$

(b) Overtime rate at time and a half $= 1\frac{1}{2} \times 72\,p$
$$= 1{\cdot}5 \times 72\,p = 108\,p \text{ or } £1{\cdot}08$$

(c) Overtime rate at double time $= 2 \times 72\,p = 144\,p \text{ or } £1{\cdot}44$

Example 4   John Smith works a 42 hour week for which he is paid a basic wage of £37·80. He works 6 hours overtime at time and a half and 4 hours overtime at double time. Calculate his gross wage for the week.

$$\text{Basic hourly rate} = \frac{£37{\cdot}80}{42} = £0{\cdot}90$$
Overtime rate at time and a half $= 1\frac{1}{2} \times £0{\cdot}90 = £1{\cdot}35$
Overtime rate at double time $\quad = 2 \times £0{\cdot}90 \quad = £1{\cdot}80$
Gross wage $= £37{\cdot}80 + 6 \times £1{\cdot}35 + 4 \times £1{\cdot}80$
$$= £37{\cdot}80 + £8{\cdot}10 + £7{\cdot}20 = £53{\cdot}10$$

Exercise 93

1) A shop girl works a 46 hour week for which she is paid £29·44. She works 4 hours overtime which is paid for at time and a quarter. How much did she earn that week?

2) Tom Brown works 54 hours in a certain week. His basic week is 42 hours for which he is paid £50·40. His overtime rate is time and a half. Calculate his gross wage for the week.

3) In an engineering firm employees work a basic week of 38 hours. Any overtime worked from Monday to Friday is paid for at time and a quarter. Overtime worked on Saturday is paid for at time and a half whilst on Sunday it is paid for at double time. If the basic rate is £1·24 per hour find the wages of a man who worked 6 hours overtime from Monday to Friday, 4 hours overtime on Saturday and 7 hours overtime on Sunday.

4) A man's basic wage for a 38 hour week is £30·40. In a certain week he earned £35·10 by working overtime. If he worked 5 hours overtime what is the overtime rate?

5) A man's basic hourly rate is 72 p. Overtime is paid for at time and a quarter. If the basic week is 40 hours, how many hours of overtime must he work in order to earn £34·20 for the week?

6) A man is paid a basic hourly rate of 80 p for a 40 hour week. On weekdays he is paid at time and a half for overtime. If his wage for a certain week was £39·20, how many hours of overtime did he work?

Piecework

Some workers are paid a fixed amount for each article or piece of work that they make. Thus the more pieces of work that they make the more they are paid. Frequently if they can do more than an agreed amount of work a bonus is paid on top of the piecework rate.

Example 5   A man is paid $1\frac{1}{2}$ p for every handle he fixes to an electric iron up to 200 per day. For each handle over 200 that he fixes he is paid a bonus of

$\frac{1}{2}$ p. If the man fixes 350 handles on a certain day, calculate how much he earns on that day.

Amount earned on the first 200 = $200 \times 1\frac{1}{2}$ p = 300 p
Amount earned on next 150   = 150×2 p = 300 p
Total earned   = 300 p + 300 p = 600 p or £6

Exercise 94

1) Nancy Jones is paid 2p for each article she completes up to 200 per day. For each article over the 200 that she completes she is paid a bonus of $\frac{1}{2}$ p. Calculate how much she earns in a day on which she completed 320 articles.

2) A man is paid 8 p for each bolt that he locks, up to 60 per day. For each bolt over the 60 that he locks he is paid 9 p. How much does he earn during a day on which he locked 95 bolts.

3) A welder is paid 12 p for each metre of weld that he makes up to 80 m per day. For each metre above this amount he is paid a bonus of 2 p. How much does the welder earn on a day when he made 115 m of weld?

4) A woman is paid $\frac{3}{4}$ p for each handle that she fixes to a saucepan up to 350 per day. For each handle over 350 she is paid 1 p. If she fixes 426 on Monday, 394 on Tuesday, 408 on Wednesday, 398 on Thursday and 378 on Friday how much does she earn in the week?

Commission

Shop assistants, salesmen and representatives are sometimes paid commission on top of their basic wage. This commission is usually a small percentage of the total value of the goods which they have sold.

Example 6 A salesman is paid a commission of $2\frac{1}{2}$ % on the value of the goods which he has sold. Calculate the amount of his commission if he sells goods to the value of £820 during a certain week.

$$\text{Commission} = 2\frac{1}{2}\% \text{ of £820} = \frac{2 \cdot 5}{100} \times £820 = £20 \cdot 50$$

Example 7 A shop assistant is paid a basic wage of £22 per week. In addition she is paid a commission of 2 % of the value of the goods which she sells. During a certain week she sells goods worth £340. How much does she earn in the week?

$$\text{Commission} = 2\% \text{ of £340} = \frac{2}{100} \times £340 = £6 \cdot 80$$
$$\text{Total wages for the week} = £22 + £6 \cdot 80 = £28 \cdot 80$$

Exercise 95

1) A salesman sells £650 of goods during a week. If he is paid a commission of 2 % how much commission will he be paid?

2) Calculate the commission due to a car salesman if he sells a car for £1850 and his commission is 3 %.

3) A sales assistant is paid a basic wage of £34 per week. In addition she is paid a commission of $2\frac{1}{2}$ % on the value of the goods she sells. How much commis-sion will she be paid on sales amounting to £520 and what are her earnings for that week?

4) An agent selling agricultural machinery is paid a basic wage of £25 per week. In addition he is paid a commission of 3 % on his sales. In one week he made sales totalling £3250. How much are his gross wages?

Salaries

People like teachers, civil servants, secretaries and company managers are paid a definite amount for one year's work. It is unusual for them to be paid overtime, commission or a bonus. The annual salary is usually divided into twelve equal parts which are paid to the employee at the end of each month.

Example 8   A teacher is employed at an annual salary of £2496. How much is he paid monthly?

$$\text{Monthly salary} = £2496 \div 12 = £208$$

Exercise 96

Calculate the monthly payment for each
of the following annual salaries:

1) £2160   2) £1572   3) £2856   4) £3600   5) £5076

Deductions from Earnings

The wages and salaries discussed above are gross earnings. From these gross earnings a number of deductions are usually made. The most important of these deductions are:

(i) Income tax (see chapter 14)
(ii) National insurance
(iii) Superannuation

After these deductions have been made from the wage or salary the amount remaining is called the *net* earnings.

Example 9   A man earns a gross wage of £48 per week. If his deductions for one week are: income tax £5·40; national insurance £2·64; and superannuation £2·88, calculate his net wage.

$$\text{Net wage} = £48 - (£5·40 + £2·64 + £2·88)$$
$$= £48 - £10·92 = £37·08$$

The amount £37·08 is often referred to as the *take home pay*.

National Insurance

National insurance is a compulsory payment by employees and employers. The contributions paid by employees is a certain percentage of their *gross* salary (at the time of going to press the percentage is $5\frac{1}{2}\%$). Most married women and most widows who are in employment pay at a reduced rate, which at the moment is 2·0% of their gross wages. The employer pays his contributions at a standard rate ($8\frac{1}{2}\%$ of the employee's wage at the present time) irrespective of whether the employee pays at the standard or reduced rates. If an employee earns less than a certain amount (at the moment, £11 per week) then he or she pays no contributions. If a person earns more than a certain amount (at the moment, £69 per week) then the contributions are paid only on the first £69. The contributions are collected in the same way as income tax and they are recorded on an official deduction card which shows the amount of income tax paid, the amount earned (including overtime, bonuses, commission, etc.) and national insurance contributions on each occasion the wage or salary is paid. Note that the contribution rate and the upper and lower earnings limits may be altered from year to year.

Examples 10 An employee earns a basic wage of £65 per week and in addition, during a certain week he was paid £22 in overtime and £7 in bonuses. If the rate for national insurance contributions for the employee is $5\frac{1}{2}\%$ of his gross wage how much did he pay? The upper limit for payment is £69 per week.

$$\text{Gross wage for the week} = £65 + £22 + £7 = £94$$

This wage is above the upper earnings limit and hence national insurance is only paid on the first £69.

$$\text{Amount paid} = 5\tfrac{1}{2}\% \text{ of } £69 = \frac{5 \cdot 5}{100} \times £69 = £3 \cdot 79$$

Superannuation

State retirement pensions are small compared to the amounts earned by people prior to retirement. Hence many firms, local authorities and other organisations provide pensions through the medium of their own superannuation schemes. Usually these schemes relate the pension to the length of service and the salary or wage earned at the time of retirement. The employee's contribution to private superannuation schemes is normally of the order of 5 to 6 per cent of gross earnings.

Exercise 97

1) A trainee earns £39 per week. His deductions are: income tax £1·27, national insurance contribution £2·14. Calculate his net wage for the week.

2) A secretary's salary is £1800 per annum. She is paid monthly and her deductions are as follows: income tax £29·89, national insurance contribution £8·25. In addition she pays superannuation at a rate of 6% of her gross salary. What is her net monthly salary?

3) A man is paid a basic hourly rate of £1·22 for a 40 hour week. He works in addition, 6 hours overtime for which he is paid time and a quarter. Calculate his gross earnings. His deductions are then as follows: income tax £13·32, national insurance contribution 5·5% of gross wage and superannuation at 5% of his basic weekly wage. Calculate the man's net wage.

4) A man earns £1·16 per hour for a 42 hour week. Any overtime which he works is paid at time and a quarter. He averages 8 hours overtime per week. He estimates his income tax as £10·50 per week and national insurance £4 per week. Estimate his net annual wage based upon a 52 week year.

5) A manager of an office earns an annual salary of £4200. His superannuation payments are 6% of his gross salary and in addition he pays a national insurance contribution of £19·25 per month. He estimates his income tax at 20% of his salary less the above deductions. Estimate his monthly net salary.

Summary

1) Hourly paid workers are paid a basic rate of so much per hour for a basic week of so many hours.

2) Overtime is time worked over and above the basic week and it is paid at enhanced rates usually $1\frac{1}{4}$, $1\frac{1}{2}$ or twice the basic hourly rate.

3) Piecework is payment according to the number of articles produced.

4) Commission is a small percentage of sales paid to salesmen etc. This commission is added to their basic wage or salary.

5) A salary is the amount paid for a year's work. The annual salary is usually divided into twelve equal parts to give a monthly salary.

6) Deductions such as income tax, national insurance contributions, superannuation payments, etc. are deducted from the gross wage or salary to leave the net wage or salary.

Mental Test 13

Try to answer the following questions without writing anything down except the answer.

1) A girl's basic wage is £28 for a 40 hour week. What is her basic hourly rate?

2) A man earns £1·20 per hour. How much will he earn in a 40 hour week?

3) A girl earns 80 p per hour and overtime is paid for at time and a quarter. How much will she be paid for 5 hours overtime?

4) Overtime in a certain factory is paid for at time and a half. A man is paid £1·20 per hour basic. How much is he paid for overtime?

5) A woman is paid 2 p for every article she completes. If she completes 450 in a day how much will she be paid?

6) A shop assistant is paid a commission of 5 % on the sales she makes. How much commission will she make on sales amounting to £300?

7) A woman employee is paid an annual salary of £2400. What is her monthly salary?

8) A sales assistant is paid a weekly wage of £20 and a commission of 3 % on her sales. If she sells £600 worth of goods in a week what will she earn?

9) A man's gross salary is £40 and his deductions are £8. What is his net wage?

10) A manager pays superannuation at a rate of 6 % of his salary. What does he pay in superannuation per month if his monthly salary is £300?

Self-Test 13

In the following state the letter (or letters) corresponding to the correct answer (or answers).

1) A man's basic wage for a 35 hour week is £56. His overtime rate is 20 pence per hour more than his basic rate. If he works 6 hours overtime his wages will be:

    a £57·20   **b** £63·00

    c £66·80   **d** £34

2) A young man's basic wage for a 40 hour week is £20 and overtime is paid for at time and a quarter. In a certain week he worked overtime and his gross wage was £25·00. He therefore worked a total of:

    a 48 hours   **b** 45 hours

    c 50 hours   **d** 47 hours

3) A female employee in a factory works at a piecework rate of 7 p for each item which she completes, up to 60 per day. After 60 per day she is paid a bonus of 2 p extra for each item she completes. In a day she completes 82. She will have earned:

    a £4·20 **b** £5·74 **c** £4·64 **d** £6·18

4) A sales assistant is paid a basic wage of £30 plus a commission of 2 % on his sales. He sells £400 worth of goods in a week. His total earnings are therefore:

    a £36   **b** £80   **c** £38   **d** £406

5) A teacher is paid an annual salary of £2160. He pays £23 a month in income tax and his other deductions amount to £12. His contribution to the teachers' superannuation fund is 6% of his gross salary. His net monthly salary is:

  a £180   **b** £134·20
  c £145   **d** £139

6) A man earns an annual salary of £2880. From this is deducted 5% for superannuation and £12·83 per month for national insurance. His income tax liability is estimated at 15% of his gross salary. His net monthly salary is therefore:

  a £179·17   **b** £2150·04
  c £182·89   **d** £181·73

7) John Smith earns £1·20 for a 40 hour week and overtime is paid for at time and a quarter. In one week he works 48 hours. His deductions are: income tax £8·90, national health contributions £3·06 and superannuation payment £1·85. His take home pay will be:

  a £48   **b** £34·19
  c £43·79   **d** £46·19

8) A sales assistant is paid a basic wage of £23 per week. In addition she is paid a commission of 2% on sales. In a certain week she sells goods worth £350. Her deductions are national insurance £1·82 and income tax £4·89. Her net pay for the week is:

  a £30   **b** £27·60
  c £23·29   **d** £19·79

14. Housing, Insurance and Taxes

Rates

Every property in a town or city is given a rateable value which is fixed by the local district valuer. This rateable value depends upon the size, condition and position of the property.

The rates of a town or city are levied at so much in the £1 of rateable value, for instance, £0·85 in the £1. The money brought in by the rates is used to pay for such things as education, police, libraries, etc.

Example 1

The rateable value of a house is £120. If the rates are £0·75 in the £1, how much must the owner pay in rates per annum?

Rates payable per annum = 120 × £0·75 = £90

Example 2

A householder pays £90 in rates on property which has a rateable value of £150. What is the local rate?

For a rateable value of £150 rates paid are £90

For a rateable value of £1 rates paid are £$\frac{90}{150}$ = £0·60

Hence the rates are levied at £0·60 in the £1.

Example 3

What rate should a council charge if they need to raise £4 510 000 from a total rateable value of £8 200 000?

Rates chargeable in the £1 = $\frac{4\,510\,000}{8\,200\,000}$ = 0·55

Hence the rates should be £0·55 in the £1.

Most councils state on their rate demand the product of a penny rate. This is the amount that would be raised if the rate levied was 1 p in the £1, that is £0·01 in the £1.

Example 4

The rateable value for a city is £9 350 000. What is the product of a penny rate?

Product of a penny rate = 9 350 000 × 0·01 = £93 500

Example 5

The cost of highways and bridges in a town is equivalent to a rate of 9·28 pence in the £1. If the rateable value of all the property in the town is £15 400 000 find how much money is available for spending on highways and bridges during the financial year.

Amount available = 9·28 × 15 400 000 pence

$$= £\frac{9·28 \times 15\,400\,000}{100} = £1\,429\,120$$

Exercise 98

1) The rateable value of a house is £90. Calculate the rates payable by a householder when the rates are £0·70 in the £1.

2) A householder pays £90 in rates when the rate levied is £0·75 in the £1. What is the rateable value of the house?

3) A house is assessed at a rateable value of £45. The owner pays £40·50 in rates for the year. What is the rate in the £1?

4) What rate should a council charge if they need to raise £100 000 from a total rateable value of £320 000?

5) Calculate the total income from the rates of a town of rateable value £2 150 000 when the rates are 54 p in the £1.

6) A town of rateable value £772 000 needs to raise £70 400 from the rates. What local rate should be charged?

7) The rateable value of all the property in a city is £8 500 000. What is the product of a penny rate?

8) The rateable value for all the property in a city is £8 796 000. Calculate the product of a penny rate. How much must the rates be if the total expenses for the city for a year are £4 837 800?

9) The total rateable value for all the property in a city is £850 000. Calculate the total cost of public libraries if a rate of 4·6 pence in the £1 must be levied for the purpose.

10) The expenditure of a town is £900 000 and its rates are 87 pence in the £1. The cost of libraries is £30 000. What rate in the £1 is needed for the upkeep of the libraries?

Rent

Rent is the charge for accommodation and it is usually paid weekly or monthly to the landlord who owns the property. The landlord may include the rates in his charge but if he does not it is the tenant's responsibility to see that these are paid.

Example 6

A landlord charges a rent of £8·50 per week for a house. The rates for the house are £101·40 per annum. What inclusive amount should the landlord charge the tenant?

$$\text{Rates per week} = £\frac{101\cdot40}{52} = £1\cdot95$$

$$\text{Inclusive charge} = £8\cdot50 + £1\cdot95 = £10\cdot45$$

Mortgages

A person buying a house usually arranges a loan or mortgage from a Building Society. The Building Society usually requires a deposit of about 5 or 10% of the purchase price of the property. The balance of the purchase price plus the interest charged is paid back over a number of years. The interest rates of the Building Societies vary from time to time.

Example 7

A Building Society quotes the repayments on a mortgage as £10·74 per month for 25 years per £1000 borrowed. What will be the monthly repayments on a mortgage of £8500

$$\text{Monthly repayments} = £\frac{8500}{1000} \times 10\cdot74 = £91\cdot29$$

Sometimes a combined mortgage and life insurance can be arranged. A life insurance policy (see Chapter 15) is taken out for the value of the loan. Interest is paid on the loan for the whole period of the loan after which the money received from the insurance policy is used to repay it.

Example 8 A man wishes to borrow £8000 to buy a house, the loan to be covered by an insurance policy for the 20 year period which costs £3·88 per £1000 per month. The Building Society charges interest on the loan of 11 %. What will be the total monthly payments?

Annual loan interest   = 11 % of £8000 = £880

Monthly repayment of interest   = £$\frac{880}{12}$ = £73·33

Life insurance premiums per month = £3·88 × 8 = £31·04

Total monthly payments   = £73·33 + £31·04 =
                                                                    £104·37

Exercise 99

1) A house is rented for £7·36 per week. Its rateable value is £174 and rates are levied at 54 p in the £1. What will be the weekly charge for rent and rates?

2) A flat is rented for £6·50 per week. Its rateable value is £162 and rates are charged at 60 p in the £1. What is the inclusive weekly charge for rent and rates?

3) A man borrows £12 000 from a Building Society in order to buy a house. The society charges £12·20 per month per £1000 borrowed. How much are the monthly payments?

4) A man borrows £6000 on a mortgage for 25 years. The mortgage costs £0·94 per £100 per month. What are his monthly repayments?

5) A man purchases a house using a combined life insurance and mortgage. He borrows £9000 from the Building Society who charge an interest rate of 11 % per annum. The insurance premiums amount to £2·95 per £1000 per month. Calculate the total monthly payments which the man must make.

6) A man takes out a £8000 mortgage over 21 years when the Building Society interest rate was 8·5 % per annum. The mortgage was covered by life insurance. If the rate is now 11 % per annum calculate the increase in the monthly payments to the Society.

Insurance

Our future is something that is far from certain. We would become too ill to work or we could be badly injured or even killed in an accident. Our house could be burnt down or burgled. We could be involved in a car accident in which we might be liable for injuries and damage. How do we take care of such eventualities? The answer is to take out insurance policies which is a way of investing in the future that we are so uncertain about.

Insurance works like this. The insurance company charges the policy holders a sum of money each year known as the *premium*. Thousands of people pay these premiums and hence the company collects a very large sum of money each year. It invests this money to earn dividends and interest which it uses to meet the claims of its policy holders.

Example 9 A person values his house and its contents at £12 000. His insurance company charges a premium of £1·25 per £1000 of insurance. How much is the annual premium?

$$\text{Annual premium} = £1{\cdot}25 \times \frac{12\,000}{1000} = £1{\cdot}25 \times 12 = £15$$

His annual premium is therefore £15.

Car Insurance

By law a vehicle must be insured and the owner of the vehicle can be prosecuted for not having third party insurance. That is a policy must be taken out in case someone is injured or damage is caused by an accident. Third party insurance covers only the other person; it does not cover the policy holder who will have to pay for damage to his own vehicle himself. A fully comprehensive policy is needed to cover damage to the policy holder's vehicle as well as to any other person or property damaged in an accident.

The size of the premium depends on:

(i) the value of the vehicle,

(ii) the engine size,

(iii) the area in which the owner lives,

(iv) special risks (sports cars and young owners),

(v) the use to which the vehicle is put (private, taxi, goods, etc.).

If a driver makes no claims during a year he gets a bonus (called a no claims bonus) which means that he will pay less next year.

Example 10

A car owner is quoted a premium of £40·85 to insure his vehicle. If his no claims bonus is 20% of the premium, how much does the owner pay?

$$\text{The no claims bonus is 20\% of } £40{\cdot}85 = \frac{20}{100} \times £40{\cdot}85 = £8{\cdot}17$$

$$\text{Actual premium payable} = £40{\cdot}85 - £8{\cdot}17 = £32{\cdot}68$$

The annual premium is £32·68.

Whole Life Assurance

With this type of assurance a sum of money, depending upon the size of the premium, etc., is paid to the dependents of the policy holder upon his death. The size of the premium depends upon:

(i) the age of the person next birthday (the younger he is the less he pays because there is less risk of him dying suddenly),

(ii) the amount of money the person wants his dependents to receive (the greater the amount the larger the premium).

Example 11

A man aged 35 years wishes to assure his life for £7500. The insurance company quotes an annual premium of £13·90 per £1000. Calculate the amount of the monthly premium.

$$\text{Annual premium} = £13{\cdot}90 \times \frac{7500}{1000} = £13{\cdot}90 \times 7{\cdot}5 = £104{\cdot}25$$

$$\text{Monthly premium} = £104{\cdot}25 \div 12 = £8{\cdot}69$$

Hence the man will pay £8·69 per month to assure his life for £7500.

Endowment Assurance

This is very similar to whole life assurance but the person can decide for how long he is going to pay the premium. At the end of the period chosen a certain sum of money will be paid to the policy holder. If however he dies before the end of the chosen period the assured sum of money will be paid to his dependents. Some endowment and life assurance policies are 'with profits' which means that the sum assured may increase over a period depending upon the profits made by the insurance company.

Example 12   A man aged 30 next birthday wishes to take out a 'with profits' endowment policy. He is quoted a price of £48·50 per £1000 assured for a term of 20 years. Calculate the monthly premiums if he wishes to assure himself for £6000.

$$\text{Annual premiums} = £48·50 \times \frac{6000}{1000} = £48·50 \times 6 = £291$$

$$\text{Monthly premiums} = £291 \div 12 = £24·25$$

Exercise 100

1) A householder wishes to insure his house for £6200. His insurance company charges a premium of 12 p for each £100 insured. Calculate his annual premium.

2) An insurance company offers the following rates to customers: buildings $-12\frac{1}{2}$ p per £100; contents -25 p per £100 insured. Calculate the annual premium paid by a householder if his house is valued at £8500 and the contents are valued at £1500.

3) A car owner is quoted an annual premium of £38·70 but he is given a $33\frac{1}{3}\%$ no claims bonus. Calculate the amount of his annual premium.

4) Calculate the actual premium paid by a vehicle owner if the premium quoted is £48·50 and he is allowed a 60% no claims bonus.

5) A man aged 25 next birthday wishes to assure his life for £3000. He is quoted a rate of £9·00 per £1000 assured per annum. If he pays monthly how much will he pay?

6) A person aged 36 next birthday is quoted a rate of £13·90 per £1000 assured per annum. He wishes to assure his life for £8000 but he wishes to pay monthly. The company states that for monthly payments the premiums will be increased by 3%. How much per month will the man actually pay?

7) A man aged 40 next birthday takes out a £2000 endowment policy for which he is charged a premium of £0·44 per £100 assured for a term of 20 years. If he pays the premiums monthly, how much will he pay?

Income Tax

Taxes are levied by the Chancellor of the Exchequer in order to produce income to pay for the armed services, the Civil Service, the National Health Services and other expenditures. The largest producer of revenue is Income Tax.

Every person who has an income above a certain minimum amount has to pay income tax to the Government. Tax is not paid on the whole income. Certain allowances are made as follows:

(i) an allowance, the amount of which varies according as to whether the taxpayer is a single person or a married man,

(ii) allowances for children, dependent relatives, etc.,

(iii) allowances for superannuation contributions, mortgage interest, etc.

(iv) an allowance for the premiums on whole life and endowment assurance policies.

The residue of the income left after the allowances have been deducted is called the taxable income. The following example shows the method used in calculating income tax.

Example 13 A man's salary is £3500 per year. His taxable income is found by deducting the following from his salary:
1. A married man's allowance of £775
2. A children's allowance of £430
3. Superannuation payments of £210
4. Interest on Building Society mortgage £295.
He then pays tax at the standard rate of 35%. Calculate his taxable income and the amount he has to pay in income tax.

To find the taxable income deduct the following from the salary of £3500:

Married man's allowance	= £775
Children's allowance	= £430
Superannuation payments	= £210
Interest to Building Society	= £295
Total allowance	£1710

Taxable income = £3500−£1710 = £1790
Total tax payable = 35% of £1790 = £626·50

P.A.Y.E.

Most people pay income tax by a method known as Pay As You Earn or PAYE for short. The tax is deducted from their wage or salary before they receive it.

The tax payer and his employer receive a notice of coding which sets the allowances to which the person is entitled and sets his code number. The employer will then know from the tax tables supplied by the Inland Revenue the amount of tax to deduct from the wages of his employees. A typical Notice of Coding is shown on page 134.

Exercise 101

Use the following allowances for the questions in this exercise:

a) Single person's allowance	£595
b) Married man's allowance	£775
c) Child under 11 years old	£200
d) Child 11-16 years old	£235
e) Child over 16 if in full time education	£265
f) Dependent relative	£100
g) Building Society interest	relief in full

1) A man's taxable income is £1200. If tax is paid at 35% find the amount paid in income tax.

2) When income tax is levied at 30% a man pays £60 in income tax. What is his taxable income?

3) Calculate the amount a single man, with no allowances except his single person's allowance, will pay in income tax when this is levied at 33%, if he earns £3500 per annum.

4) A married man with two children under 11 years old earns £3500 per annum. If he has no other allowances find the amount of tax he will pay when income tax is levied at 35%.

5) A married man with one child aged 15 years and a second aged 10 years earns £4000 per annum. He has a dependent relative whom he helps to support and he also pays Building Society interest of £300 per annum. If his superannuation payments are 5% of his salary calculate the amount he pays in income tax per annum when this is levied at 30%.

NOTICE OF CODING

CODING ALLOWANCES	£
Expenses	210
Building Society interest	295
Personal	775
Wife's earned income	——
Children	430
Dependent relatives	——
Life assurance	——
Total allowances due	1710
Less	
Allowances given against other income	——
Income from property	——
Interest	40
Family allowances	——
Family Allowance deduction	——
Net allowance	1670
Less	
Tax unpaid for earlier years	——
Allowances given against pay	1670

Your code for 1976/77 is　　 167H

Summary

1) Rates are charged at so much in the £1 of rateable value.

   Rates payable per annum = rate in the £1 × rateable value

2) Rent is the charge for accommodation. It is usually paid weekly or monthly.

3) A person buying a house often arranges a loan or mortgage from a Building Society.

4) Insurance premiums are charged by insurance companies to give cover for any stated eventuality. The premiums may be paid weekly, monthly or yearly.

5) Income tax is paid on the taxable income which is the total income less the allowances. The standard rate is so much per cent which means that the amount of tax payable is this percentage of the taxable income.

Mental Test 14

Try to answer the following questions without writing anything down except the answer.

1) The rateable value of a house is £150. How much is paid in rates when rates are levied at 50 p in the £1?

2) The rateable value for a city is £4 000 000. What is the product of a penny rate?

3) A man pays £80 per annum in rates. If the rateable value of his house is £160 what is the rate in the £1?

4) A householder pays £75 in rates when the rate is levied at 50 p in the £1. What is the rateable value of his house?

5) A landlord charges a rent of £240 per annum. What is the monthly rent?

6) The annual rates for a house are £104. If the rent is £5 per week find the inclusive weekly charge for rent and rates.

7) A Building Society charges a man £12 per month per £1000 borrowed. If the man borrows £8000 how much does he pay each month to the society?

8) A man borrows £5000 on a mortgage. The repayments are £0·80 per £100 borrowed per month. How much does he pay per month?

9) A man wishes to insure his property for £12 000. The insurance company quotes a rate of £1·25 per £1000 insured. How much are the annual premiums?

10) A car owner is quoted a premium of £40 to insure his vehicle. If he gets a no claims bonus of 20% how much does he pay?

11) A man has a taxable income of £2000 and he pays tax at the rate of 30%. How much does he pay in income tax?

12) A person earns £3000 per annum. For income tax purposes his allowances are £1800. What is the taxable income?

Self-Test 14

In the following state the letter or letters corresponding to the correct answer or answers.

1) The rateable value of a house is £150. If the rates are 80 p in the £1 the rates payable are:
   a £150 **b** £12 **c** £120 **d** £140

2) In a certain city the rateable value of all the property is £8 000 000. The product of a penny rate is:
   a £80 000   **b** £8000
   c £16 000   **d** £20 000

3) The cost of highways in a town is equivalent to a rate of 6·2 pence in the £1. If the rateable value of all the property in the town is £3 500 000 then the cost of highways is:
   a £21 700   **b** £22 000
   c £220 000   **d** £217 000

4) The expenditure of a town is £300 000 and its rates are 75 p in the £1. The cost of the library is £20 000. The rate needed for the upkeep of the library is:
   a 4 p in the £1   **b** 5 p in the £1
   c 8 p in the £1   **d** 7·5 p in the £1

5) A landlord charges a rent of £416 per annum and the rates amount to £104 per annum. The inclusive charge for rent and rates per week is:
   a £43·33   **b** £10
   c £12   **d** £8

6) The rateable value of a property is £186 and the rates are 55 p in the £1. The rent charged is £364 per annum. The inclusive charge for rent and rates per month is:
   a £38·86   **b** £8·52½
   c £30·33   **d** £45·83

7) A Building Society charges an interest rate of 11%. A man borrows £9000 in order to purchase a house the loan to be

covered by an insurance policy for which the premiums of £48·24 per £1000 insured per annum are paid. The man's total monthly outgoings are therefore:

a £82·50   b £19·04
c £118·68   d £27·39

8) A car owner is quoted a premium of £49·80 to insure his vehicle. If his no claims bonus is 40% the amount he pays for the insurance is:

a £49·80   b £19·92
c £29·88   d £69·72

9) When income tax is levied at 30% a man paid £90 income tax. His taxable income was therefore:

a £30   b £27   c £270   d £300

10) A man's annual income is £3500 per year and his allowances, for income tax purposes, are £1500. If he pays tax at 35% then the amount of tax he pays in a year is:

a £1225   b £525   c £1750   d £700

15. Household Bills and Personal Loans

Gas Bills

Gas is charged according to the number of therms used (1 therm is 5·66 cubic metres of town gas or 2·83 cubic metres of natural gas). The gas corporation offers a choice of tariffs to its customers. The following are typical:

Tariff 1 A quarterly standing charge of £3·75
A charge per therm of 12·225 p

Tariff 2 A quarterly standing charge of £6·90
A charge per therm of 9·072 p per therm.

The second tariff is intended for customers who use large quantities of gas in a year since it encourages the greater use of gas because of the lower charge per therm.

Example 1 A householder has the choice of paying for his gas by either of the tariffs shown above. If he uses 110 therms per quarter which should he choose?

Tariff 1:
Cost of gas = £3·75+110×12·225 p = £3·75+£13·45 = £17·20
Tariff 2:
Cost of gas = £6·90+110×9·072 p = £6·90+£9·98 = £16·88

The customer should choose the second tariff as this will save him 32 p per quarter.

Electricity Bills

Electricity is charged according to the number of units used (1 unit is 1 kilowatt-hour). The electricity board offer its customers a choice of tariffs. The following are typical:

Tariff 1 (Flat rate)
Lighting   5·324 p per unit
Cooking, heating, etc. 2·218 p per unit

Tariff 2 (Two part)
A quarterly charge of £2·50
Cost per unit 1·228 p

Tariff 3 (Night rate)
A quarterly charge of £3·95
Cost per unit used between 10·30 p.m. and 7·30 a.m. 0·511 p
Cost per unit used at other times 1·296 p

Tariff 1 is suitable when the amount of electricity used is small whilst tariff 2 is suitable for the average household. Tariff 3 is suitable for households with central heating (storage heaters) which is switched on at night time.

Example 2   A user of electricity estimates that he will use 2500 units during a quarter of which 1200 units will be used at night time. He has the choice of tariffs 2 or 3 (see above). Which should he choose?

Tariff 2:
Cost of electricity $= £2·50 + 2500 \times 1·228\,p = £2·50 + £30·70$
$$= £33·20$$

Tariff 3:

Standing charge	£3·95
1300 units at 1·296 p per unit	£16·85
1200 units at 0·511 p per unit	£6·132
Total cost	£26·93

The householder should choose tariff 3 because he will then save £6·27 per quarter.

Exercise 102

1) A householder pays for his electricity by tariff 1 (above). If he uses 225 units for lighting and 470 units for cooking, etc., how much will he pay?

2) In a certain area electricity is charged for at a fixed rate of 2·3 p for every unit used. If a householder receives a bill for £16·79, how many units has she used?

3) A customer uses 90 therms of gas in a quarter. He is charged 12·225 p per therm plus a standing charge of £3·75. How much is his gas bill?

4) A householder receives a gas bill for £38·23. He is charged 9·072 p per therm plus a standing charge of £6·90. How many therms has he used?

5) An electricity user consumes 4200 units in a quarter. He uses tariff 3 (above) and he uses 2300 of these units at night time. How much does he pay for electricity?

6) A householder has the choice of paying for his electricity as follows:
    (i) at a fixed rate of 2·8 p per unit for each unit used,
    (ii) a standing charge of £8·00 plus 1·43 p per unit for each unit used.
If the householder estimates that he will use 650 units of electricity which method of payment should he choose?

7) A man is charged for his electricity as follows: 4 p per unit for the first 80 units used and 1·3 p per unit for the remainder. If he uses 800 units how much will he pay?

8) A householder has a choice of tariffs 2 or 3 (see above) when paying for the electricity he consumes. If he uses 2800 units during the night and 1800 units during the day how much will he save by choosing tariff 3?

Cost of Running a Car

When calculating the cost of running a car, the costs of tax, insurance, petrol, maintenance and depreciation should all be taken into account. Every motor vehicles requires a Road Fund Licence which has to be paid when the vehicle is first registered and renewed periodically. It is also a legal requirement that every motor vehicle must be insured to protect a third party who may be injured in an accident. The vehicle will need maintaining and its value will depreciate with age.

Example 3 A car is bought for £800 and used for one year. It is then sold for £650. During this year it did 20 000 km averaging 12 km per litre of petrol which cost 19 p per litre. Insurance cost £28·50, tax £40, repairs and maintenance £42. What is the total cost for a year's motoring and what is the cost per kilometre?

$$\text{Depreciation} = £150$$
$$\text{Insurance} = £28\text{·}50$$
$$\text{Tax} = £40$$
$$\text{Repairs and maintenance} = £42$$
$$\text{Cost of petrol} = £\frac{20\,000}{12} \times \frac{19}{100} = £316\text{·}67$$
$$\text{Total cost for the year} = £577\text{·}17$$
$$\text{Cost per kilometre} = \frac{£\,577\text{·}17 \times 100\,\text{p}}{20\,000}$$
$$= 2\text{·}89\,\text{p}$$

Value Added Tax

Value added tax or VAT is a tax on goods and services which are purchased. Some goods and services bear no tax, for instance food and water. Services which are exempt are insurance, education and the postal service. The rate of tax varies from time to time and luxury goods bear a higher rate of tax than other goods.

Example 4 A man buys a lawnmower which is priced at £40 plus VAT. How much will he pay for the mower if the rate of tax is 25%?

$$\text{VAT} = 25\% \text{ of } £40 = \frac{25}{100} \times £40 = £10$$

$$\text{Total cost of mower} = £40 + £10 = £50$$

Example 5 A person buys a table for £54 the price including VAT. If the rate of tax is 8% what is the price of the table exclusive of VAT?

Let 100% be the price exclusive of VAT
then 108% is the price inclusive of VAT
108% represents £54
$$1\% \text{ represents } £\frac{54}{108} = £0\text{·}50$$
100% represents £0·50 × 100 = £50

Exercise 103

1) A man drives 15 000 km in a year. If he averages 10 km per litre of petrol costing 20 p per litre how much does petrol cost him?

2) A second hand car is bought for £450. It is run for a year and then sold for £320. The cost of insurance is £22·60, tax £28, repairs £38 and maintenance £8. It is driven 12 000 km in the year and it averages 11 km per litre of petrol costing 18 p per litre. What is the cost of a year's motoring and how much is the cost per kilometre?

3) A new car is bought for £1500 and it is sold two years later for £950. During this time it travelled 42 000 km at an average petrol consumption of 14 km per litre. If petrol costs 20 p per litre and other expenses were £105, calcuate the cost per kilometre of running the car.

4) At the beginning of a year a man bought a car for £950 and then sold it for £800. The tax for the year was £40 and insurance cost £32·50. The car averaged 11 km per litre of petrol costing 19 p per litre. Oil was used at the rate of 1 litre for each 900 km travelled. If oil costs 55 p per litre and the car travelled 9900 km in the year, calculate the cost per kilometre of running the car.

5) A man buys a washing machine whose price, exclusive of VAT, is £96. If VAT is charged at 25% how much did the man actually pay?

6) A chair is priced at £27 inclusive of VAT which is charged at 8%. What is the price exclusive of VAT?

7) A set of saucepans are priced at £12·96 inclusive of VAT. If VAT is charged at 8% calculate the price exclusive of VAT.

Hire Purchase

When we purchase goods and pay for them by instalments we are said to have purchased them on hire purchase. Usually the purchaser pays a deposit and the balance of the purchase price plus interest is repaid in a number of instalments.

Example 6

A woman buys a suite of furniture for £280. A deposit of 25% is paid and interest at 12% per annum is charged on the outstanding balance. The balance is paid in 12 monthly instalments. Calculate how much each instalment will be.

Price of suite = £280
Less deposit = £70 (25% of £280)
Outstanding balance = £280−£70 = £210
Plus interest at 12% on balance for 1 year = 12% of £210 = £25·20
Total amount to be repaid = £210+£25·20 = £235·20
Amount of each instalment = $£\dfrac{235\cdot20}{12}$ = £19·60

In Example 6, 12% would only be the true rate of interest if all of the outstanding balance was paid at the end of the year. However as each instalment is paid the amount outstanding is reduced and hence a larger proportion of each successive payment is interest. The true rate of interest is much higher than 12%; it is in fact about 22%.

Example 7

A woman buys a refrigerator for £80 and pays a deposit of 20% of the purchase price. The outstanding balance plus interest at 10% on this balance for the whole period of the repayment is to be repayed in four quarterly instalments. What is the true rate of interest?

Outstanding balance = £80−20% of £80 = £80−£16 = £64
Interest at 10% for 1 year = 10% of £64 = £6·40
Total to be repayed = £64+£6·40 = £70·40
Amount of each instalment = $£\dfrac{70\cdot40}{4}$ = £17·60

£64·00 is the balance outstanding for 3 months
£48·00 is the balance outstanding for the next 3 months
£32·00 is the balance outstanding for the next 3 months
£16·00 is the balance outstanding for the final 3 months
Average amount of the loan for the entire year:

$$= £\dfrac{64+48+32+16}{4} = £40$$

If £6·40 is the interest paid on a loan of £40 the true rate of interest may be found from the simple interest formula:

$$I = \frac{PRT}{100}$$

$$6·40 = \frac{40 \times R \times 1}{100}$$

$$640 = 40R$$

$$R = \frac{640}{40} = 16$$

The true rate of interest is 16%.

Note that in calculating the outstanding balance we have said that the interest payable every 3 months is £1·60. Thus the amount actually paid off the balance is £17·60−£1·60 = £16. The method of Example 7 is called the average loan method.

Bank Loans

Many people take out personal loans from a bank. The bank will calculate the interest for the whole period of the loan and the loan plus the interest is usually repaid in equal monthly payments.

Example 8

A man borrows £300 from his bank. The bank charges 18% interest for the whole period of the loan. If the repayments are in 12 equal monthly instalments calculate the amount of each payment.

Interest = 18% of £300 = £54
Total amount to be repaid = £300+£54 = £354
Amount of each instalment = £$\frac{354}{12}$ = £29·50

Exercise 104

1) A man buys a television set for £320. He pays a deposit of £50 and he is to pay the outstanding balance plus interest in 12 equal monthly instalments. If the interest is charged at 10% on the outstanding balance for the full period of the loan calculate the amount of the instalments.

2) A woman buys a suite of furniture for £320. A deposit of 20% is paid and interest at 12% per annum is charged on the outstanding balance for the full period of the loan. The balance is to be paid in 4 quarterly payments. How much is each payment?

3) A vacuum cleaner is bought for £50 and a deposit of £10 is paid. The outstanding balance plus interest at 10% on this balance for the whole period of the repayment is to be repaid in 4 quar-

terly instalments. What is the true rate of interest?

4) A radio is priced at £84. It can be purchased on hire purchase by paying a deposit of £21 and 12 monthly instalments of £5·88. What rate of interest is being charged on the outstanding balance for the whole period of the loan?

5) A man borrows £250 from a bank who charge interest of 15% over the whole period of the loan. If the loan plus interest is to be repaid in 12 equal monthly instalments calculate the amount of the instalments.

6) A suite of furniture is priced at £240. Hire purchase terms are available which are: deposit 25% and 18 equal instalments of £11·80. Calculate the total hire purchase price and find the difference

between the cash price and the hire purchase price.

7) An article of furniture can be purchased for £80 cash or by hire purchase. When purchased on the instalment system nine monthly repayments are required in which case interest at 18% per annum for nine months is added to

the cash price. Calculate the amount of each instalment.

8) A bank lends a man £500. They charge interest at 12% per annum which is added to the amount of the loan. If the loan is repayed in 24 monthly instalments calculate the amount of each instalment.

Summary

1) Gas is charged according to the number of therms used and the type of tariff chosen.

2) Electricity is charged according to the number of units used and the type of tariff chosen.

3) The costs of tax, insurance, petrol, maintenance and repairs should be taken into account when assessing the cost of running a car.

4) Value added tax (VAT) is a tax on goods and services. The rate of tax is a percentage of the selling price of the goods.

5) Hire purchase is the term used when goods are purchased on an instalment system. Interest is added to the balance outstanding (the purchase price minus the deposit) and this total is paid in a number of equal instalments.

6) When a personal loan is taken out through a bank the bank calculates the interest for the whole period of the loan (similar to the way in which hire purchase interest is calculated) and the loan plus the interest is repaid in equal instalments.

Mental Test 15

Try to answer the following without writing anything down except the answer.

1) Gas is charged at 20p per therm. If 250 therms are used how much does it cost?

2) The tariff for gas users is a fixed charge of £5 plus 10p per therm. Calculate the amount of a gas bill if 300 therms are used.

3) A householder uses 500 units of electricity. The tariff is a fixed charge of £4 plus 1·5p per unit. How much is the bill?

4) A car does 10 km to the litre of petrol. How many litres are needed for the car to travel 5000 km?

5) What is the cost of 200 litres of petrol at 20p per litre?

6) A woman purchases household goods for £120. She pays a deposit of £20 and interest of 10% is added to the balance outstanding. She then pays the loan plus interest in 10 equal instalments. How much is each instalment?

7) A bank gives a man a loan of £500. Interest is charged at 12%. If the loan plus interest is repaid in 10 equal instalments how much is each instalment?

8) The total cost of running a car for a year is £600. If it travels 6000 km in the year what is the cost per kilometre?

Self-Test 15

In the following questions state the letter (or letters) corresponding to the correct answer (or answers).

1) A householder is charged for electricity as follows: the first 80 units are charged for at 3 p per unit and each subsequent unit used is charged at 1·3 p per unit. If the electricity bill amounted to £8·12 the total number of units used is:

 a 600   **b** 550   **c** 440   **d** 520

2) A householder pays for his electricity by means of a fixed charge of £3·60 plus 1·2 p per unit for each unit used. If he used 330 units his bill would be:

 a £3·96   **b** £7·56   **c** £8·05   **d** £4·36

3) A workbench is priced at £22. It can be bought on easy terms of £5 deposit plus 12 equal payments of £1·56. The rate of interest charged is:

 a 10%   **b** 15·5%   **c** 3·4%   **d** 5%

4) A stereo-unit is priced at £50. It can be had on hire purchase for a 25% deposit and 12 equal payments. The interest charged is 15% for the whole period. How much is each repayment?

 a £4·67   **b** £5·21   **c** £3·59   **d** £4·58

5) The expenses of running a car for a year are: depreciation £155; tax £40; insurance £32; maintenance £45. The car does 8000 km at 10 km to the litre of petrol. If petrol costs 20 p per litre how much per kilometre does it cost to run the car?

 a 3·4 p   **b** 2 p   **c** 5·4 p
 d none of these

6) The price of a car is £1320 inclusive of VAT. If VAT is charged at 10% what is the price of the car exclusive of VAT?

 a £1188   **b** £1200
 c £1306·80   **d** £1310

7) A man wishes to borrow £480 from his bank. The bank agrees to the loan at 12% interest per annum. The repayments will be in 24 equal monthly instalments. The amount of each instalment is:

 a £20   **b** £22·40
 c £32   **d** £24·80

8) A carpet is sold for £3·50 per square metre. A customer buys 8 square metres and agrees to easy terms of a deposit of £2·80 and 6 monthly payments of £4·52. The rate of interest charged is:

 a 15%   **b** 10%   **c** 26%   **d** 8%

16. Investment and Bankruptcy

Shares

Many people at some time or another will have money to invest. It could be deposited in a bank, a building society or in the National Savings Bank where it will earn a fixed rate of interest. It could also be invested in a company by buying some of its shares.

Companies obtain their capital by the issue of shares to the public. Shares have a nominal value of 25 p, £1, £5, etc. which cannot be divided into fractional amounts. If the company does well the price of the shares will appreciate to a value above the nominal price. On the other hand if the company does badly the price will fall below the nominal value. Shares can be bought and sold through the Stock Exchange. Companies issue different kinds of shares, two of the most important kinds being as follows:

Preference shares which carry a fixed rate of interest. The holders of these shares have first call on any profits the company may make in order that payments due to them can be made.

Ordinary shares, the dividends on which vary according to the amount of profit that the company makes. The directors of the company decide what dividend shall be paid.

The dividends payable on the shares are a percentage of the nominal value of the shares.

Example 1

A man buys 200 Emperor 25 p shares at 44 p. How much does he pay for the shares?

25 p is the nominal value of the shares
44 p is the price he actually pays for the shares
Amount paid $= 200 \times 44\,p = 8800\,p = £88$

Example 2

Tom Jones sells 500 Tuxo £5 shares at £4. How much does he get?

£5 is the nominal value of the shares
£4 is the price at which he sells the shares
Amount received $= 500 \times £4 = £2000$

Example 3

A man owns 300 Ludo shares. The company declares a dividend of 32 p per share. How much does he get in dividends?

Amount payable $= 300 \times 32\,p = 9600\,p = £96$

Example 4

A man holds 600 Snake 50 p shares which he bought for 35 p. The declared dividend is 8 % of the nominal value of the shares. How much does he get in dividends and what is the yield per cent on his investment?

Dividend per share $= 8\%$ of $50\,p = 4\,p$
Amount obtained in dividends $= 600 \times 4\,p = 2400\,p = £24$

$$\text{Yield per cent} = \frac{\text{dividend per share}}{\text{price paid per share}} \times 100$$

$$= \frac{4}{35} \times 100 = 11\cdot4\%$$

Example 5   The paid up capital of a company consists of 50 000 6% preference shares of £1 each and 200 000 ordinary shares of 50 p each. The profits available for distribution are £11 973. What dividend can be paid to the ordinary shareholders? What is the dividend per cent?

Preference dividend $= 6\%$ of £50 000 $=$ £3000
Amount of profit remaining $=$ £11 973 $-$ £3000 $=$ £8973
Dividend per share $= £\dfrac{8973}{200\,000} =$ £0·448 or 4·48 p
Dividend per cent $= \dfrac{4\cdot48}{50} \times 100 = 8\cdot96\%$

Exercise 105

1) Find the cost of the following shares:
(a) 400 Oak £2 shares at 314 p
(b) 900 Staite 50 p shares at 39 p
(c) 280 Mako 25 p shares at 59 p

2) Find the amount raised by selling the following shares:
(a) 180 Kneck 80 p shares at 97 p
(b) 350 Truck £5 shares at 87 p
(c) 490 Mill 50 p shares at 117 p

3) Calculate the dividend received from the following investments:
(a) 300 Proof shares; dividend is 8 p per share
(b) 450 Shock shares; dividend is 18 p per share
(c) 750 Stairways shares; dividend is 85 p per share

4) Calculate the amount of dividend received from the following investments:
(a) 300 Well 75 p shares; declared dividend is 10%
(b) 500 Toomet £5 shares; declared dividend is 5%
(c) 1200 Boom 50 p shares; declared dividend is 16%

5) Calculate the yield per cent on the following investments:
(a) 200 Salto £3 shares bought at 250 p; declared dividend is 9%
(b) 500 Melting 40 p shares bought at 85 p; declared dividend is 5%
(c) 85 Penn £2 shares bought at 98 p; declared dividend is 3%

6) Calculate the yearly income from 500 Imperial £2 shares at 150 p when a dividend of 8% is declared. What is the yield per cent on the money invested?

7) Find the cost, income and yield per cent from 900 £1 shares at 82 p when a dividend of 7% is declared.

8) 500 Flag 25 p shares are sold for £160. What is the cash value of each share?

9) How much profit does a man make when he sells 900 Emblem £3 shares for 390 p, having bought them for 265 p?

10) The paid up capital of a company consists of 100 000 8% preference shares of £2 each and 250 000 ordinary shares of £1 each. The profits available for distribution are £27 000. What is the dividend per cent that can be paid to the ordinary shareholders?

11) The issued capital of a company is 200 000 8% preference £1 shares, 150 000 6% £2 preference shares and 500 000 ordinary 25 p shares. If the profits available for distribution to the shareholders is £92 000, what dividend per cent is payable to the ordinary shareholders?

12) The paid up capital of a company consists of 90 000 7% preference £1 shares and 110 000 ordinary 50 p shares. If a dividend of 10% is declared, what is the profit of the company?

Stock

Stock is issued by the Government and Local Authorities when they need cash. This stock is issued at a fixed rate of interest and it can be redeemed after a certain number of years. Stock is always issued in £100 units but an investor need not necessarily buy whole units of stock. The price of stock varies in the same way as does the price of shares.

If you look in the financial section of your newspaper you will see statements like this:

Treasury 5% 1986-89 52

This means that £100 worth of Treasury Stock, paying 5% interest and redeemable between 1986 and 1989, can be bought for £52.

Example 6   How much 9% Treasury Stock at 70 can be bought for £280? How much in dividends are payable and what is the yield per cent?

$$£70 \text{ buys } £100 \text{ stock}$$
$$£280 \text{ buys } £\frac{100}{70} \times 280 = £400 \text{ stock}$$

Interest payable = 9% of £400 = £36

$$\text{Yield per cent} = \frac{\text{Interest payable}}{\text{Amount paid for stock}} \times 100$$

$$= \frac{36}{280} \times 100 = 12 \cdot 86\%$$

Brokerage

Brokerage is the commission charged by a broker for the purchase or sale of stocks and shares. It is calculated as a percentage of the sum for which they are bought or sold.

When buying *add* the brokerage to the price paid
When selling *deduct* the brokerage from the sum received

Example 7   Find the change in income resulting from selling £2500 5% stock at 105 and investing the proceeds in 3% stock at 55. Brokerage is $1\frac{1}{2}$%.

Original income = 5% of £2500 = £125 per annum

$$\text{Amount received for stock sold} = £2500 \times \frac{105}{100} = £2625$$

Brokerage $= 1\frac{1}{2}\%$ of £2625 = £39·37

Amount received for stock sold less brokerage = £2625 − £39·37
$$= £2585 \cdot 63$$

$$\text{Amount available for reinvestment} = £2585 \cdot 63 \times \frac{100}{101\frac{1}{2}}$$

$$= £2547 \cdot 41$$

$$\text{Stock bought at } 55 = £2547 \cdot 41 \times \frac{100}{55} = £4631 \cdot 67$$

New income $= 3\%$ of £4631·67 = £138·95
Change in income $=$ £138·95 − £125 = £13·95

Exercise 106

1) Calculate the amount of stock that can be bought in each case:
   (a) £300 invested in 5% Crewe at 75

(b) £250 invested in Treasury stock at 69

(c) £700 invested in Devon at 120

2) Calculate the amount of interest received each year from the following:
(a) £800 stock at $3\frac{1}{2}\%$
(b) £1200 stock at 5%
(c) £500 stock at 4%

3) Calculate the amount of 6% Cambridge stock that can be bought for £600 if the price is 88. What is the interest earned per annum and what is the yield per cent?

4) How much does it cost to buy £300 of Railway stock at 80?

5) What are the proceeds from selling £400 of Dorset 3% stock at 75?

6) A man sells £800 worth of Argentine stock at 30 and buys German 8% stock at 110. How much German stock does he buy?

7) A man buys £500 of a certain stock at 75 and sells when they reach 57. How much does he lose on the transaction?

8) An investor sold £5000 of 4% American stock at 80 and invested the proceeds in French 6% stock at 90. Calculate the amount of French stock bought and the change in income.

9) Find the change in income which results from selling £4000 of 5% stock at 102 and investing the proceeds in 4% stock at 92. Brokerage is 2% on each transaction.

10) A 6% stock is quoted at 130. Allowing for brokerage at $1\frac{1}{2}\%$ calculate:
(a) how much stock can be bought for £2000,
(b) how much is realised by the sale of £2000 of this stock,
(c) the net income from £2000 stock less income tax at 35%.

Bankruptcy

A person or company is *insolvent* when the liabilities of the person or company exceed the assets. Under certain conditions the person or company may be declared bankrupt. In this case the creditors (the people who are owed money) may appoint a trustee to sell the debtor's (the person or company owing the money) assets. After expenses and certain prior claims have been met the remainder of the proceeds will be distributed amongst the creditors.

To do this a dividend is declared which is worked out as follows:

$$\text{Dividend} = \frac{\text{Net assets}}{\text{total liabilities}}$$

Example 8

A bankrupt has liabilities of £10 000 and assets of £2000. Find the dividend. How much will a creditor owed £3000 be paid?

$$\text{Dividend} = £\frac{2000}{10\,000} = £0\cdot20 \text{ in the £1 or 20p in the £1}$$

This means that each creditor will receive 20p for each £1 that he is owed.

Amount received by creditor owed £3000 = £3000 × £0·20
= £600

Secured creditors do not rank for dividend unless the security does not realise the amount of the claim. In this case the balance of the claim ranks for dividend in the usual way. If however the security raises more than the amount of the claim the residue is added to the assets thus increasing the amount of the dividend.

Example 9

A company, declared bankrupt, owes £85 873 to fully secured creditors and £98 748 to unsecured creditors. If the assets of the company realise

£150 786 net find the dividend payable to the unsecured creditors.

Net assets	£150 786
Secured creditors	£85 873
Available for dividend	£64 913

$$\text{Dividend} = £\frac{64\,913}{98\,748} = £0.66 \text{ in the £1 or 66 p in the £1}$$

Exercise 107

1) Find the dividends payable in the following cases:
   (a) Net assets £20 000.
      Creditors £50 000.
   (b) Net assets £7532.
      Creditors £82 516.
   (c) Net assets £190 632.
      Creditors £567 826.

2) Find the amounts paid to the following creditors:
   (a) Dividend 30 p in the £1.
      Creditor owed £7000.
   (b) Dividend 8 p in the £1.
      Creditor owed £6378.
   (c) Dividend 19 p in the £1.
      Creditor owed £15 678.

3) The total assets of a company are sold for £358 907 but the expenses incurred are £28 712. If the company owes £739 054 to unsecured creditors find the amount of the dividend which can be paid.

4) The liabilities of a man in bankruptcy are £25 832 to fully secured creditors and £48 798 to unsecured creditors. If his assets realise £35 746 net what dividend can be paid?

5) A bankrupt owed £8572 to his ordinary (unsecured) creditors and £1750 to his secured creditors. If the expenses of the winding up were £125 and a dividend of 20 p in the £1 was declared, how much were his assets?

Summary

1) Companies obtain their capital by selling shares to the public. Shares have a nominal value, for instance, 25 p but if the company does well the price of the shares will rise above the nominal value. If the company does badly the price of the shares will fall below the nominal price.

2) Preference shares carry a fixed rate of interest. The dividends payable on ordinary shares varies according to the profit the company makes.

3) The dividends payable are a percentage of the nominal value of the shares.

4) Stock is issued at a fixed rate of interest and it can be redeemed after a certain number of years. Stock is always issued in units of £100 but an investor need not buy a whole number of units. The price of stock varies in the same way as the price of shares.

5) Brokerage is commission charged by a broker when he purchases or sells stock or shares for an investor.

6) A person may be declared a bankrupt if his liabilities exceed his assets. The bankrupt then pays a dividend of so much in the £1 to his creditors.

Mental Test 16

Try to answer the following without writing anything down except the answer.

1) A man buys 100 shares at 50 p. How much do they cost him?

2) A man sells 200 shares at 30 p. How much does he get?

3) A company declares a dividend of 8 p per share. How much does an investor with 200 shares receive?

4) A dividend of 10 % is declared. How much does an investor with 100 £2 shares get in dividends?

5) How much 9 % Treasury stock at 80 can be bought for £160?

6) How much is received when £300 of stock at 105 is sold?

7) What is the interest per annum on £200 stock at 3 %.

8) A man buys £500 of stock at 75 and sells at 70. How much does he lose?

9) Calculate the brokerage at 2 % when £500 stock at 80 is sold.

10) Calculate the brokerage when £100 stock at 7p is sold if 3 % brokerage is charged.

11) A bankrupt has liabilities of £10 000 and assets of £3000. What dividend can be paid?

12) A bankrupt declares a dividend of 20 p in the £1. How much will a creditor owed £2000 be paid?

Self Test 16

In each of the following state the letter (or letters) corresponding to the correct answer (or answers).

1) A man buys 500 Empress 50 p shares at 40 p. He therefore pays for the shares:
   a £50 **b** £250 **c** £40 **d** £200

2) A person sells 400 Tuxedo £2 shares at 150 p. He gets:
   a £60 **b** £600 **c** £80 **d** £800

3) A man holds 500 Ladder 80 p shares which he bought at 70 p. The declared dividend is 8 %. He therefore receives:
   a £32 **b** £28 **c** £40 **d** £56

4) A person holds 800 Persona 50 p shares which he bought at 75 p. The declared dividend is 10 %. The yield per cent on the shares is
   a 10 % **b** $6\frac{2}{3}$ % **c** 15 % **d** 7·5 %

5) How much 8 % stock at 75 can be bought for £150?
   a £200 **b** £75 **c** £150 **d** £1200

6) Calculate the interest received per annum from £800 stock at 5 %
   a £50 **b** £400 **c** £40 **d** £500

7) A man sells £600 French stock at 50 and buys Belgian stock at 40. How much Belgian stock does he buy?
   a £600 **b** £1200 **c** £750 **d** £400

8) A bankrupt has liabilities of £7000 and assets of £3500. How much will a creditor owed £2000 be paid?
   a £2000 **b** £1000 **c** £500 **d** £700

Miscellaneous Exercise

Exercise 108

All these questions are of the type set in examinations. The questions in section A are intended to take only a minute or two to solve but those in section B are intended to take up to 20 minutes to solve.

Section A

1) For all goods sold to the value of £1 a salesman receives a commission of $4\frac{1}{2}$ p. Find the amount of his commission after he has sold goods to the value of £350.

2) After 6% of a trainee's wages have been deducted he receives a net amount of £32·90. Calculate the amount deducted.

3) The rent of a house was £1·25 per week and the rates in a certain year were £0·81 in the £1 on a rateable value of £80. Find the total rent and rates paid in a year of 52 weeks.

4) A man's salary of £3150 is increased by 6%. Find the new salary.

5) Find the rateable value of a house on which the amount paid in rates was £96 when the rate was 80 p in the £1.

6) A car runs 4 km on a litre of petrol which costs 16 p. What would be the cost of a journey of 392 km?

7) The rates paid on a house were £46·00 and the rateable value was £92. What was the rate in the £1?

8) A man is paid £1·20 per hour for a 40 hour working week and time and a quarter for overtime. How much does he earn for a working week of 48 hours?

9) In a certain country Income Tax is levied at 20% on the first £700 of income and then at 40% on any remaining income. Calculate the tax paid by a man who earned £2800 per annum.

10) Find the cost of buying £3000 6% stock standing at 70. What is the annual income from this purchase?

11) Each calendar month a man earns £152. What is his annual income?

12) The rateable value of a house is £92 and the rate is fixed at £0·65 in the £1. If an additional water rate of £7·42 per year is charged calculate the annual amount paid in rates.

13) A firm's representative receives a fixed salary of £1500 per annum and a commission of 15% based on the gross value of all his orders over £4000 per year. Find his income in a year when the value of his orders amounts to £14 890.

14) The meter readings in units for an electricity consumer at the beginning and end of a quarter were as follows:

    Beginning of quarter 57 469
    End of quarter   58 196

The electricity is charged for at 0·978 p per unit. Calculate the amount of the electricity bill for the quarter.

15) In a certain town the rates are 62 p in the £1. A three-bedroomed house has a rateable value of £168 whilst a four-bedroomed house has a rateable value of £196. How much more is paid in rates by the owner of the four-bedroomed house?

16) A bankrupt's liabilities are £16 520. This includes £3200 owed to secured creditors which must be paid in full. His assets realise £7250. How much dividend in the £1 can be paid to his other creditors?

17) What net income will a man receive by investing £6785 in 7% stock at 92 if tax at 35% is deducted?

18) Find the change in income when £4200 of 4% stock at 98 is sold and the proceeds invested in 6% stock at 107.

19) A rise of 8% would increase a man's wages by £220 per annum. Estimate his salary at present.

20) The cash price for an electric fire is £37·10. If it is bought on the instalment system the price is increased by £1·50. A deposit of £5 is paid at once and the residue of the balance paid in 12 monthly instalments. How much is each instalment?

21) Payment of electricity is at the rate of 4·50 p per unit for the first 64 units and then 0·965 p per unit for each additional unit. If a man's bill for electricity was £6·74 how many units did he use?

22) When a man bought a stereo-unit he paid a deposit of 10% of the purchase price of £160. Simple interest of 8% per annum was added to the balance outstanding and the debt was paid in 24 equal monthly instalments. Calculate the amount of each instalment.

23) The tenant of a house makes an arrangement with his landlord to pay two-fifths of the rates for the house, the landlord paying the rest. Calculate how much more the landlord pays than the tenant if the rateable value of the house is £115 and the rate levied is 64 p in the £1.

24) The wages for a normal week of 42 hours are £52·08. The rate for overtime is $1\frac{1}{2}$ times the normal rate. If the total wages for a certain week are £66·96 calculate the number of hours of overtime worked.

Section B

25) The total rateable value of the property in a locality is £1 800 000. Calculate the income from a penny rate. The rateable value of a house on which the owner pays £52·50 in rates per half year is £150. Find the rate in the £1 which is levied. Find to the nearest penny the rate which must be levied to pay for the collection of refuse in the area if it costs £70 765 to collect annually.

26) A car uses petrol at the rate of 10 km per litre when being driven in rural areas and at the rate of 5 km per litre when being driven in towns. If one litre of petrol costs 20 p calculate the cost of petrol consumed on a 450 km journey five-sixths of which is through rural areas and the rest through towns. If other expenses for the journey amounted to 6 p per kilometre calculate the total cost of the journey. Calculate also the cost per kilometre.

27) A man finds that in one year his total cost of running his car is £255. This includes £40 road tax and £75 petrol tax. If on every pound he earned the man had to pay 30% income tax how much does the man have to earn to pay for the running of his car? Find the percentage of this amount that he paid in taxes.

28) A television set can be bought for £135, maintained at £17·30 per year for 7 years, then sold for £21. Renting the set, maintenance included, costs £4 per month (calendar) for 3 years, £3·80 per month for the next two years and £3·50 per month thereafter. Find how much is saved in 7 years by buying the set.

29) A bankrupt has assets of £81 60 and liabilities of £18 914. Of his liabilities, £1934 must be paid first and in full. Calculate:

(a) the rate in the £ which a creditor will receive,

(b) the amount a creditor will receive if he is owed £2450,

(c) the amount a creditor is owed if he receives £664.

30) In calculating the amount of Income Tax due for the year the following allowances were made:

A personal allowance of £775

£200 for each child under 11 years of age

£235 for each child between the ages of 11 and 16 years of age.

When all his allowances had been deducted from the income, the remainder (= the taxable income) was taxed as follows:

  35% on the first £5000
  40% on the next £500
  45% on the next £500

A man with three children aged 5, 13 and 14 years had an income of £6960 per annum. Calculate:

  (a) his taxable income,
  (b) the amount of tax due,
  (c) the ratio of the tax to his original income, expressing the answer as a percentage correct to three significant figures.

31) For the next year the expenditure of a borough is estimated at £313 780, some of which is to pay for a car park. The total rateable value of the borough is £432 800. Calculate:

  (a) the estimated rate in the £1,
  (b) the rates to be paid on a house whose rateable value is £156,
  (c) the estimated cost of the car park if the rate levied to meet the cost is 7·8 p in the £1. Give the answer to the nearest £100.

32) A man buys a house in which he has been living and for which he paid a weekly rent of £9·40; he also paid the rates at 55 p in the £1, the rateable value of the house being £160. The cost of heating and lighting is included in the rent. The house is valued at £8000 and to purchase the house the man borrows £5400 from a building society. His expenses now are:

  a monthly premium of £0·90 for every £100 borrowed,
  insurance at the rate of 0·125% per annum on the value of the house,
  rates now at 62 p in the £1,
  heating and lighting at an average of £32·50 per quarter,
  miscellaneous expenses estimated at £54 per annum.

Giving your answer to the nearest pound, find how much extra the man pays per annum than formerly.

33) How much must be invested in a 5% stock at 75 to yield a gross income of £75? If tax is deducted at 35% calculate the yield per cent on this investment.

34) A man invests in £1800 $4\frac{1}{2}$% stock at 30. Calculate his income from this stock. He sells them when they stand at 43. Calculate the profit he makes on the deal.

35) The paid up capital of a company consists of 8000 6% preference shares of £5 each and 300 000 ordinary shares at £1 each. The total amount available for distribution as dividend to the ordinary shareholders is £18 000. Ignoring income tax how much would an investor receive who owned 120 preference shares and 6500 ordinary shares?

36) A person holds 40 £3 shares which are paying a dividend of 5%. He sells them when they are priced at £2·50 each and reinvests the proceeds in £5 shares at £5·62 each. Find:

  (a) how many £5 shares he buys,
  (b) the change in the income if the new shares pay a dividend of 8%.

37) A man bought £600 of 7% stock at 80 and 900 50 p shares at 65 p each. The dividend declared on the shares was 15%. Calculate:

  (a) the amount of money invested,
  (b) the income in one year from his investments in stocks and shares.

38) The expenses of running a car were as follows for one year:

  Tax £40
  Insurance £64
  Depreciation £170
  Maintenance and repairs £42

During the year the owner travelled 9200 km with an average petrol consumption of 8 km per litre. If the cost of petrol was 20 p per litre calculate the total cost of the year's motoring. What is the average cost per kilometre in pence correct to the nearest one-tenth of a penny?

39) On personal loans a bank charges 15% interest per annum on the sum borrowed for the full period of repayment. A man borrows £450 on this basis and arranges to pay the loan with interest

in 24 monthly instalments. How much is the amount of each instalment?

40) A man earns a weekly wage of £45. Before income tax is charged the following allowances are deducted from his gross pay:

Personal allowance £775

Children's allowance £235

Other allowances £185

Calculate:

(a) his annual taxable income,

(b) the annual tax payable if this is charged at 30%,

(c) his average weekly tax payments.

17. Averages

To find the average of a set of quantities, add the quantities together and divide by the number of quantities in the set. Thus

$$\text{average} = \frac{\text{sum of the quantities}}{\text{number of quantities}}$$

Example 1

A batsman makes the following scores at cricket: 8, 20, 3, 0, 5, 9, 15 and 12. What is his average score.

$$\text{Average score} = \frac{8+20+3+0+5+9+15+12}{8}$$

$$= \frac{72}{8} = 9$$

Thus the batsman has an average score of 9 runs per innings.

Example 2

The apples in a box have a mass of 4·68 kg. If each apple has a mass of 97·5 g on the average, how many apples are there in the box?

Total mass = average mass of an apple × number of apples in the box

$$\text{Number of apples in the box} = \frac{\text{total mass}}{\text{average mass of an apple}}$$

$$= \frac{4680}{97·5} = 48$$

Example 3

Find the average age of a team of girls given that 4 of them are each 15 years 4 months and the other three girls are each 14 years 9 months old.

Total age of 4 girls at 15 years 4 months each
$$= 4 \times 15 \text{ years 4 months} = 61 \text{ years 4 months}$$

Total age of 3 girls at 14 years 9 months
$$= 3 \times 14 \text{ years 9 months} = 44 \text{ years 3 months}$$

Total age of 7 girls = 61 years 4 months + 44 years 3 months
$$= 105 \text{ years 7 months}$$

$$\text{Average age} = \frac{105 \text{ years 7 months}}{7} = 15 \text{ years 1 month}$$

Example 4

200 candidates sat for an examination and the average mark was 62. If the top 70 gained an average mark of 87 and the bottom 50 gained an average mark of 42 what was the average mark for the remainder of the candidates?

Total marks gained by all the candidates = 200 × 62 = 12 400
Marks gained by the top 70 candidates = 70 × 87 = 6090
Marks gained by the bottom 50 candidates = 50 × 42 = 2100
Marks gained by remaining 80 candidates = 12 400 − 6090 − 2100
$$= 4210$$

Average mark gained by the remaining 80 candidates

$$= \frac{4210}{80} = 52 \cdot 625$$

Exercise 109

1) Find the average of the following measurements: 22·3, 22·5, 22·6, 21·8 and 22·0 mm.

2) Find the average of the following numbers: 95, 128, 38, 97 and 217.

3) 12 metal castings have a mass of 12 kg each and 8 have a mass of $12\frac{1}{2}$ kg. Find the average mass of the 20 castings.

4) In an office 5 people earn a wage of £36 each, 3 earn a wage of £40 each and 2 earn a wage of £42 each. Calculate the average wage.

5) A business employs 125 people. The wage bill for a certain week was £3537·50. What was the average wage?

6) A batsman's average for 20 innings is 16·2 runs. How many runs did he score altogether?

7) The average of nine numbers is 72 and the average of four of them is 40. What is the average of the other five?

8) Find the average age of a team of boys if 5 of them are each 15 years old and the other 6 are each 14 years 1 month old.

9) The average of three numbers is 58 and the average of two of them is 49. Calculate the third number.

10) A grocer sells 40 tins of soup at 8 p per tin, 50 at 9 p per tin and 60 tins at 10 p per tin. Find the average price per tin.

Average Speed

The average speed of a vehicle is defined as the total distance travelled divided by the total time taken. The unit of speed depends upon the unit of distance and the unit of time. For instance if the distance is measured in kilometres (km) and the time is measured in hours (h) then the average speed will be stated in kilometres per hour (km/h). If the distance is measured in metres (m) and the time in seconds (s) then the average speed will be measured in metres per second (m/s).

Example 5   A car travels a total distance of 200 km in 4 hours. What is the average speed?

$$\text{Average speed} = \frac{\text{distance travelled}}{\text{time taken}} = \frac{200 \text{ km}}{4 \text{ h}} = 50 \text{ km/h}$$

Example 6   A car travels 30 km at 40 km/h and 30 km at 50 km/h. Find its average speed.

$$\text{Time taken to travel 30 km at 40 km/h} = \frac{30}{40} = 0 \cdot 75 \text{ h}$$

$$\text{Time taken to travel 30 km at 50 km/h} = \frac{30}{50} = 0 \cdot 6 \text{ h}$$

$$\text{Average speed} = \frac{\text{total distance travelled}}{\text{total time taken}} = \frac{60}{1 \cdot 35} = 44 \cdot 44 \text{ km/h}$$

Example 7   A train travels for 4 hours at an average speed of 64 km/h. For the first 2 hours its average speed is 50 km/h. What is the average speed for the last 2 hours?

Total distance travelled in the 4 hours
$$= \text{average speed} \times \text{time taken} = 64 \times 4 = 256 \text{ km}$$
Distance travelled in first 2 hours $= 50 \times 2 = 100 \text{ km}$
Distance travelled in last 2 hours $= 256 - 100 = 156 \text{ km}$
Average speed for the last 2 hours $= \dfrac{156}{2} = 78 \text{ km/h}$

Exercise 110

1) A train travels 300 km in 4 hours. Calculate its average speed.

2) A car travels 200 km at an average speed of 50 km/h. How long does it take?

3) If a car travels for 5 hours at an average speed of 70 km/h how far has it gone?

4) For the first $1\frac{1}{2}$ hours of a 91 km journey the average speed was 30 km/h. If the average speed for the remainder of the journey was 23 km/h, calculate the average speed for the entire journey.

5) A motorist travelling at a steady speed of 90 km/h covers a section of motorway in 25 minutes. After a speed limit is imposed he finds that when travelling at the maximum speed allowed he takes 5 minutes longer than before to cover the same section. Calculate the speed limit.

6) In winter a train travels between two towns 264 km apart at an average speed of 72 km/h. In summer the journey takes 22 minutes less than in winter. Find the average speed in summer.

7) A train travels between two towns 135 km apart in $4\frac{1}{2}$ hours. If on the return journey the average speed is reduced by 3 km/h, calculate the time taken for the return journey.

8) A car travels 272 km at an average speed of 32 km/h. On the return journey the average speed is increased to 48 km/h. Calculate the average speed over the entire journey.

Mixtures

It is common practice in the retail trade for a grocer to make his own blends of tea, coffee, etc. by mixing together two or three kinds of different types. Clearly the price of the blend will depend upon the quantities and the prices of the ingredients.

Example 8

30 litres of petrol costing 16 p per litre is mixed with 40 litres costing 18 p per litre. Find the price of the mixture.

30 litres at 16 p per litre cost $30 \times 16 \text{ p} = 480 \text{ p}$
40 litres at 18 p per litre cost $40 \times 18 \text{ p} = 720 \text{ p}$
Total cost of 70 litres of the mixture $= 480 + 720 = 1200 \text{ p}$

Cost per litre of the mixture $\qquad = \dfrac{1200}{70} = 17 \cdot 14 \text{ p}$

Example 9

A bronze consists of copper, lead and tin in the ratios of $7 : 2 : 1$. If copper costs 20 p per kilogramme and lead and tin cost 15 p and 25 p per kilogramme respectively, find the cost of 1 kg of the alloy.

Since there are 10 parts in all it will be convenient to work out the cost of 10 kg of the bronze. In 10 kg there will be 7 kg of copper, 2 kg of lead and 1 kg of tin.

Cost of 7 kg of copper $= 7 \times 20 \text{p} = 140 \text{p}$
Cost of 2 kg of lead $= 2 \times 15 \text{p} = 30 \text{p}$
Cost of 1 kg of tin $= 1 \times 25 \text{p} = 25 \text{p}$
Cost of 10 kg of alloy $= 140 + 30 + 25 = 195 \text{p}$
Cost of 1 kg of the alloy $= \dfrac{195}{10} = 19 \cdot 5 \text{p}$

Exercise 111

1) 4 kg of apples costing 20 p per kilogramme are mixed with 8 kg costing 14 p per kilogramme. What is the average price per kilogramme?

2) 60 litres of petrol costing 24 p per litre is mixed with 80 litres costing 27 p per litre. What is the average price of the mixture?

3) A grocer mixes together 5 kg of Brazilian coffee costing £1·30 per kg with 3 kg of Kenyan coffee costing 95 p per kg. Work out the price he should charge for the blend to the nearest penny.

4) A supermarket blends its own butter by mixing 3 types in the ratios of 5 : 3 : 2. If the prices of these grades are 72 p, 84 p and 63 p per kg respectively find the price that should be charged per kilogramme.

5) A wine merchant mixes together 8 litres of wine costing £2·50 per litre with 4 litres costing £1·80 per litre. What price should he charge for the resulting mixture?

6) A brass is composed of copper and zinc in the ratio of 3 : 1. If copper costs 25 p per kg and zinc costs 18 p per kg find the cost of 1 kg of brass.

Weighted Averages

In a set of quantities it often happens that some of the quantities are repeated several times. When this happens we must give due weighting to these repeated items in order to arrive at a true average.

Example 10   An industrial organisation gives an aptitude test to all applicants for employment. The results of 150 people taking the test was as follows:

Score (out of 10)	1	2	3	4	5	6	7	8	9	10
No. of applicants	6	12	15	21	35	24	20	10	6	1

What was the average score obtained by all the applicants?

Total score $= 1 \times 6 + 2 \times 12 + 3 \times 15 + 4 \times 21 + 5 \times 35 + 6 \times 24 + 7 \times 20 + 8 \times 10 + 9 \times 6 + 10 \times 1 = 762$

Total number of applicants $= 150$

Average score $= \dfrac{\text{total mark}}{\text{no. of applicants}} = \dfrac{762}{150} = 5 \cdot 08$

In calculating a weighted average it often helps if the information is tabulated as shown over.

Score	No. of applicants	Product
1	6	6
2	12	24
3	15	45
4	21	84
5	35	175
6	24	144
7	20	140
8	10	80
9	6	54
10	1	10
Totals	150	762

$$\text{Average score} = \frac{762}{150} = 5{\cdot}08$$

Statistical Averages

There are three statistical averages which are in common use. They are the arithmetic mean, the median and the mode.

The arithmetic mean. This is the commonest statistical average and it is determined by adding up all the quantities in a set of quantities and dividing by the number of quantities in the set. Thus:

$$\text{arithmetic mean} = \frac{\text{sum of the quantities}}{\text{no. of quantities}}$$

Hence the arithmetic mean is evaluated in exactly the same way as the averages considered in the previous section of this chapter. In Example 10, for instance, we could have said that the mean score was 5·08.

Example 11   A 100 ball bearings were measured, the results being as follows:

Diameter (mm)	14·96	14·97	14·98	14·99	15·00	15·01	15·02
No. of ball bearings	3	5	13	21	26	24	8

Calculate the mean diameter of these ball bearings.

Problems like this are best tabulated as follows:

Diameter (mm)	No. of ball bearings	Product
14·96	3	14·96 × 3 = 44·88
14·97	5	14·97 × 5 = 74·85
14·98	13	14·98 × 13 = 194·74
14·99	21	14·99 × 21 = 314·79
15·00	26	15·00 × 26 = 390·00
15·01	24	15·01 × 24 = 360·24
15·02	8	15·02 × 8 = 120·16
Totals	100	1499·66

$$\text{Mean diameter} = \frac{1499{\cdot}66}{100} = 14{\cdot}9966 \text{ mm}$$

The median. If a set of quantities is arranged in ascending (or descending) order of size, the median is the value which is half-way along the set. Thus the median of 3, 5, 7, 8, 10 is 7. If the number of quantities in the set is even then the median is the average of the two middle values. Thus the median of 2, 3, 5, 7, 8, 9 is $\frac{1}{2} \times (5+7) = \frac{1}{2} \times 12 = 6$.

Example 12

The wages of 7 people working in an office are £1·20, £1·08, £0·75, £2·49, £1·36, £0·67 and £1·98 per hour. What is the median wage?

The first step is to arrange the wages in ascending order.

$$0·67 \quad 0·75 \quad 1·08 \quad 1·20 \quad 1·36 \quad 1·98 \quad 2·49$$

The median is now the middle value which is 1·20. Hence the median wage is £1·20.

Example 13

The heights of 8 students at a college were as follows: 177·8, 162·6, 167·6, 182·0, 165·3, 157·5, 185·4 and 169·8 cm. Find the median height.

Arranging the heights in ascending order of size we have:

$$157·5 \quad 162·6 \quad 165·3 \quad 167·6 \quad 169·8 \quad 177·8 \quad 182·0 \quad 185·4$$

The two middle values are 167·6 and 169·8 and hence the median height is $\frac{1}{2} \times (167·6 + 169·8) = \frac{1}{2} \times 337·4 = 168·7$ cm.

The mode. The quantity which occurs most frequently in a set of quantities is called the mode. Thus the mode of the set of numbers 20, 22, 25, 25, 27, 27, 27, 30, 30, 31, 33 and 35 is 27 since this number occurs three times which is more than any of the other numbers.

Example 14

In an aptitude test 12 candidates obtained the following scores out of 20. 3, 4, 4, 7, 7, 8, 9, 9, 9, 12, 12, 15. Find the mode.

Three of the candidates scored 9 marks which is the most frequently occurring mark. Hence the mode is 9 marks.

The arithmetic mean takes into account extreme values which may not be truly representative of the group as a whole. The median and the mode avoid this and in many cases will give a better average than the arithmetic mean. The median can often be located with greater accuracy than the mode because there may be more than one mode in a set of quantities. However the mode is useful for such things as stock sizes. It is not much good if a manufacturerer of men's trousers finds that the mean length of men's legs is 81·28 cm since this may not be a stock size. What he wants to know is which stock size is the most popular and the mode will give him this information.

In Chapter 18 methods of finding the mode and median by graphical methods are discussed.

Exercise 112

1) Find the arithmetic mean of the following:

Length (cm)							
29·5	29·6	29·7	29·8	29·9	30·0	30·1	30·2
No. of lengths							
3	7	22	28	18	12	7	3

2) The wages of 60 employees in a company were as follows:

Wage £	40	41	42	43	44	45	46
No. of wages	7	9	16	13	9	5	1

Calculate the mean wage.

3) The marks of 50 students taking a test were as follows (marks out of 20):

Mark	12	13	14	15	16	17	18
No. of students	3	8	11	18	7	2	1

Find the mean mark.

4) The rainfall in millimetres falling on a town in 5 successive days was as follows: 23, 28, 13, 42, 17. Find the median.

5) The wages of 8 people working on a small section of a factory are as follows: £1·89, £2·06, £1·75, £2·48, £1·63, £2·08, £1·97, £1·42. Find the median wage.

6) Find the median of the following sets of numbers:
(a) 2, 3, 3, 5, 6, 7, 8
(b) 4, 4, 6, 8, 9, 11, 14, 16
(c) 8, 9, 8, 7, 9, 6, 10, 7, 9

7) The figures below represent the daily output of a factory on 14 successive working days:

27, 42, 35, 63, 38, 75, 63, 72, 75, 61, 63, 65, 63, 75

Find the median and the mode.

8) Find the mode of the following set of numbers:

2, 8, 11, 3, 7, 8, 11, 12, 8, 15, 9, 8, 11, 8, 6, 4, 10, 2.

Summary

1) Average = $\dfrac{\text{sum of the quantities}}{\text{no. of quantities}}$

2) Average speed = $\dfrac{\text{distance travelled}}{\text{time taken}}$

3) Arithmetic mean = $\dfrac{\text{sum of the quantities}}{\text{no. of quantities}}$

4) When a set of quantities is arranged in ascending (or descending) order of size the median is the middle value of the set. If the set contains an even number of quantities then the median value is the average of the two middle values.

5) The mode is the value which occurs most frequently in a set of quantities.

Mental Test 17

Try to write down the answers to the following without writing down anything else.

1) Find the average of 3, 5 and 10.

2) Find the average of 2, 4, 6 and 8.

3) 200 candidates sat for an examination and the average mark was 12. How many marks were scored altogether?

4) 3 apples have a mass of 60 g each and 5 have a mass of 100 g each. What is the average mass of an apple?

5) A cricketer's batting average is 8 runs per innings. If he batted 20 times how many runs did he score in all?

6) A grocer sells 10 tins of peas at 7 p per tin and 5 tins at 4 p per tin. Find the average price for a tin of peas.

7) A car travels 80 km in 2 hours. What is its average speed?

8) A car's average speed is 50 km/h. It travels for 3 hours. How far does it go?

9) A car travels 120 km at an average speed of 40 km/h. How long does it take?

10) 2 kg of tea costing 84 p per kg are mixed with 3 kg costing 72 p per kg. Find the price of the mixture.

11) An alloy consists of copper and zinc in the ratio 7 : 3. If copper costs 20 p per kg and zinc costs 24 p per kg, find the cost of 1 kg of the alloy.

12) Find the median of 3, 5, 7, 9, 11, 13.

13) Find the median of 1·5, 1·8, 2·0, 3·2, 5·8.

14) Find the mode of 2, 2, 4, 4, 4, 6, 6, 7, 7, 8, 9, 10, 11, 11.

Self-Test 17

In the following questions state the letter (or letters) corresponding to the correct answer (or answers).

1) The mean of 11·2, 11·3, 11·5, 11·1 and 11·2 is:

   a 11·3 **b** 11·5 **c** 11·22 **d** 11·26

2) The average weight of two adults in a family is 81 kg and the average weight of three children in the same family is 23 kg. The average weight for the whole family is:

   a 45·3 kg   **b** 46·2 kg
   c 52·0 kg   **d** 20·8 kg

3) 50 litres of oil costing 16 p per litre is mixed with 70 litres costing 18 p per litre. The average price of a litre is:

   a 17·2 p **b** 17 p **c** 19·2 p **d** 21·6 p

4) A grocer sells 20 tins of soup at 10 p per tin, 30 at 16 p per tin and 40 at 14 p per tin. The average price per tin is:

   a $13\frac{1}{3}$ p **b** $13\frac{7}{9}$ p **c** 12 p **d** 15 p

5) The average of three numbers is 116. The average of two of them is 98. The third number is:

   a 18   **b** 107 **c** 110   **d** 152

6) An aeroplane flies non-stop for $2\frac{1}{4}$ hours and travels 1620 km. Its average speed in km/h is:

   a 720 **b** 800   **c** 3645 **d** 364·5

7) A car travels 50 km at 50 km/h and 70 km at 70 km/h. Its average speed is:

   a 60 km/h   **b** 65 km/h
   c 58 km/h   **d** 62 km/h

8) A car travels for 3 hours at a speed of 45 km/h and for 4 hours at a speed of 50 km/h. It has travelled a distance of:

   a 27·5 km   **b** 95 km
   c 335 km   **d** 353 km

9) A car travels 540 km at an average speed of 30 km/h. On the return journey the average speed is doubled to 60 km/h. The average speed over the entire journey is:

   a 45 km/h   **b** 42 km/h
   c 40 km/h   **d** 35 km/h

10) A car travels between two towns 270 km apart in 9 hours. On the return journey the speed is increased by 10 km/h. The time taken for the return journey is:

   a $6\frac{1}{4}$ hours   **b** $6\frac{3}{4}$ hours
   c 2·7 hours   **d** $4\frac{1}{2}$ hours

11) The heights of a group of boys are measured with the results shown below:

Height	157	158	159	160	161
No. of boys	20	36	44	46	39

Height	162	163	164	165	166
No. of boys	30	22	17	10	6

The mean height of the boys is:

   a 161·5   **b** 161
   c 160   **d** 160·5

12) The mode of the numbers 23, 27, 28, 29, 32, 33, 35, 37 is:

   a 29   **b** 28   **c** 28·5 **d** 30·2

18. Graphs and Charts

In newspapers, business reports and government publications use is made of pictorial illustrations to present and compare quantities of the same kind. These diagrams help the reader to understand what deductions can be drawn from the quantities represented. The most common forms are charts and graphs.

Axes of Reference

To plot a graph we first take two lines at right angles to each other (Fig. 18.1). These lines are called the axes of reference. Their intersection, the point O, is called the origin. The vertical axis is often called the y-axis and the horizontal axis is then called the x-axis.

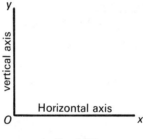

Fig. 18.1

Scales

The number of units represented by a unit length along an axis is called the scale on that axis. For instance 1 cm could represent 2 units. The scale is determined from the highest and lowest values to be plotted along an axis. It should be as large as possible but it must also be chosen so that it is easy to read. The scales need not be the same on both axes.

Coordinates

Coordinates are used to mark the points of a graph. In Fig. 18.2, values of x are to be plotted against values of y. The point P has been plotted so that $x = 8$ and $y = 10$. The values of 8 and 10 are said to be the rectangular coordinates of the point P.

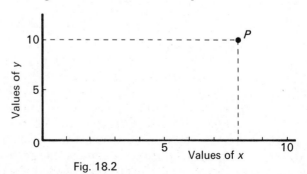

Fig. 18.2

Drawing a Graph

Every graph shows a relation between two sets of numbers. The table below gives the average diameter of ash trees of varying ages.

Age in years								
5	10	15	20	25	30	40	50	70

Diameter (cm)								
7·6	9·3	12·2	16·2	21·4	27·7	43·8	64·5	119·7

To plot the graph we first draw the two axes of reference (Fig. 18.3)· We then choose suitable scales to represent the age in years along the horizontal axis and the diameter along the vertical axis. Scales of 7mm = 10 years (horizontally) and 7mm = 20 cm (vertically) have been chosen. On plotting the graph we see that it is a smooth curve which passes through all of the plotted points.

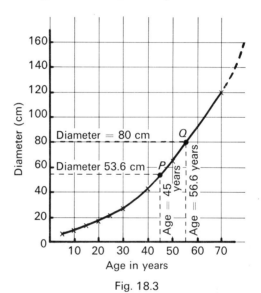

Fig. 18.3

When a graph is either a smooth curve or a straight line we can use the graph to deduce corresponding values not given in the table of values. Thus to find the diameter of a tree which is 45 years old we first find 45 on the horizontal axis and from this point we draw a vertical line to meet the curve at P. From P we now draw a horizontal line to the vertical axis and read off the value. It is found to be 53·6. Hence a tree which is 45 years old will have a diameter of 53·6 cm.

Suppose now that we wish to know the age of a tree with a diameter of 80 cm. We find 80 cm on the vertical axis and from this point we draw a horizontal line to meet the curve at Q. From Q we draw a vertical line to the horizontal axis and read off the value. It is found to be 56·6. Hence a tree with a diameter of 80 cm is 56·6 years old.

Using a graph in this way to find values which are not given in the table is called *interpolation*. If we extend the curve so that it follows the general trend we can estimate values of the diameter and age which lie just beyond the range of the given values. Thus in Fig. 18.3 by extending the curve we can find the probable diameter of a tree which is 75 years old. This is found to be 136·4 cm.

Finding a value in this way is called *extrapolation*. An extrapolated value can usually be relied upon, but in certain cases it may contain a substantial amount of error. Extrapolated values must therefore be used with care. It must be clearly understood that interpolation can only be used if the graph is a smooth curve or a straight line. It is no good applying interpolation to the graph of Example 1.

Example 1

The table below gives the temperature at 12.00 noon on seven successive days. Plot a graph to illustrate this information with the day horizontal.

Day June	1	2	3	4	5	6	7
Temp. °C	16	20	16	18	22	15	16·5

As before we draw two axes at right-angles to each other, indicating the day on the horizontal axis. Since the temperatures range from 15° to 22°C we can make 14°C (say) our starting point on the vertical axis. This will allow us to use a larger scale on that axis which makes for greater accuracy in plotting the graph.

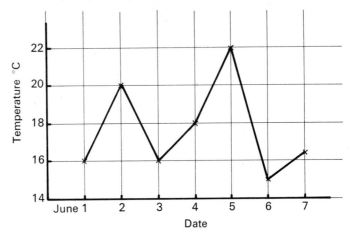

Fig. 18.4

On plotting the points (Fig. 18.4) we see that it is impossible to join the points by means of a smooth curve. The best we can do is to join the points by means of a series of straight lines. The graph then presents in pictorial form the variations in temperature and we can see at a glance that the 1st, 3rd and 6th June were cool days whilst the 2nd and 5th were warm days.

Exercise 113

1) The table below shows the amount of steel delivered to a factory during five successive weeks. Plot a graph to show this with the number of weeks on the horizontal axis.

Week number	1	2	3
Amount delivered (kg)	25 000	65 000	80 000

Week number	4	5
Amount delivered (kg)	30 000	50 000

2) The areas of circles for various diameters is shown in the table below. Plot a graph with the diameter on the horizontal axis and from it estimate the area of a circle whose diameter is 18 cm.

Diameter (cm)	5	10	15	20	25
Area (cm²)	19·6	78·5	177·6	314·2	492·2

3) The output of a factory in 8 successive

weeks is given in the table below. Plot a graph to show this with the number of weeks on the horizontal axis.

Week number	1	2	3	4	5	6	7	8
Output (units)	83	65	78	89	96	88	73	69

4) The table below gives the amounts for £1 invested at 8% interest per annum for the periods stated.

Years	2	4	6	8	10	12	14
Amounts in £	1·17	1·36	1·59	1·85	2·16	2·52	2·94

Plot the years horizontally and find the amount after 7 years.

5) Two quantities W and P are connected as shown by the following table of values:

W	28	50	59	67	74	79	84
P	2·0	5·4	6·8	8·0	9·1	9·9	10·6

Plot a graph with P plotted horizontally and find the value of W when $P = 7·4$. What is the value of P when $W = 77$?

Straight Line Graphs

When one quantity varies with another quantity we can show the relationship by drawing a graph. The method is shown in Example 2.

Example 2   If the rate of exchange between the pound and the mark is 5·4 marks = £1, construct a graph to show the value of the mark in pounds up to £60. From the graph find the value of £25 in marks and 120 marks in £.

The first step is to draw up a table of corresponding values as follows:

£	0	10	20	30	40	50	60
marks	0	54	108	162	216	270	324

The graph is shown plotted in Fig. 18.5 and it is seen to be a straight line. By using the graph we find that £25 = 135 marks and that 120 marks = £22·22.

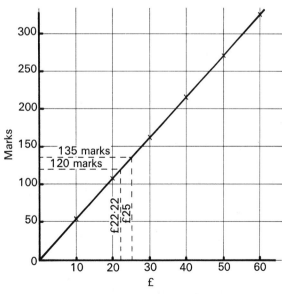

Fig. 18.5

Graphs of Formulae

The volume of a sphere is given by the formula

$$V = \tfrac{4}{3}\pi r^3, \text{ where } r \text{ is the radius.}$$

By taking values of r we can calculate the corresponding values of V and so plot a graph which shows the relationship between r and V. We can then use this graph to read off the volume of a sphere of given radius.

Example 3

The volume of a sphere is given by the formula $V = \frac{4}{3}\pi r^3$, where r is the radius. Taking values of r from 1 to 10 draw a graph of V against r and using the graph find the volume of a sphere whose diameter is 9.

We first select suitable values for r and then calculate the corresponding values of V as shown below.

$$r = 1 \qquad V = \tfrac{4}{3}\times3{\cdot}142\times1^3 = 4{\cdot}19$$
$$r = 2 \qquad V = \tfrac{4}{3}\times3{\cdot}142\times2^3 = 33{\cdot}51$$
$$r = 3 \qquad V = \tfrac{4}{3}\times3{\cdot}142\times3^3 = 113{\cdot}1 \quad \text{and so on.}$$

Drawing up a table of these corresponding values we have

r	1	2	3	4	5	6	7	8	9	10
V	4·19	33·51	113·1	268·1	523·7	904·9	1437	2145	3054	4189

The graph is shown in Fig. 18.6 and it is seen to be a smooth curve. Using the graph as shown in the diagram we find the volume of a sphere whose diameter is 9 (radius = 4·5) to be 381.

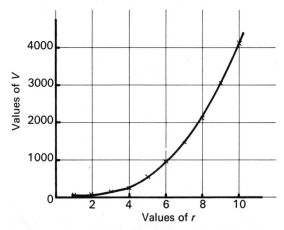

Fig. 18.6

Exercise 114

1) The rate of exchange between the franc and the £ is 9·20 francs = £1. Construct a graph to show the value of the franc in £'s up to £50. From the graph find the value of £22 in francs and 180 francs in £'s.

2) £200 is invested at 9% simple interest. Draw a graph to show the amount of money accruing for any period up to 10 years. From the graph find the amount accruing after 7 years.

3) A dealer marks the price of his goods at a profit of 25% on his cost price. Draw a graph showing the relationship between cost price and selling price for cost prices up to £50 and from the graph find the cost price of an article selling for £38.

4) A man is paid £52 for a basic week of 40 hours. When he works overtime he is paid at time and a half. Draw a graph to show the man's earnings when he works overtime up to 12 hours. From the graph find how much overtime he must work to earn £63·70.

5) The area of a circle is given by the formula $A = \pi r^2$. Draw a graph to show the relationship between the area and the radius, r, of the circle for values of r up to 8.

6) The surface area of a sphere is given by $A = 4\pi r^2$ where r is the radius. Draw a graph of A against r for values of r up to 6.

7) The formula for connecting two quantities x and y is $y = 3x+5$. Draw a graph of x against y for values of x up to 16.

8) The circumference of a circle is found from the formula $C = \pi d$ where d is the diameter. Find the diameter of a circle whose circumference is 24 by constructing a suitable graph.

Distance-Time Graphs

Since distance $=$ speed $\times$ time, when the speed is constant the distance travelled is proportional to the time. This may be illustrated on a graph which will be a straight line.

Example 4

A car travels a distance of 180 km in a time of 3 hours. Draw a distance time graph to illustrate and from the graph find the average speed for the whole journey.

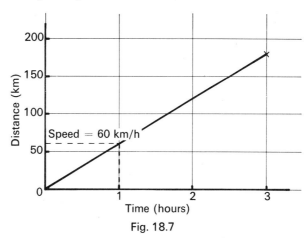

Fig. 18.7

The graph is shown in Fig. 18.7 and time (in hours) is plotted horizontally and distance vertically which is the usual way. Note that the straight line is obtained by taking the two points as follows: time $= 0$, distance $= 0$; time $= 3$ hours, distance $= 180$ km. To find the average speed we find the distance the car travelled in 1 hour. From the graph this is 60 km. Hence the average speed is 60 km/h.

Example 5

A train travels at a speed of 70 km/h. Draw a graph to illustrate and from the graph find the distance travelled in 2 hours and how long it will take to travel 175 km.

To draw the graph take the following points: time $= 0$, distance $= 0$; time $= 1$ hour, distance $= 70$ km (since speed is 70 km/h). The graph is drawn in Fig. 18.8.

To find the distance travelled in 2 hours we find 2 hours on the horizontal axis and draw a vertical line to meet the straight line graph at P. From P we draw a horizontal line to meet the vertical axis and read off the value which is 140 km.

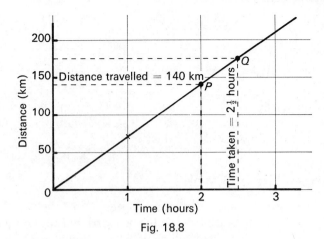

Fig. 18.8

To find how long it takes to travel 175 km we find 175 km on the vertical axis and draw a horizontal line to meet the graph at Q. From Q we draw a vertical line to meet the horizontal axis and read off the value which is $2\frac{1}{2}$ hours.

Example 6   A man travels a distance of 80 km by car at a speed of 40 km/h. He then cycles a distance of 20 km at a speed of 15 km/h and finally walks a distance of 8 km at a speed of 6 km/h. Draw a graph to illustrate and from it find the average speed for the entire journey.

The graph is drawn in the usual way (Fig. 18.9) and it consists of three straight lines to represent each stage of the journey. The average speed is found by drawing the straight line $0A$. Using the line $0A$ we find the distance travelled in 1 hour, i.e. 23·1 km. The average speed is therefore 23·1 km/h.

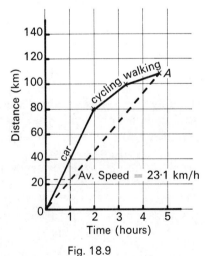

Fig. 18.9

Exercise 115

1) A train travels a distance of 200 km in a time of 4 hours. Draw a graph to illustrate and find:
   (a) the average speed,
   (b) the distance travelled in 2 hours,
   (c) the time taken to travel 150 km.

2) A car travels at a speed of 60 km/h. Use a graph to find the distance travelled in 3 hours and the time taken to travel 40 km.

3) A car travels a distance of 80 km in 2 hours. It then changes speed and travels a further 60 km in $1\frac{1}{2}$ hours. Draw a time-distance graph and from it find the average speed for the entire journey.

4) A girl cycles a distance of 20 km at a speed of 12 km/h. She rests for 20 minutes and then continues the journey at 10 km/h for $1\frac{1}{2}$ hours. From the graph which you plot find the average speed for the entire journey and the total distance travelled.

5) A man travels a distance of 90 km by car at a speed of 60 km/h. He then cycles a distance of 18 km at a speed of 12 km/h. He then rests for 15 minutes before continuing on foot during which he walks a distance of 8 km in 2 hours. Find the average speed for the entire journey using a suitable graph.

Break Even Points

By plotting two graphs on the same axes the break-even point can be discovered. The method is shown in Examples 7 and 8.

Example 7

A consumer of electricity has the choice of the following tariffs:

(1) A fixed charge of £4 per quarter plus 0·8 p per unit used.
(2) A charge of 1·2 p for all the units used.

What is the break-even point?

To plot the graphs we draw up the following table:

Units used	400	800	1200	1600
Tariff 1 (pence)	720	1040	1360	1680
Tariff 2 (pence)	480	960	1440	1920

We now plot the graphs of cost of electricity against units used on the same axes and to the same scales as shown in Fig. 18.10. We see that the graphs cross at the point where the number of units used is 1000. This is the break-even point and it means that if a consumer is going to use more than 1000 units he should use tariff 1; if less he should use tariff 2.

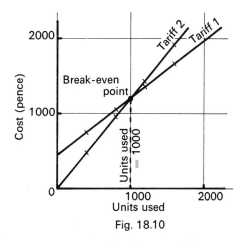

Fig. 18.10

Example 8

A factory manufactures a product which is sold to retailers at £10 each. The cost of producing the articles consists of a fixed charge of £1500 plus a manufacturing cost of £8 per article. Use this information

to draw graphs showing income and costs against the number produced. From the graphs find:

   (a) the break-even point,
   (b) the loss when the output is 400,
   (c) the profit when the output is 900.

Drawing up a table giving the number produced per year, income and
costs, we have

Number produced per year	0	400	800	1200
Annual income £	0	4000	8000	12 000
Annual costs £	1500	4700	7900	11 100

The graphs are shown plotted on the same axes and to the same
scales in Fig. 18.11. The break-even point occurs when the two graphs
cross and this is seen to be at 750 units produced per annum. Thus to
show a profit the manufacturer must produce more than 750 units
per annum. The loss when the output is 400 is found by finding the
difference between the heights of the two graphs at this point. It is
£700. The profit is found in a similar way and when the output is 900
the profit is £300.

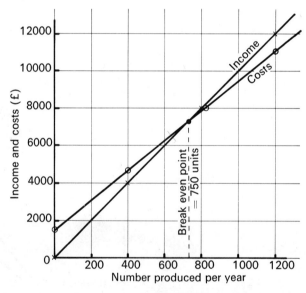

Fig. 18.11

Exercise 116

1) Using hand methods the cost of
making an article is constant at £0·80
each. By using special tools the cost of
making the article falls uniformly from
£1·50 each when 10 are made to £0·40
when 1000 are made. Find the break-
even point.

2) A factory manufactures a product
which is sold to retailers at £15 each.
Production costs vary with the numbers

produced as shown in the table below.

Number produced per year	0	1000	2000	3000
Total cost per year £	15 000	33 000	46 000	54 000

Number produced per year	4000	5000
Total cost per year £	61 000	65 000

Use this information to draw graphs on
the same axes showing income and cost
against the number produced per year.

From the graphs find:
  (a) the annual output for which income equals costs,
  (b) the output corresponding to the maximum loss per year,
  (c) the profit when 4500 units are produced per year.

3) A user of gas can choose between the following two tariffs:
  (1) A fixed charge of £8 plus a charge of 12 p per therm used.
  (2) A charge of 14 p per therm for all the gas used.
Using this information draw graphs on the same axes of number of therms used against cost for both tariffs. Hence find the break-even point.

4) The table below shows the amounts accruing when £100 is invested at 7% compound interest.

Number of years	1	2	3	5
Amount accruing	107	114	122	140
Number of years	10	15	20	
Amount accruing	197	276	387	

A man can either invest cash at 7% compound interest or 12% simple interest. Find the number of years for which both methods will yield the same amount of capital.

5) A person can travel to work by either train or car. By car he can achieve an average speed of 40 km/h but by train the average speed is 60 km/h. However by train there is a waiting time at each end of the journey of 20 minutes. Find the shortest journey for which it is quicker to go by train by drawing two graphs on the same axes.

The Pie Chart

Suppose that in a factory the number of persons employed on various jobs is as shown in the following table:

Type of personnel	Number employed
Unskilled workers	45
Craftsmen	25
Draughtsmen	5
Clerical staff	10
Total	85

The pie charts displays the information as angles, the size of the angle being proportional to the number employed. Thus for unskilled workers the angle is $\frac{45}{85} \times 360° = 190°$ and for craftsmen the angle is $\frac{25}{85} \times 360° = 106°$, etc. The resulting pie chart is shown in Fig. 18.12.

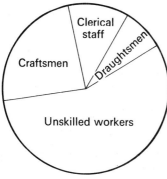

Fig. 18.12

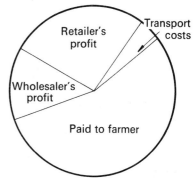

Fig. 18.13

Example 9   An analysis of the cost of potatoes retailed at 15 p per kilogramme was as follows:

Paid to farmer	8 p per kilogramme
Wholesaler's profit	2 p
Retailer's profit	4 p
Transport costs	1 p

Represent this information on a pie chart.

Item	Pence	Centre angle
Paid to farmer	8	$\frac{8}{15} \times 360° = 192°$
Wholesaler's profit	2	$\frac{2}{15} \times 360° = 48°$
Retailer's profit	4	$\frac{4}{15} \times 360° = 96°$
Transport costs	1	$\frac{1}{15} \times 360° = 24°$
Totals	15	360°

The pie chart is shown in Fig. 18.13.

The Bar Chart

This diagram relies upon heights (or areas) to convey the proportions, the total height of the diagram representing the total or 100%.

Example 10   Represent the information given in Example 9 in the form of a bar chart.

Item	Pence	Percentage
Paid to farmer	8	$\frac{8}{15} \times 100 = 53\%$
Wholesaler's profit	2	$\frac{2}{15} \times 100 = 13\%$
Retailer's profit	4	$\frac{4}{15} \times 100 = 27\%$
Transport costs	1	$\frac{1}{15} \times 100 = 7\%$
Totals	15	100%

The bar chart is shown in Fig. 18.14.

The Horizontal Bar Chart

This gives a better comparison of the costs involved (see Example 9) but it does not readily display the total costs.

Example 11   Draw a horizontal bar chart for the information given in Example 9. The diagram is shown in Fig. 18.15.

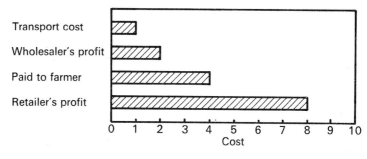

Transport costs	7%
Retailer's profit	27%
Wholesaler's profit	13%
Paid to farmer	53%

Fig. 18.14

Fig. 18.15

Frequency Distributions

Suppose that we measure the diameters of 100 ball bearings. We might get the following readings, in millimetres:

```
15·02  15·03  14·98  14·98  15·00  15·01  15·00  15·01  14·99
15·02  14·99  15·03  15·02  15·01  15·01  15·02  15·04  14·98
15·01  15·02  14·98  15·01  15·01  15·01  14·99  15·00  15·00
15·00  15·01  15·01  15·01  15·03  14·98  14·99  14·99  15·00
14·99  15·00  15·00  15·02  14·96  15·01  14·98  15·01  15·00
15·01  15·00  15·01  14·99  15·01  15·00  14·99  15·02  14·99
15·01  15·00  15·01  15·00  14·99  14·98  14·97  14·99  15·00
14·98  14·97  15·00  14·99  14·98  15·03  14·99  15·03  15·00
14·99  14·97  15·02  15·03  15·03  14·99  15·00  14·99  14·99
14·96  15·04  14·99  15·01  15·00  15·00  15·00  15·03  14·98
14·99  15·01  14·99  14·98  15·00  14·97  15·00  15·02  15·00
15·01
```

These figures do not mean very much as they stand and so we rearrange them into what is called a frequency distribution. To do this we collect all the 14·96 measurements together, all the 14·97 measurements together and so on. A tally chart (Table 1) is the best way of doing this. Each time a measurement arises we place a tally mark opposite the appropriate measurement. The fifth tally mark is usually made in an oblique direction thus tying the tally marks into bundles of five to make counting easier. When the tally marks are completed the marks are counted and the numerical value recorded in the column headed frequency. The frequency is the number of times each measurement occurs. From Table 1 it will be seen that the measurement 14·96 mm occurs twice (that is, it has a frequency of 2), the measurement 14·97 occurs four times (a frequency of 4) and so on.

TABLE 1

Measurement (mm)	Tally marks	Frequency
14·96	11	2
14·97	1111	4
14·98	LHH LHH 1	11
14·99	LHH LHH LHH LHH	20
15·00	LHH LHH LHH LHH 111	23
15·01	LHH LHH LHH LHH 1	21
15·02	LHH 1111	9
15·03	LHH 111	8
15·04	11	2

The Histogram

The frequency distribution becomes even more understandable if we draw a diagram to represent it. The best type of diagram is the histogram (Fig. 18.16) which consists of a set of rectangles, each of the same width whose areas represent the frequencies. Since the rectangles are all of the same width the heights of the rectangles represent the frequencies. On studying the histogram the pattern of the variation in the size of the ball bearings is easily understood. Most of the values are near to the centre of the diagram with a few values more widely dispersed.

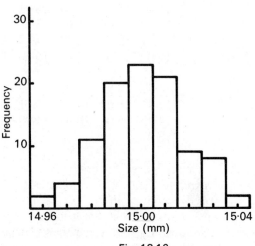

Fig. 18.16

Grouped Data

When dealing with a large number of observations it is often useful to group the data into classes or categories. We can then determine the number of items which belong to each class thus obtaining a class frequency. Table 2 shows the result of a test given to 200 students, the maximum mark being 20.

TABLE 2

Mark	Frequency
1–5	22
6–10	55
11–15	93
16–20	30

From the table we see that the first class consists of marks from 1 to 5. 22 students obtained marks in this range and hence the class frequency is 22. A histogram of this data may be drawn (Fig. 18.17) by using the mid-points of the class intervals as the centres of the rectangles.

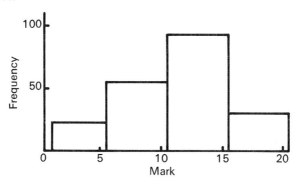

Fig. 18.17

The Median of a Frequency Distribution

In Chapter 17 we discovered that the median of a set of numbers arranged in ascending (or descending) order of size is the middle value of the set. Thus the median of

2   4   5   6   6   7   8   8   8   9   10

is 7 since there are five numbers below this value and 5 numbers above it.

Since, in a histogram, area corresponds to frequency, the median divides the histogram into two equal areas (Fig. 18.18). Hence the median occurs at half of the total frequency. However the easiest way of finding the median of a frequency distribution is to draw a cumulative frequency curve as shown in Example 12.

Example 12   The information in the table below relates to the masses of packets of chemical. By drawing a cumulative frequency curve determine the median of the distribution.

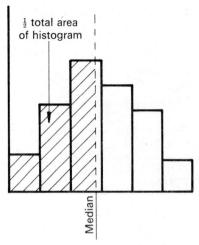

Fig. 18.18

Mass (grammes)	119	120	121	122	123	124
Frequency	5	9	19	25	18	4

The cumulative frequencies are given below:

Mass (grammes)	Cumulative frequency
not more than 119·5	5
not more than 120·5	5+9 = 14
not more than 121·5	5+9+19 = 33
not more than 122·5	5+9+19+25 = 58
not more than 123·5	5+9+19+25+18 = 76
not more than 124·5	5+9+19+25+18+4 = 80

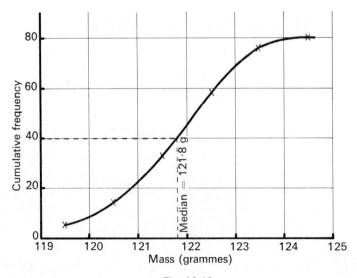

Fig. 18.19

Notice that the mass of 119 grammes includes all the masses between 118·5 and 119·5 grammes. Similarly the mass 120 grammes includes all the packets between 119·5 and 120·5 grammes.

The cumulative frequency curve is shown in Fig. 18.19. Since the total frequency is 80 the median is the mass corresponding to a frequency of 40, that is, 121·8 grammes.

The Mode of a Frequency Distribution

It was shown in Chapter 17 that the mode of a set of values is the most frequently occurring value. Thus the mode of

2   4   5   6   6   7   8   8   8   9   10

is 8 because this value occurs three times which is more than any of the other values.

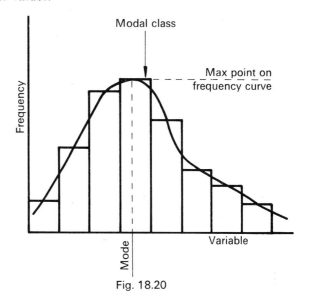

Fig. 18.20

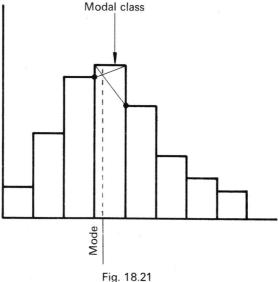

Fig. 18.21

To find the mode of a frequency distribution we draw a histogram and hence a frequency curve. The mode is then the value of the variable corresponding to the maximum point on the curve (Fig. 18.20). The mode can also be obtained directly from the histogram as shown in Fig. 18.21.

Example 13   The heights of a group of boys are measured to the nearest centimetre with the following results:

Height (cm)	157	158	159	160	161	162	163	164	165	166	167
Frequency	20	36	44	46	39	30	22	17	10	4	2

Find the mode of distribution.

By constructing the histogram (Fig. 18·22) the mode is found to be 159·7. It is worthwhile noting that the modal class is 159·5 to 160·5 cm.

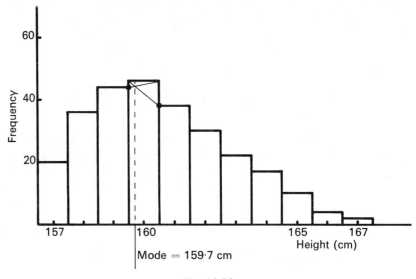

Fig. 18.22

Exercise 117

1) A building contractor surveying his labour force finds that 35% are engaged on factories, 40% are engaged on house building and 25% are engaged on public works (schools, hospitals, etc.).

    (a) Draw a pie chart of this information.

    (b) Present the information in the form of a single bar chart.

2) A firm finds that each pound received from sales is spent in the following way:

Raw materials	£0·38
Wages and salaries	£0·29
Machinery etc.	£0·08
Advertising etc.	£0·15
Profit	£0·10

Construct a pie chart of this information.

3) A department store has monthly takings of £40 000. It is divided between the various departments as follows:

Men's clothing	£10 000
Women's clothing	£15 000
Hardware	£ 5 000
Electrical	£ 8 000
Stationery	£ 2 000

Draw a pie chart of this information.

4) Draw a horizontal bar chart for the information given in Question 3.

5) In a certain factory the number of personel employed on various jobs as follows: Machinists 140, Fitters 120, Clerical staff 80, Labourers 10, Draughtsmen 20. Represent this information:

(a) in a pie chart,
(b) in a single bar chart,
(c) in a horizontal bar chart.

6) An industrial organisation gives an aptitude test to all applicants for employment. The results of 150 people taking the test were:

Score (out of 10)	1	2	3	4	5
Frequency	6	12	15	21	35

Score (out of 10)	6	7	8	9	10
Frequency	24	20	10	6	1

Draw a histogram of this information.

7) The diameters of 40 steel bars were measured (in millimetres) with the following results:

24·98 24·96 24·97 24·98 24·99 25·02 24·99 25·01
25·03 25·01 25·00 25·02 25·00 25·02 25·01 25·02
25·01 24·97 24·98 25·01 25·03 25·05 24·95 24·98
24·99 24·99 25·02 24·97 25·04 25·00 24·97 25·04
25·00 25·00 24·99 25·01 25·03 25·03 25·02 25·01

Draw up a frequency table and then draw a histogram to represent the frequency distribution.

8) The data below relates to the marks of a class of 30 students in an end of term test. The marks are out of 10.

4 3 8 8 9 7 7 6 5 6 7 8 4 6 4 8 7 6 7 8
5 5 7 9 6 9 5 7 6 9

Draw up a frequency distribution table and from that draw a histogram.

9) The lengths of 100 pieces of wood were measured with the following results:

Length (cm)	29·5	29·6	29·7	29·8	29·9
Frequency	2	4	11	18	31

Length (cm)	30·0	30·1	30·2	30·3
Frequency	22	8	3	1

Find the median of this distribution.

10) 200 candidates sat an examination. The following table shows the frequency distribution obtained.

Mark	0–10	11–20	21–30	31–40	41–50
Frequency	4	12	20	25	38

Mark	51–60	61–70	71–80	81–90	91–100
Frequency	43	30	16	8	4

Draw a histogram to represent this information.

11) By drawing a histogram find the mode of the frequency distribution given in Question 9.

12) The wages of 60 employees of a company are as follows:

Wage £	30	31	32	33	34	35	36
Frequency	6	10	16	13	9	5	1

Find the median and the mode of this distribution.

Summary

1) Coordinates are used to mark the points on a graph. When a graph is either a smooth curve or a straight line we can use the graph to deduce values not given in the table from which the graph was drawn. Using a graph in this way is called interpolation.

2) If we extend a graph so that it follows the general trend we can find values which are outside of the range of values given. Using a graph in this way is called extrapolation.

3) Since distance = speed × time when the speed is constant, the graph of distance plotted against time is a straight line.

4) To find the break-even point draw two graphs on the same axes to the same scales.

5) Pie charts are used to represent the relative sizes of a number of quantities. The angle at the centre is proportional to the size of the quantity represented.

6) A bar chart relies upon heights (or areas) to represent the proportions of the quantities represented. The total height of the

diagram is equal to the total of the quantities.

7) The horizontal bar chart represents each of the quantities given but it does not readily display the total of the quantities.

8) A histogram is used to represent a frequency distribution. It consists of a set of rectangles each of the same width and the frequency is represented by the area of the rectangle (or by the height of the rectangles).

9) When dealing with grouped data the histogram is drawn by using the mid-points of each class or category as the mid-point of the rectangles.

10) The median of a frequency distribution is the value of the variable corresponding to half of the total frequency. The median can be found by drawing a cumulative frequency diagram.

11) The mode of a frequency distribution can be found by drawing the frequency curve. It is the value of the variable corresponding to the maximum value on the curve. The mode may also be found directly from a histogram.

Miscellaneous Excercise

Exercise 118

All these questions are of the type set in examinations. The questions in section A are intended to take only a minute or two to solve but those in section B are intended to take up to 20 minutes to solve.

Section A

1) The average amount of oil in 3 cans is 16 litres per can. Two of the cans contain amounts which have an average of 13 litres. Find the number of litres contained in the third can.

2) The total yield of apples from 144 trees was 23 400 kg. Find in kilogrammes the average yield per tree.

3) In a class of 24 children the average height was 138 cm. After 4 children left the average height of the remainder was 135 cm. Calculate the average height of the 4 children who left.

4) 5 men earn £40 each and 2 men earn £68 each. What were the average earnings per man?

5) A man walked a distance of 80 m in 2 minutes. What is his average speed in kilometres per hour?

6) A train leaves Paddington station at 12.00 noon and travels 350 km to its destination at an average speed of 75 km/h. Find the time of arrival.

7) In a hospital the number of babies born each week for 13 weeks were as follows:

Week number	1	2	3	4	5	6	7
Number	35	11	15	6	8	11	42

Week number	8	9	10	11	12	13
Number	16	13	15	9	15	24

Find the median and the mode.

8) What is the average of 8, 10, 11, 14, 17 and 22?

9) A man makes a journey in two parts: the first part of 60 km is by road and takes $1\frac{1}{2}$ hours; the second part of 250 km is by rail and takes 4 hours. Calculate the average speed for the entire journey.

10) A motorist makes a journey of 430 km. He covers the first 100 km at an average speed of 50 km/h and the remainder of the journey at an average speed of 55 km/h. What is his average speed for the whole journey?

11) A motorist travelled a total distance of 420 km at an average speed of 90 km/h. The first 220 km of this journey were travelled at an average speed of 100 km/h. Find the average speed for the last 200 km, to the nearest km/h.

12) A retailer's weekly takings in one month were as follows: £105·75, £96·74, £106·38, £90·95. What were his average weekly takings? What might he expect to take in one year (52 weeks) estimated from this average?

Section B

13) The basic cost of running a car is £250 per annum, but there is an additional cost of 8 p for every kilometre travelled. Draw a graph to compare total cost with distance travelled. From your graph find:
(a) the total cost of running a car for 30 000 km,
(b) how many kilometres can be travelled for a total cost of £1850.

14) A retailer has two kinds of tea for which he paid £1·20 per kg and £1·40 per kg. He blends them in the proportions of 3 kg of the cheaper to 2 kg of the dearer. At what price must he sell the mixture to

make a profit of 25% on his outlay?

15) The average diameter of a certain specie of tree of varying ages is shown in the table below:

Age in years	5	10	15	20	30	50
Diameter (cm)	4·5	6	8·5	12	22	54

Draw a graph of this information plotting age on the horizontal axis. From your graph find the average diameter of a tree which is 40 years old and the age at which the average diameter will be 17 cm.

16) A blend of coffee is made from the following grades of coffee using the amounts stated:

    15 kg of grade A at £1·30 per kg
    20 kg of grade B at £1·50 per kg
    25 kg of grade C at £1·74 per kg

(a) What is the cost of the blend per kilogramme?
(b) At what price per kilogramme should the blend be sold in order that a profit of $33\frac{1}{3}\%$ shall be made?

17) Given that £1 is equivalent to 2·05 U.S.A. dollars, draw a graph for use as a ready reckoner to convert British money into American money and vice versa. Use your graph to find:

(a) the value of £4·80 in dollars,
(b) the value of 23 dollars in £'s.

18) The formula for the volume of a right cone is $V = \frac{1}{3}\pi r^2 h$ where r is the radius and h is the vertical height. For cones having a constant vertical height of 12 cm draw a graph showing the volumes of cones up to 20 cm radius. From your graph find the volume of a cone having a radius of 12 cm and a height of 12 cm.

19) Packets of chemical were weighed with the following results:

Mass (kg)	0·996	0·997	0·998	0·999	1·000
Frequency	1	8	23	36	28

Mass (kg)	1·001	1·002
Frequency	3	1

Calculate the arithmetic mean.

20) The table below gives the distribution of marks in a test for which the maximum mark was 20.

Marks	1–4	5–7	8	9	10
Frequency	11	20	23	24	30

Marks	11	12	13–15	16–20
Frequency	25	21	33	13

Calculate the mean mark.

21) The diameters of 100 wooden rods were measured (in centimetres) with the following results.

Diameter	15·8	15·9	16·0	16·1	16·2	16·3
Frequency	4	15	26	35	15	5

(a) Find the median.
(b) Find the mode.

22) In an experiment a fixed quantity of water is poured into each of a number of cylinders which have bases of different areas. The results of the experiment showing the relation between the height h centimetres and the perimeter p centimetres of the base, are given in the following table:

p	6	7	8	9	10	12	14	16	18
h	24	17·6	13·5	10·7	8·6	6	4·4	3·4	2·7

Draw a graph to show the relation between p and h plotting p on the horizontal axis and from your graph estimate:

(a) the height of water when the base perimeter is 11 cm,
(b) the perimeter of the base when the height of the water is 12 cm,
(c) the height of the water when it is equal to the perimiter of the base.

23) The following table shows the relation between the height, in metres, above the ground of a ball thrown upwards and the time, in seconds, after it was thrown. Plotting the time on the horizontal axis, draw a smooth graph to illustrate the relationship and from it state:

(a) the greatest height which the ball reaches,
(b) the height after 5·5 seconds,
(c) for how long the ball is more than 6 metres above the ground.

Time (seconds)	0	1	2	3	4
Height (metres)	0	5	7	7·9	8

Time (seconds)	5	6	7	8	9
Height (metres)	7·6	6·6	5	2·8	0

19. Areas

Unit of Length

In Chapter 7 we saw that the standard unit of length is the metre (abbreviation: m) and that it is split up into smaller units as follows:

$$1 \text{ metre (m)} = 10 \text{ decimetres (dm)}$$
$$= 100 \text{ centimetres (cm)}$$
$$= 1000 \text{ millimetres (mm)}$$

Units of Area

The area of a plane figure is measured by seeing how many square units it contains. 1 square metre is the area contained inside a square which has a side of 1 metre (Fig. 19.1). Similarly 1 square centimetre is the area inside a square whose side is 1 cm and 1 square millimetre is the area inside a square whose side is 1 mm.

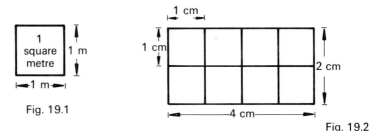

Fig. 19.1

Fig. 19.2

The standard abbreviations for units of area are:

square metre $= \text{m}^2$
square centimetre $= \text{cm}^2$
square millimetre $= \text{mm}^2$

Area of a Rectangle

The rectangle (Fig. 19.2) has been divided into 4 rows of 2 squares, each square having an area of 1 cm². The rectangle, therefore, has an area of $4 \times 2 \text{ cm}^2 = 8 \text{ cm}^2$. All that we have done to find the area is to multiply the length by the breadth. The same rule will apply to any rectangle. Hence:

$$\text{Area of rectangle} = \text{length} \times \text{breadth}$$

If we let $A =$ the area of the rectangle
$l =$ the length of the rectangle
and $b =$ the breadth of the rectangle
$A = lb$

In using this formula the units of l and b must be the same, that is they both must be in metres, centimetres or millimetres.

Example 1

A carpet measures 5·2 m by 6·3 m. What is its area?

We are given that $l = 5\cdot2$ m and $b = 6\cdot3$ m. Hence the area is:

$$A = 5\cdot2 \times 6\cdot3 = 32\cdot76 \text{ m}^2$$

Example 2   Find the area of a piece of sheet metal measuring 184 cm by 73 cm. Express the answer in square metres.

In problems of this type it is best to express each of the dimensions in metres before attempting to find the area. Thus:

$$184 \text{ cm} = 1 \cdot 84 \text{ m and } 73 \text{ cm} = 0 \cdot 73 \text{ m}$$

The area of sheet metal is then

$$A = 1 \cdot 84 \times 0 \cdot 73 = 1 \cdot 3432 \text{ m}^2$$

Example 3   A room 9·3 m long and 7·6 m wide is to be carpeted so as to leave a surround 50 cm wide as shown in Fig. 19.3. Find the area of the surround.

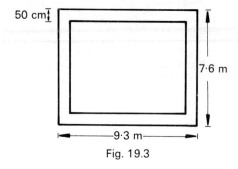

Fig. 19.3

The easiest way of solving this problem is to find the area of the room and subtract from it the area of the carpet.

Area of room $= 9 \cdot 3 \times 7 \cdot 6 = 70 \cdot 68 \text{ m}^2$
Area of carpet $= 8 \cdot 3 \times 6 \cdot 6 = 54 \cdot 78 \text{ m}^2$
Area of surround $= 70 \cdot 68 - 54 \cdot 78 = 15 \cdot 90 \text{ m}^2$

The areas of may shapes can be found by splitting the shape up into rectangles and finding the area of each rectangle separately. The area of the shape is then found by adding the areas of the separate rectangles together.

Example 4   Find the area of the shape shown in Fig. 19.4.

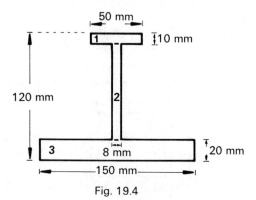

Fig. 19.4

The shape can be divided up into three rectangles as shown in the diagram.

Area of shape = area of 1+area of 2+area of 3
$$= (50 \times 10) \text{ mm}^2 + (90 \times 8) \text{ mm}^2 + (150 \times 20) \text{ mm}^2$$
$$= 500 \text{ mm}^2 + 720 \text{ mm}^2 + 3000 \text{ mm}^2 = 4220 \text{ mm}^2$$

Exercise 119

1) Find the areas of the following rectangles:
   (a) 7 cm by 8 cm
   (b) 20 mm by 11 mm
   (c) 18 m by 35 m.

2) A piece of wood is 3·7 m long and 28 cm wide. What is its area in square metres?

3) A rectangular piece of metal is 198 cm long and 88 cm wide. What is its area in square metres?

4) A room 5·8 m long and 4·9 m wide is to be covered with vinyl. What area of vinyl is needed?

5) What is the total area of the walls of a room which is 6·7 m long, 5·7 m wide and 2·5 m high?

6) A rectangular lawn is 32 m long and 23 m wide. A path 1·5 m wide is made around the lawn. What is the area of the path?

7) A room 8·5 m long and 6·3 m wide is to be carpeted to leave a surround 60 cm wide around the carpet. What is:
   (a) the area of the room?
   (b) the area of the carpet?
   (c) the area of the surround?

8) Find the areas of the shapes shown in Fig. 19.5.

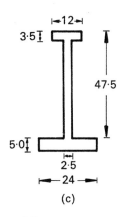

(c)

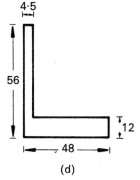

(d)

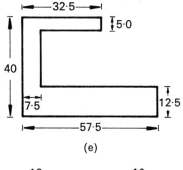

(e)

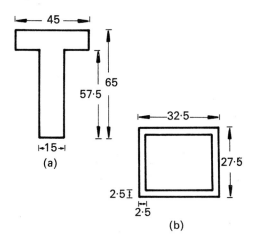

(a)

(b)

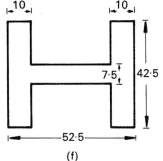

(f)

Fig. 19.5 (all dimensions in mm)

We can find the length of a rectangle given its area and its breadth by solving an equation as shown in Chapter 11.

Example 5   A rectangle has an area of 60 cm² and its breadth is 12 cm. What is its length?

We are given that $A = 60$ and $b = 12$. Hence:

$$60 = 12 \times l$$
$$l = \frac{60}{12} = 5$$

Therefore the length of the rectangle is 5 cm.

Example 6   A piece of wood has an area of 1·8 m² and a width of 30 cm. What is its length?

We must first convert 30 cm into metres, that is 30 cm = 0.3 m. We now have that $A = 1·8$ and $b = 0·3$. Substituting these values in the formula for the area of a rectangle we have:

$$1·8 = 0·3 \times l$$
$$l = \frac{1·8}{0·3} = 6$$

Hence the length of the piece of wood is 6 m.

The Square

A square is a rectangle with all its sides equal in length. Hence:

$$\text{area of square} = \text{side} \times \text{side} = \text{side}^2$$

We can express this as a formula by letting A represent the area of the square and l the length of the side. Thus:
$$A = l^2$$

Example 7   A square has an area of 20·25 cm². What is the length of its side?

$$\text{Length of side} = \sqrt{\text{area}} = \sqrt{20·25} = 4·5 \text{ cm}$$

Exercise 120

1) The area of a rectangle is 72 m². If its length is 12 m find its width.

2) The area of a room is 44·82 m². It is 5·4 m wide. How long is it?

3) A carpet measuring 6 m by 7 m is laid in a room measuring 6·5 m by 8 m. Calculate the area not covered by the carpet.

4) A carpet has an area of $30\frac{1}{4}$ m². If it is square calculate the length.

5) A piece of vinyl has an area of 12·3 m². If its length is $20\frac{1}{2}$ m, what is its width in centimetres?

6) A room is 5·4 m long and 4·2 m wide. It takes 1575 square tiles to cover the floor. Calculate the area of each tile and state its dimensions.

7) How many square tiles each 15 cm square are needed to cover a floor 4·5 m long by 12 m wide?

8) A householder makes a square lawn in his garden which has a side of 12 m. If the plot of ground is 15 m by 14 m, what area is left?

The Parallelogram

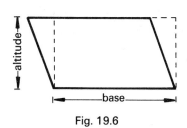

Fig. 19.6

A parallelogram is a plane figure bounded by four straight lines whose opposite sides are parallel (Fig. 19.6). A parallelogram is, in effect, a rectangle pushed out of square as shown in Fig. 19.6 where the equivalent rectangle is shown dotted. Hence:

$$\text{area of parallelogram} = \text{length of base} \times \text{vertical height}$$
$$A = bh$$

where A = area, b = length of base and h = vertical height (or altitude).

Example 8

Find the area of a parallelogram whose base is 15 cm long and whose altitude is 8 cm.

$$\text{Area} = 15 \times 8 = 120 \text{ cm}^2$$

Example 9

A parallelogram has an area of 36 cm². If its base is 9 cm find its altitude.

We are given that $A = 36$ and that $b = 9$. Hence:

$$36 = 9 \times h \text{ or } h = \frac{36}{9} = 4$$

Hence the altitude is 4 cm.

Exercise 121

1) Find the area of a parallelogram whose base is 7 cm long and whose vertical height is 8 cm.

2) What is the area of a parallelogram whose base is 7 cm long and whose altitude is 65 cm? Give the answer in square metres.

3) The area of a parallelogram is 64 m². Its base is 16 m long. Calculate its altitude.

4) A parallelogram has an area of 25·92 cm². Its altitude is 3·6 cm. Find its length of base.

5) Fig. 19.7 shows a steel section. Find its area in square centimetres.

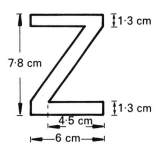

Fig. 19.7

Angles

When two lines meet at a point they form an angle. The size of the angle depends only upon the amount of opening between the lines. It does not depend upon the lengths of the lines forming the angle. In

Fig. 19.8 the angle A is larger than the angle B despite the fact that the lengths of the arms are shorter.

Fig. 19.8

Angular Measurement

An angle may be looked upon as the amount of rotation or turning. In Fig. 19.9 the line OA has been turned about O until it takes up the position OB. The angle through which the line has turned is the amount of opening between the lines OA and OB.

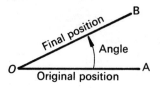

Fig. 19.9

If the line OA is rotated until it returns to its original position it will have described one revolution. Hence we can measure an angle as a fraction of a revolution. Fig. 19.10 shows a circle divided up into 36 equal parts. The first division is split up into 10 equal parts so that each small division is $\frac{1}{360}$ of a complete revolution. We call this division a *degree*.

$$1 \text{ degree } = \tfrac{1}{360} \text{ of a revolution}$$
$$360 \text{ degrees} = 1 \text{ revolution}$$

When writing angles we write seventy degrees 70°. The small ° at the right hand corner of the figure replaces the word degrees. Thus 87° reads 87 degrees.

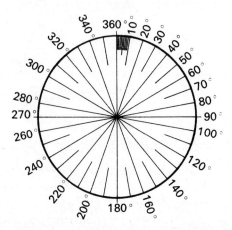

Fig. 19.10

The right-angle is $\frac{1}{4}$ of a revolution and hence it contains $\frac{1}{4}$ of $360° = 90°$. Two right-angles contain $180°$ and three right-angles contain $270°$.

Example 10   Find the angle in degrees corresponding to $\frac{1}{8}$ of a revolution.

$$\text{Since 1 revolution} = 360°$$
$$\tfrac{1}{8}\text{ revolution} = \tfrac{1}{8} \times 360° = 45°$$

Example 11   Find the angle in degrees corresponding to $0·6$ of a revolution.

$$1 \text{ revolution} = 360°$$
$$0·6 \text{ revolution} = 0·6 \times 360° = 216°$$

Exercise 122

1) How many degrees are there in $1\frac{1}{2}$ right-angles?

2) How many degrees are there in $\frac{3}{5}$ of a right-angle?

3) How many degrees are there in $\frac{2}{3}$ of a right-angle?

4) How many degrees are there in $0·7$ of a right-angle?

Find the angle in degrees corresponding to the following:

5) $\frac{1}{20}$ revolution

6) $\frac{3}{8}$ revolution

7) $\frac{4}{5}$ revolution

8) $0·8$ revolution

9) $0·3$ revolution

10) $0·25$ revolution.

Types of Triangles

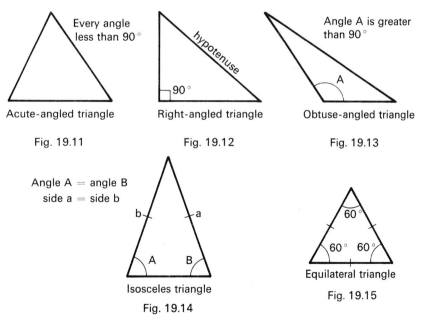

Acute-angled triangle
Fig. 19.11

Right-angled triangle
Fig. 19.12

Obtuse-angled triangle
Fig. 19.13

Isosceles triangle
Fig. 19.14

Equilateral triangle
Fig. 19.15

(i) An acute angled triangle has all its angles less than $90°$ (Fig. 19.11).

(ii) A right-angled triangle has one of its angles equal to $90°$ (Fig. 19.12). The side opposite to the right-angle is the longest side and is called the hypotenuse.

(iii) An obtuse angled triangle has one angle greater than $90°$ (Fig. 19.13).

(iv) An isosceles triangle has two sides and two angles equal. The equal angles lie opposite to the equal sides (Fig. 19.14).

(v) An equilateral triangle has all its sides and all its angles equal. Each angle of the triangle is 60° (Fig. 19.15).

Properties of a Right-Angled Triangle

In a right-angled triangle the square described on the hypotenuse is equal to the sum of the squares on the other two sides (Fig. 19.16). This statement is known as the theorem of Pythagoras. As shown in Fig. 19.16:

The square on the hypotenuse $= AC^2$
The square on the side AB $= AB^2$
The square on the side BC $= BC^2$
$$AC^2 = AB^2 + BC^2$$

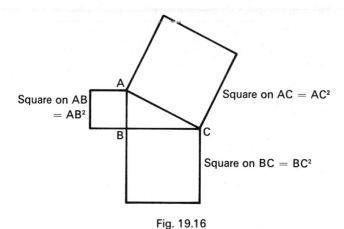

Fig. 19.16

Example 12   In a right-angled triangle the two sides forming the right-angle are 6 cm and 8 cm long respectively. Find the length of the hypotenuse.

From Fig. 19.17, $AC^2 = AB^2 + BC^2 = 6^2 + 8^2 = 36 + 64 = 100$
$$AC = \sqrt{100} = 10 \text{ cm}$$

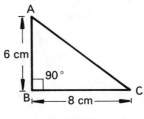

Fig. 19.17

Example 13   A rectangle is 9 cm long and 5 cm wide. What is the length of the diagonal of the rectangle?

From Fig. 19.18 it will be seen that we have to find the length AC, which is the hypotenuse of the triangle ABC.

$$AC^2 = AB^2 + BC^2 = 9^2 + 5^2 = 81 + 25 = 106$$

Using the square root tables:

$$AC = \sqrt{106} = 10 \cdot 3 \text{ cm}$$

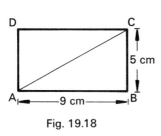

Fig. 19.18

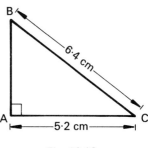

Fig. 19.19

When we are given the length of the hypotenuse and the length of one of the other sides of a right-angled triangle, then to find the length of the remaining side we have to proceed as shown in Example 14.

Example 14   In a triangle ABC, BC is the hypotenuse and is 6·4 cm long. If AC is 5·2 cm long, how long is the side AB?

In Fig. 19.19, by Pythagoras' theorem:

$$BC^2 = AB^2 + AC^2$$
$$\text{or } AB^2 = BC^2 - AC^2 = 6\cdot4^2 - 5\cdot2^2 = 40\cdot96 - 27\cdot04 = 13\cdot92$$

By using the square root tables:

$$AB = \sqrt{13\cdot92} = 3\cdot731 \text{ cm}$$

Exercise 123

1) In a triangle ABC, AC is the hypotenuse, AB = 5 cm long and BC = 5 cm long. Find the length of AC.

2) In a right-angled triangle the two sides forming the right-angle are 30 mm and 40 mm long respectively. Find the length of the hypotenuse.

3) In a right-angled triangle the two sides forming the right-angle are 2 cm and 4 cm long respectively. Find the length of the hypotenuse.

4) For each of the triangles shown in Fig. 19.20, find the length of the side marked x.

5) Find the diagonal of a square whose side is 3 cm long.

6) Find the diagonal of a rectangle which is 8 cm long and 3 cm wide.

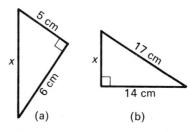

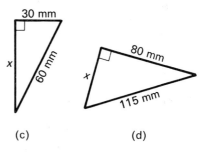

Fig. 19.20

Properties of the Isosceles Triangle

The most important property of an isosceles triangle is that the perpendicular dropped from the apex to the unequal side:

(i) bisects the unequal side. Thus in Fig. 19.21, BD = CD

(ii) bisects the apex angle. Thus in Fig. 19.21, angle BAD = angle CAD.

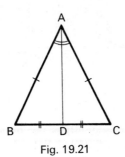

Fig. 19.21

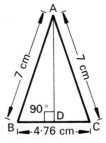

Fig. 19.22

Example 15   For the isosceles triangle shown in Fig. 19.22 find:
(a) the length BD
(b) the height AD.

(a) Because AD is perpendicular to the base BC, the base is bisected. Hence:

$$BD = \tfrac{1}{2}BC = \tfrac{1}{2} \times 4{\cdot}76 = 2{\cdot}38 \text{ cm}$$

(b) To find the height AD, we apply Pythagoras's theorem to the triangle ABD.

$$AD^2 = AB^2 - BD^2 = 7^2 - 2{\cdot}38^2 = 49 - 5{\cdot}664 = 43{\cdot}336$$

By using the square root tables:

$$AD = \sqrt{43{\cdot}336} = 6{\cdot}583 \text{ cm}$$

Exercise 124

1) An isosceles triangle has a base of 8 cm and a height of $4\tfrac{1}{2}$ cm. Find the lengths of the equal sides.

2) An isosceles triangle has a base 18 cm long and the equal sides are each 16 cm long. What is the vertical height of the triangle?

3) The equal sides of an isosceles triangle are each 18 cm long. If the vertical height of the triangle is 11 cm, find the length of the base.

4) An equilateral triangle has sides 9·6 cm long. What is the vertical height of the triangle?

5) An equilateral triangle has a base which is 8·2 cm long. What is the vertical height of the triangle?

Area of a Triangle

The diagonal of the parallelogram shown in Fig. 19.23 splits the parallelogram into two equal triangles. Hence:

$$\text{area of triangle} = \tfrac{1}{2} \times \text{base} \times \text{vertical height}$$

Sometimes the vertical height is called the altitude and:

$$\text{area of triangle} = \tfrac{1}{2} \times \text{base} \times \text{altitude}$$

As a formula the statement becomes:

$$A = \tfrac{1}{2}bh \text{ where } b = \text{the base and } h = \text{the altitude}$$

Example 16   A triangle has a base 5 cm long and a vertical height of 12 cm. Calculate its area.

$$\text{Area of triangle} = \tfrac{1}{2} \times \text{base} \times \text{height} = \tfrac{1}{2} \times 5 \times 12 = 30 \text{ cm}^2$$

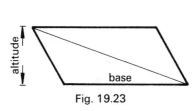

Fig. 19.23

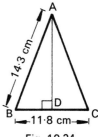

Fig. 19.24

Example 17   An isosceles triangle has a base 11·8 cm long and the two equal sides are each 14·3 cm long. Calculate the area of the triangle.

We must first calculate the altitude of the triangle. Referring to Fig. 19.24 we see that, by Pythagoras' theorem,

$$AD^2 = AB^2 - BD^2 = 14 \cdot 3^2 - 5 \cdot 9^2 = 204 \cdot 5 - 34 \cdot 8 = 169 \cdot 7$$
$$AD = \sqrt{169 \cdot 7} = 13 \cdot 03 \text{ cm}$$

$$\text{Area of triangle} = \tfrac{1}{2} \times \text{base} \times \text{height} = \tfrac{1}{2} \times 11 \cdot 8 \times 13 \cdot 03 = 76 \cdot 9 \text{ cm}^2$$

When we are given the lengths of three sides of a triangle we can find its area by using the formula given below:

$$A = \sqrt{s \times (s-a) \times (s-b) \times (s-c)}$$

where s stands for half of the perimeter of the triangle and a, b and c are the lengths of the sides of the triangle.

Example 18   The sides of a triangle are 13 cm, 8 cm and 7 cm long. Calculate the area of the triangle.

$$s = \tfrac{1}{2} \text{ perimeter} = \tfrac{1}{2} \times (13 + 8 + 7) = \tfrac{1}{2} \times 28 = 14 \text{ cm}$$
$$a = 13 \text{ cm}, \ b = 8 \text{ cm and } c = 7 \text{ cm}.$$

$$\text{Area of triangle} = \sqrt{14 \times (14 - 13) \times (14 - 8) \times (14 - 7)}$$
$$= \sqrt{14 \times 1 \times 6 \times 7} = \sqrt{588} = 24 \cdot 25 \text{ cm}^2$$

Exercise 125

1) Find the area of a triangle whose base is 18 cm and whose altitude is 12 cm.

2) Find the area of a triangle whose base is 7·5 cm and whose altitude is 5·9 cm.

3) A triangle has sides 4 cm, 7 cm and 9 cm. What is its area?

4) A triangle has sides 37 mm, 52 mm and 63 mm long. What is its area in square centimetres?

5) An isosceles triangle has a base 12·4 cm long and equal sides each 16·3 cm long. Calculate the area of the triangle.

Area of a Trapezium

A trapezium is a plane figure bounded by four straight lines which has one pair of parallel sides (Fig. 19.25).

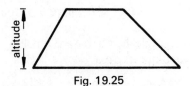

Fig. 19.25

Area of trapezium = ½ the sum of the lengths of the parallel sides × the distance between them

Example 19   The parallel sides of a trapezium are 12 cm and 16 cm long. The distance between the parallel sides is 9 cm. What is the area of the trapezium?

$$\text{Area of trapezium} = \tfrac{1}{2} \times (12+16) \times 9 = \tfrac{1}{2} \times 28 \times 9 = 126 \text{ cm}^2$$

Example 20   The area of a trapezium is 220 cm² and the parallel sides are 26 cm and 14 cm long. Find the distance between the parallel sides.

$$\tfrac{1}{2} \text{ the sum of the parallel sides} = \tfrac{1}{2} \times (26+14) = \tfrac{1}{2} \times 40 = 20$$

$$\text{distance between the parallel sides} = 220 \div 20 = 11 \text{ cm}$$

Exercise 126

1) Find the area of a trapezium whose parallel sides are 7 cm and 9 cm long and whose altitude is 5 cm.

2) The parallel sides of a trapezium are 15 cm and 9·8 cm long. If the distance between the parallel sides is 7·6 cm, what is the area of the trapezium?

3) The area of a trapezium is 500 cm² and its parallel sides are 35 cm and 65 cm long. Find the altitude of the trapezium.

4) Find the area of a trapezium whose parallel sides are 75 mm and 82 mm and whose vertical height is 39 mm. Give the answer in square centimetres.

5) Find the area of the trapezium shown in Fig. 19.26.

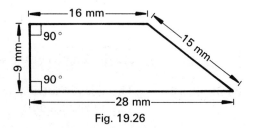

Fig. 19.26

Mensuration of the Circle

The names of the main parts of a circle are shown in Fig. 19.27. The value

$$\frac{\text{circumference}}{\text{diameter}} = 3 \cdot 141 \, 59 \ldots \ldots$$

The exact value has never been worked out but for most problems a value of 3·142 is sufficiently accurate when working in decimals. When working in fractions a value of $\frac{22}{7}$ can be taken.

The value $\dfrac{\text{circumference}}{\text{diameter}}$ is so important that it has been given the special symbol π (the Greek letter pi). We take π as being 3·142 or $\frac{22}{7}$.

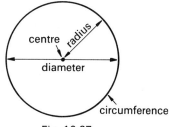

Fig. 19.27

Since $\dfrac{\text{circumference}}{\text{diameter}} = \pi$

circumference $= \pi \times \text{diameter}$

or circumference $= 2 \times \pi \times \text{radius}$ or $C = 2\pi r = \pi d$

Example 21   The diameter of a circle is 300 mm. What is its circumference?

Circumference $= \pi \times 300 = 3\cdot142 \times 300 = 942\cdot6$ mm

Example 22   The radius of a circle is 14 cm. What is its circumference?

Circumference $= 2 \times \pi \times \text{radius} = 2 \times \frac{22}{7} \times 14 = 88$ cm

Example 23   A wheel 700 mm diameter makes 30 revolutions. How far does a point on the rim travel?

Distance travelled in 1 revolution
$$= \pi \times \text{diameter} = \tfrac{22}{7} \times 700 = 2200 \text{ mm}$$
Distance travelled in 30 revolutions
$$= 30 \times 2200 = 66\,000 \text{ mm} = 66 \text{ m}$$

Example 24   Find the radius of a circle whose circumference is 93·8 cm.

$$\text{Radius} = \frac{\text{circumference}}{2 \times \pi} = \frac{93\cdot8}{2 \times 3\cdot142} = \frac{93\cdot8}{6\cdot284}$$

The best way of calculating the answer is to use logs:

number	log
93·8	1·9722
6·284	0·7983
14·92	1·1739

Hence the radius of the circle is 14·92 cm.

Exercise 127

Find the circumference of the following circles:

1) Radius 21 cm

2) Radius 350 mm

3) Radius 43 m

4) Radius 3·16 cm

5) Diameter 28 cm

6) Diameter 85 mm

7) Diameter 8·423 m

8) Diameter 1400 mm

9) A wheel has a diameter of 560 mm. How far, in meters, will a point on the rim travel in 50 revolutions?

10) A circular flower bed has a circumference of 64 m. What is its radius?

11) 8 circular cushion covers whose radius is 60 cm are to be decorated with braiding around their circumference. How many metres of braiding is needed?

12) A pond which is circular has a circumference of 12·62 m. What is its radius?

13) Find the diameter of a circle whose circumference is 110 cm.

14) Find the diameter of a circle whose circumference is 956 mm

The Area of a Circle

It can be shown that:

$$\text{Area of circle} = \pi \times \text{radius}^2 = \pi r^2$$

Example 25   Find the area of a circle whose radius is 30 cm.

$$\text{Area of circle} = \pi \times 30^2 = 3\cdot142 \times 900 = 2827\cdot8 \text{ cm}^2$$

Example 26   Find the area of a circle whose diameter is 28 cm.

Since diameter = 28 cm, radius = 14 cm

$$\text{Area of circle} = \pi \times \text{radius}^2 = \tfrac{22}{7} \times 14^2 = 616 \text{ cm}^2$$

Example 27   Find the area of the annulus shown in Fig. 19.28.

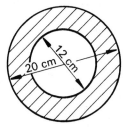

Fig. 19.28

Outer radius   = 10 cm; inner radius = 6 cm
Area of outer circle = $\pi \times 10^2 = 314\cdot2$ cm^2
Area of inner circle = $\pi \times 6^2 = 113\cdot1$ cm^2
Area of annulus   = $314\cdot2 - 113\cdot1 = 201\cdot1$ cm^2

Exercise 128

Find the areas of the following circles:

1) 14 cm radius

2) 350 mm radius

3) 2·82 m radius

4) 42 cm diameter

5) 7·78 m diameter

6) 197·6 mm diameter

7) An annulus has an inside radius of 6 cm and an outside radius of 9 cm. Calculate its area.

8) A copper pipe has a bore of 32 mm and an outside diameter of 42 mm. Find the area of its cross section.

9) A pond having a diameter of 36 m has to have a path 1 m wide laid around its circumference. What is the area of the path?

10) A circular flower bed is to have a path laid around its circumference. If the flower bed has a diameter of 60 m and the path is to be $1\frac{1}{2}$ m wide, find the area of the path.

Sector of a Circle

The area and the arc of a sector of a circle (Fig. 19.29) depend upon the angle that the sector subtends at the centre of the circle of which the sector is part.

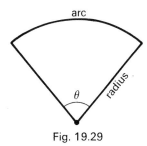

Fig. 19.29

Referring to the diagram (Fig. 19.29)

Arc of the sector $= 2\times\pi\times\text{radius}\times\dfrac{\theta}{360}$ or $C = 2\pi r\times\dfrac{\theta}{360}$

Area of the sector $= \pi\times\text{radius}^2\times\dfrac{\theta}{360}$ or $A = \pi r^2\times\dfrac{\theta}{360}$

Example 28   Find the length of arc and the area of a sector of a circle which subtends an angle of $108°$ at the centre, if its radius is 8 cm.

Length of arc $= 2\times\pi\times8\times\dfrac{108}{360} = \dfrac{24\times\pi}{5} = 15\cdot08$ cm

Area of sector $= \pi\times8^2\times\dfrac{108}{360} = \dfrac{96\times\pi}{5} = 60\cdot33$ cm^2

Exercise 129

Find the length of arc and the area of the following sectors of a circle:

1) Radius 4 cm; sector angle $45°$.

2) Radius 10 cm; sector angle $90°$.

3) Radius 3 cm; sector angle $60°$.

4) Radius 2·7 m; sector angle $84°$.

5) Radius 78 mm; sector angle $175°$.

6) Calculate the shaded area shown in Fig. 19.30.

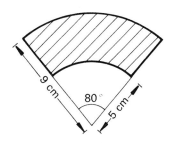

Fig. 19.30

Areas of Composite Figures

Many shapes are composed of straight lines and arcs of circles. The areas of such shapes are found by splitting up the shape into figures such as rectangles, triangles, etc. and sectors of circles.

Example 29   A table top is the shape shown in Fig. 19.31. Find its area.

The table top can be spit up into 4 quarter circles and 5 rectangles as shown in Fig. 19.32.

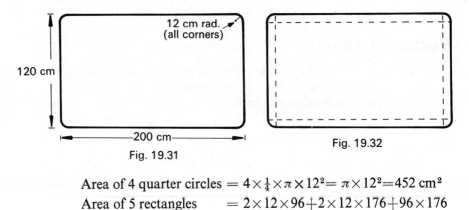

Fig. 19.31

Fig. 19.32

Area of 4 quarter circles $= 4 \times \frac{1}{4} \times \pi \times 12^2 = \pi \times 12^2 = 452$ cm²

Area of 5 rectangles $= 2 \times 12 \times 96 + 2 \times 12 \times 176 + 96 \times 176$

$= 2304 + 4224 + 16\,896 = 23\,424$ cm²

Area of table top $= 452 + 23\,424 = 23\,876$ cm²

Exercise 130

Find the areas of the shaded portions of the figures shown in Fig. 19.33.

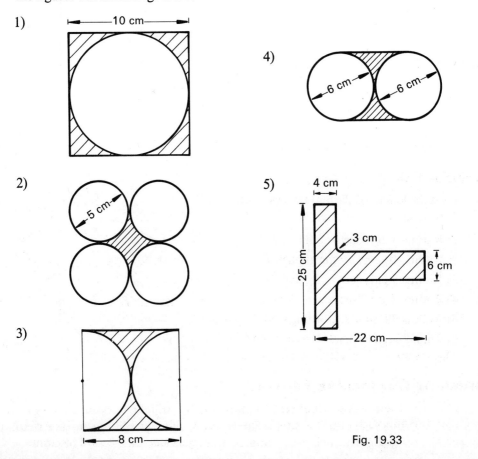

Fig. 19.33

Summary

1) The area of a figure is measured by seeing how many square units it contains.
   1 square metre is the area contained in a square of 1 m side.
   1 square centimetre is the area inside a square whose side is 1 cm.
   1 square millimetre is the area inside a square whose side is 1 mm.

2) Area of rectangle = length × breadth.

3) Area of square = side².

4) Area of parallelogram = base × altitude.

5) Pythagoras' theorem states that the square on the hypotenuse is equal to the sum of the squares on the other two sides.

6) Area of triangle = $\frac{1}{2}$ × base × altitude.

7) When three sides of a triangle are given the following formula may be used:
$$\text{Area} = \sqrt{s \times (s-a) \times (s-b) \times (s-c)}$$
where s stands for half the perimeter and a, b and c are the lengths of the three sides of the triangle.

8) Area of trapezium = $\frac{1}{2}$ of the sum of the parallel sides × altitude.

9) Circumference of a circle = 2 × π × radius = π × diameter.

10) Area of circle = π × radius²

11) Length of arc of a sector of a circle
$$= 2 \times \pi \times \text{radius} \times \frac{\text{sector angle}}{360}$$

12) Area of sector of a circle
$$= \pi \times \text{radius}^2 \times \frac{\text{sector angle}}{360}$$

Mental Test 19

1) What is the area of a rectangle 8 cm long and 5 cm wide?

2) A square has an area of 36 m². What is the length of its side?

3) A rectangle has an area of 48 cm². It is 8 cm long. What is its width?

4) A parallelogram has a base 12 cm long and an altitude of 8 cm. What is its area?

5) A parallelogram has an area of 700 mm². Its altitude is 35 mm. Find its length of base.

6) A triangle has a base of 8 cm long and an altitude of 4 cm. What is its area?

7) A triangle has an area of 18 m² and a base 9 m long. What is its altitude?

8) A right-angled triangle has the sides forming the right-angle 6 cm and 8 cm long. What is the length of the hypotenuse?

9) A trapezium has an altitude of 6 cm and the parallel sides are 3 cm and 7 cm long. What is its area?

10) Find the circumference of a circle whose radius is 7 cm.

11) Find the circumference of a circle whose diameter is 28 cm.

12) Find the area of a circle whose radius is 7 cm.

Self Test 19

1) A rectangle has a length of 80 mm and a width of 30 mm. Its area is therefore:

a 240 mm²   **b** 2400 mm²
c 24 cm ²   **d** 240 cm²

2) A triangle has an altitude of 100 mm and a base of 50 mm. Its area is:

  a 2500 mm²   **b** 5000 mm²
  c 25 cm²   **d** 50 cm²

3) A parallelogram has a base 10 cm long and a vertical height of 5 cm. Its area is:

  a 25 cm²   **b** 50 cm²
  c 2500 mm²   **d** 5000 mm²

4) A trapezium has parallel sides whose lengths are 18 cm and 22 cm. The distance between the parallel sides is 10 cm. Hence the area of the trapezium is:

  a 400 cm²   **b** 200 cm²
  c 3960 cm²   **d** 495 cm²

5) The area of a circle is given by the formula:

  a $2 \times \pi \times radius^2$ **b** $2 \times \pi \times radius$
  c $\pi \times radius^2$ **d** $\pi \times radius$

6) The circumference of a circle is given by the formula:

  a $\pi \times radius^2$ **b** $2 \times \pi \times radius$
  c $\pi \times radius$ **d** $\pi \times diameter$

7) A ring has an outside diameter of 8cm and an inside diameter of 4 cm. Its area is:

  a $\pi \times 8^2 - \pi \times 4^2$ **b** $8 \times \pi - 4 \times \pi$
  c $4 \times \pi - 2 \times \pi$ **d** $\pi \times 4^2 - \pi \times 2^2$

8) A wheel has a diameter of 70 cm. The number of revolutions that it will make in travelling 55 km is:

  a 2500   **b** 5000   **c** 50000 **d** 10000

9) A sector of a circle subtends an angle of 120°. If the radius of the circle is 42 cm then the area of the sector is:

  a 88 cm²   **b** 1848 cm²
  c 3696 cm²   **d** 176 cm²

10) A rectangular plot of ground is 40 m long and 80 m wide. Its area is:

  a 320 m²   **b** 3200 m²
  c 32000000 cm²   **d** 32000 cm²

20. Volume and Capacity

Introduction

In this chapter we deal with the unit of volume and the volumes of solid figures such as prisms, cylinders, cones and spheres. We then deal with the units of capacity and finally we discuss density and the methods of finding the mass of solid figures.

The Unit of Volume

We measure volume by seeing how many cubic units an object contains. 1 cubic centimetre (abbreviation: cm³) is the volume contained inside a cube whose edge is 1 cm (Fig. 20.1). Similarly, 1 cubic metre (abbreviation: m³) is the volume contained in a cube whose edge is 1 m.

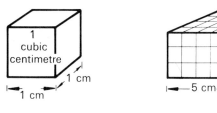

| Fig. 20.1 | Fig. 20.2 |

We can divide up the rectangular solid shown in Fig. 20.2 into three layers of small cubes each having a volume of 1 cm³. There are 5×4 cubes in each layer and, therefore, the total number of cubes is $5 \times 4 \times 3 = 60$. The solid therefore has a volume of 60 cm³.

All that we have done in order to find the volume is to multiply the length by the breadth by the height. This rule applies to any rectangular solid and hence:

Volume of a rectangular solid = length × breadth × height or $V = lbh$

Since the area of the end of a rectangular solid = length × breadth we can write:

Volume of rectangular solid = area of end × height

This statement is true for any solid which has the same shape (i.e. cross-section) throughout its length. For solids of this type:

Volume of solid = cross-sectional area × length
$$V = Al$$

where A = cross-sectional area and l = length

Example 1   Find the volume of a rectangular block which is 32 cm long, 28 cm wide and 2 cm high.

Volume = length × breadth × height = $32 \times 28 \times 2 = 1792$ cm³

Example 2   Calculate the volume of a rectangular solid which is 120 cm long, 82 cm wide and 52 cm high. Give the answer in cubic metres.

It is best to express the dimensions of the solid in metres before attempting to find the volume. Thus:

length = 1·20 m, breadth = 0·82 m and height = 0·52 m

Volume = length × breadth × height = 1·20 × 0·82 × 0·52 = 0·5117 m³

Example 3   Find the volume of the steel bar shown in Fig. 20.3.

Since the bar has the same cross-section throughout its length

Volume = area of cross-section × length

Area of cross-section = 50 × 6 + 50 × 6 + 88 × 6 = 300 + 300 + 528
= 1128 mm²
Volume = 1128 × 300 = 338 400 mm³

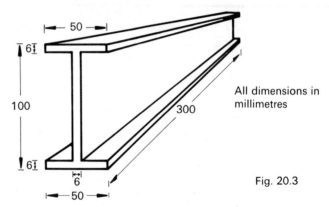

All dimensions in millimetres

Fig. 20.3

Example 4   A block of wood has the cross-section shown in Fig. 20.4. If it is 9 m long calculate its volume.

Because the length is given in metres it will be convenient to find the volume in cubic metres.

Area of cross-section = 0·100 × 0·150 + ½ × π × 0·075²
= 0·015 + 0·0088 = 0·0238 m²

Volume = area of cross-section × length = 0·0238 × 9 = 0·2142 m³

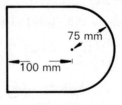

75 mm

100 mm

Fig. 20.4

Volume of a Cylinder

A cylinder (Fig. 20.5) has a constant cross-section which is a circle. Hence:

Volume of cylinder = π × radius² × length (or height) or $V = \pi r^2 h$

Example 5   Find the volume of a cylinder which has a radius of 14 cm and a height of 12 cm.

$$\text{Volume} = \tfrac{22}{7} \times 14^2 \times 12 = 22 \times 2 \times 14 \times 12 = 7392 \text{ cm}^3$$

Example 6   A pipe has the dimensions shown in Fig. 20.6. Calculate its volume.

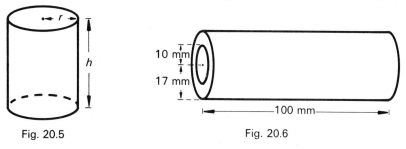

Fig. 20.5   Fig. 20.6

$$\text{Volume} = \text{cross-sectional area} \times \text{length}$$
$$\text{Cross-sectional area} = \pi \times 17^2 - \pi \times 10^2 = 593 \cdot 8 \text{ mm}^2$$
$$\text{Volume} = 593 \cdot 8 \times 100 = 59\,380 \text{ mm}^3$$

Exercise 131

1) Find the volume of a rectangular block 8 cm long, 5 cm wide and 3·5 cm high.

2) The diagram (Fig. 20.7) shows the cross-section of a steel bar. If it is 250 mm long, calculate its volume.

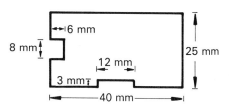

Fig. 20.8

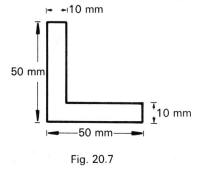

Fig. 20.7

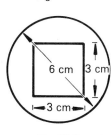

Fig. 20.9

3) Find the volume of a cylinder whose radius is 7 cm and whose height is 50 cm.

4) A hole 40 mm diameter is drilled in a plate 25 mm thick. What volume of metal is removed from the plate?

5) A block of wood has the cross-section shown in Fig. 20.8. If it is 8 cm long calculate its volume in cubic centimetres.

6) Calculate the volume of a metal tube whose bore is 50 mm and whose thickness is 8 mm if it is 6 m long. Give the answer in cubic metres.

7) Fig. 20.9 shows a washer which is 0·2 cm thick. Calculate its volume.

8) Fig. 20.10 shows a triangular prism. Calculate its volume.

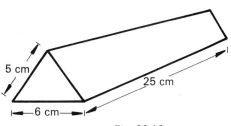

Fig. 20.10

9) A tent has a triangular cross-section whose base is 3 m and whose height is 2·2 m. If it is 7 m long, what is the volume inside the tent?

10) A pipe is 8 m long. It has a bore of 8 cm and an outside diameter of 10 cm. Calculate the volume of the pipe in cubic centimetres.

Surface Areas

We frequently need to find the surface areas of solid figures such as cylinders and rectangular blocks. The surface area is composed of the areas of the ends and the lateral surface area. The lateral surface area of a solid with a constant cross-section is found by multiplying the perimeter of the cross-section by the length. That is:

$$\text{lateral surface area} = \text{perimeter of cross-section} \times \text{length}$$

Example 7

Find the total surface area of a cylinder whose diameter is 28 cm and whose height is 50 cm.

The total surface area is composed of the areas of the two ends and the area of the curved surface. Thus:

$$\text{Area of one end} = \pi \times \text{radius}^2 = \tfrac{22}{7} \times 14^2 = 616 \text{ cm}^2$$

$$\text{Area of curved surface} = \pi \times \text{diameter} \times \text{height} = \tfrac{22}{7} \times 28 \times 50$$
$$= 4400 \text{ cm}^2$$

$$\text{Total surface area} = 2 \times 616 + 4400 = 5632 \text{ cm}^2$$

Example 8

Find the lateral surface area of the triangular prism shown in Fig. 20.11.

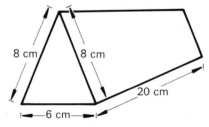

Fig. 20.11

$$\text{Lateral surface area} = \text{perimeter of the end} \times \text{length}$$
$$\text{Perimeter of end} = 8 + 8 + 6 = 22 \text{ cm}$$
$$\text{Lateral surface area} = 22 \times 20 = 440 \text{ cm}^2$$

Exercise 132

1) A room is 5 m long, 4·5 m wide and 2·5 m high. What is the surface area of the walls?

2) A rectangular block of wood is 50 cm long, 10 cm wide and 8 cm high. Find its total surface area.

3) A tent is in the shape of a triangular prism. It is 8 m long, 5 m wide and 3 m high. How much canvas was used in its construction?

4) A cylinder is 5 m long and it has a diameter of 28 cm. What is its total surface area in square metres?

5) A cylinderical tank is 1·5 m diameter and 3 m high. Its curved surface and the top are to be lagged. What area of lagging is required?

6) A closed water tank with vertical sides has a horizontal base in the shape of a rectangle with semi-circular ends as

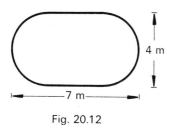

Fig. 20.12

shown in Fig. 20.12. The total inside length of the tank is 7 m, its width 4 m and its height 2 m. Calculate the total surface area of the tank.

7) Find the curved surface area of a cylinder whose diameter is 3·25 m and whose height is 8·12 m.

The Cone

The volume of a cone (Fig. 20.13) is one-third of the volume of the equivalent cylinder. That is:

volume of cone $= \frac{1}{3} \times \pi \times \text{radius}^2 \times \text{vertical height}$ or $V = \frac{1}{3}\pi r^2 h$

The surface area of a cone depends upon the slant height and the radius.

Curved surface area of cone $= \pi \times \text{radius} \times \text{slant height}$ or $A = \pi r l$

Example 9

Find the volume and total surface area of a cone which has a vertical height of 8 cm and a radius of 6 cm.

$$\text{Volume} = \frac{1}{3} \times \pi \times \text{radius}^2 \times \text{vertical height} = \frac{1}{3} \times 3 \cdot 142 \times 6^2 \times 8$$
$$= 301 \cdot 6 \text{ cm}^3$$

To find the surface area we must first calculate the slant height. From Fig. 20.13:

$$\text{Slant height} = \sqrt{6^2 + 8^2} = \sqrt{36 + 64} = \sqrt{100} = 10 \text{ cm}$$
$$\text{Curved surface area} = \pi \times \text{radius} \times \text{slant height} = 3 \cdot 142 \times 6 \times 10$$
$$= 188 \cdot 5 \text{ cm}^2$$
$$\text{Area of base} = \pi \times \text{radius}^2 = 3 \cdot 142 \times 6^2 = 113 \cdot 1$$
$$\text{Total surface area} = 188 \cdot 5 + 113 \cdot 1 = 301 \cdot 6 \text{ cm}^2$$

Fig. 20.13

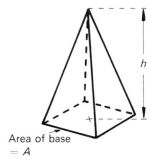

Area of base
$= A$

Fig. 20.14

The Pyramid

The volume of a pyramid (Fig. 20.14) is one-third of the equivalent prism. That is:

Volume of pyramid $= \frac{1}{3} \times \text{area of base} \times \text{vertical height}$ or $V = \frac{1}{3}Ah$

Example 10

Find the volume of a pyramid which has a rectangular base 8 cm long and 5 cm wide and a vertical height of 7 cm.

$$\text{Volume of pyramid} = \tfrac{1}{3} \times \text{area of base} \times \text{vertical height}$$
$$= \tfrac{1}{3} \times 8 \times 5 \times 7 = 93 \cdot 33 \text{ cm}^3$$

The Sphere

$$\text{Volume of a sphere} = \tfrac{4}{3} \times \pi \times \text{radius}^3 \text{ or } V = \tfrac{4}{3}\pi r^3$$

$$\text{Surface area of a sphere} = 4 \times \pi \times \text{radius}^2 \text{ or } A = 4\pi r^2$$

Example 11   A sphere has a diameter of 12 cm. Calculate its volume and surface area.

$$\text{Volume of sphere} = \tfrac{4}{3} \times \pi \times \text{radius}^3 = \tfrac{4}{3} \times \pi \times 6^3 = 904 \cdot 9 \text{ cm}^3$$

$$\text{Surface area of sphere} = 4 \times \pi \times \text{radius}^2 = 4 \times 3 \cdot 142 \times 6^2$$
$$= 452 \cdot 4 \text{ cm}^2$$

Exercise 133

1) Find the volume and curved surface area of a cone with a radius of 4 cm and a vertical height of 3 cm.

2) A cone has a diameter of 12 cm and a slant height of 8 cm. Calculate its total surface area and its volume.

3) A pyramid has a base which is an equilateral triangle of side 6 cm. If its altitude is 4 cm, calculate the volume of the pyramid.

4) A pyramid has a square base of side 12 cm and an altitude of 6 cm. What is its volume?

5) A sphere has a diameter of 10 cm. Calculate its volume and surface area.

6) A hemisphere has a radius of 9 cm. What is its volume?

7) Fig. 20.15 represents a bird cage in the form of a cylinder surmounted by a cone. Calculate:
(a) the total volume of the cage,
(b) the total surface area except for the base.

8) Fig. 20.16 shows a flask which may be considered to be a sphere with a cylinderical neck. Calculate the volume of the flask.

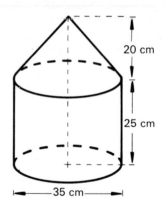

Fig. 20.15

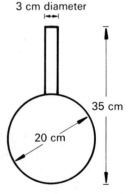

Fig. 20.16

Capacity

The capacity of a container is the volume that it will contain. It is sometimes measured in the same units as for volume, that is, in cubic metres, cubic centimetres or cubic millimetres.

However, for liquid measure the litre (abbreviation: l) is frequently used. The litre is not a precise measurement because 1 litre = 1000·028 cm³. However for most practical problems the litre can be assumed to be 1000 cm³.

Example 12

A rectangular tank has inside measurements of 3 m long, 2 m wide and 1·5 m high. How many litres of liquid will it hold?

Since 1 litre is 1000 cm³ it is best to calculate the volume (or capacity) in cubic centimetres to start with. Thus:

$$\text{Capacity} = 300 \times 200 \times 150 = 9\,000\,000 \text{ cm}^3$$
$$= \frac{9\,000\,000}{1000} = 9000 \text{ litres}$$

Small capacities are often measured in millilitres and:

$$1000 \text{ millilitres (ml)} = 1 \text{ litre}$$

Example 13

How many doses of 5 millilitres can be obtained from a cylindrical medicine bottle which is 5 cm in diameter and 12 cm high?

$$\text{Volume of cylinder} = \pi \times \text{radius}^2 \times \text{height} = 3 \cdot 142 \times 2 \cdot 5^2 \times 12$$
$$= 235 \cdot 7 \text{ cm}^3$$

Since there are 1000 cm³ to 1 litre, 1 cm³ = 1 millilitre. Hence:

$$\text{Number of 5 ml doses} = \frac{235 \cdot 7}{5} = 47 \text{ full doses}$$

The Flow of Water

When a tank or container is being filled with water the time taken to fill the tank depends upon the quantity of water entering the tank in unit time. The rate of flow if often stated in cubic centimetres per second (cm³/s) or cubic metres per minute (m³/min). In the case of water flowing through a pipe the speed of flow, usually in metres per minute (m/min), is often given.

Example 14

A tank which contains 250 m³ of water when full is to be filled through a pipe which delivers water at a rate of 2 m³/min. How long does it take to fill the tank?

$$\text{Time taken} = \frac{\text{volume to fill tank}}{\text{rate of flow}} = \frac{250}{2} = 125 \text{ min}$$

Example 15

Water is flowing through a pipe whose bore is 75 mm at a speed of 2 m/s. Calculate the discharge from the pipe in:
(a) cubic metres per second
(b) litres per minute

(a) Bore of pipe = 75 mm = 0·075 m

Area of pipe $= \pi \times (0 \cdot 0375)^2 = 0 \cdot 0044 \text{ m}^2$

Discharge from the pipe = speed of flow × area of the pipe
$$= 2 \times 0 \cdot 0044 = 0 \cdot 0088 \text{ m}^3/\text{s}$$

(b) Since 1 m = 100 cm, 1 m³ = 100³ cm³ = 1 000 000 cm³

Discharge from pipe $= 0 \cdot 0088 \times 1\,000\,000 \text{ cm}^3/\text{s} = 8800 \text{ cm}^3/\text{s}$

Since 1 litre = 1000 cm³

$$\text{Discharge from the pipe} = \frac{8800}{1000} = 8\cdot 8 \text{ litres per second}$$

$$= 8\cdot 8 \times 60 = 528 \text{ litres per minute}$$

Exercise 134

1) A rectangular tank is 2·5 m long, 1·4 m wide and 0·8 m high. How many litres of water will it hold?

2) A cylindrical garden pool has a radius of 3 m. How many litres of water will it hold if it is filled to a depth of 140 cm?

3) What is the volume of a cylindrical tank 2 m diameter and 3 m high? Give the answer in cubic metres. How many litres does the tank hold?

4) A water pipe has a diameter of 20 mm and a length of 25 m. How many litres of water are contained in the pipe?

5) A cylindrical tank contains 15 375 cm³ of water when full. How many litres does it contain?

6) A rectangular medicine bottle is 8 cm wide, 4 cm long and 12 cm high. What is its capacity in millilitres? How many doses of 4 ml can be obtained from a full bottle?

7) A conical wine glass is 4·5 cm diameter and 6 cm high. What is its capacity in millilitres? How many glasses could be filled from a bottle of wine containing half a litre?

8) A petrol storage tank measures 3 m by 2m by 1·5 m being rectangular in shape. Calculate the number of litres of petrol that it will contain when full.

9) An ice cream carton is cylindrical in shape being 6 cm diameter and 8 cm high. How many litres of ice cream are needed to fill 50 such cartons?

10) A container is in the form of a hemisphere with an internal diameter of 24 cm. How many litres of liquid will it hold?

11) Water is poured into a container at a rate of 300 cm³/s. How long does it take for the container to contain 45 000 cm³?

12) Water is flowing through a pipe whose bore is 15 cm at a speed of 3 m/s. Find the discharge from the pipe:
(a) in cubic metres per second.
(b) in litres per minute.

13) Water flows along a channel at a rate of 3 m/s. Calculate the number of litres of water flowing along the channel each minute if its cross-sectional area is 10 m².

14) A tank is in the form of a cylinder 3 m diameter and 5 m high. Calculate the volume of water it will hold when full. If water flows into the tank at a rate of 50 cm³/s find how long it will take to fill the tank.

15) Water is poured into a cylindrical reservoir 10 m in diameter at a rate of 3000 litres per minute. At what rate does the water level rise in cm/min?

Mass and Density

The density of a substance is the mass per unit volume. Densities are usually measured in kilogrammes per cubic metre (kg/m³) or in grammes per cubic centimetre (g/cm³). The mass of an object may be found by using the formula:

Mass = density × volume of material in the object

The table below gives the densities of various common substances.

Example 16   Find the mass of a block of copper 5 cm by 6 cm by 8 cm. Take the density of copper to be 9 g/cm³.

DENSITIES OF VARIOUS SUBSTANCIES			
Substance	**Density (g/cm³)**	**Substance**	**Density (g/cm³)**
Alcohol	0·79	Gravel	1·8
Aluminium	2·7	Ice	0·90
Asbestos	2·8	Iron	7·9
Brick, common	1·8	Kerosene	0·80
Cement	3·1	Lead	11·4
Coal, bituminous	1·3	Masonry	2·4
Concrete	2·2	Petroleum oil	0·82
Copper	8·9	Salt, common	2·1
Gasoline	0·70	Sand, dry	1·6
Glass	2·6	Silver	10·5
Gold	19·3	Water, fresh	1·0

$$\text{Volume of block} = 5 \times 6 \times 8 = 240 \text{ cm}^3$$
$$\text{Mass of block} = \text{volume} \times \text{density} = 240 \times 9$$
$$= 2160 \text{ g or } 2 \cdot 16 \text{ kg}$$

Example 17   Fig. 20.17 shows the cross-section of a cast iron pillar. If the pillar is 3 m high, calculate its mass given that the density of cast iron is 8 g/cm³.

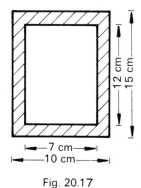

Fig. 20.17

Since the density is given in grammes per cubic centimetre it will be best to calculate the volume in cubic centimetres. Thus:

$$\text{Volume of pillar} = (15 \times 10 - 12 \times 7) \times 300 = (150 - 84) \times 300$$
$$= 66 \times 300 = 19\,800 \text{ cm}^3$$
$$\text{Mass of pillar} = \text{volume} \times \text{density} = 19\,800 \times 8$$
$$= 158\,400 \text{ g or } 158 \cdot 4 \text{ kg}$$

Exercise 135

1) A piece of masonry has a volume of 250 cm³. If the density of masonry is 2·4 g/cm³, calculate the mass of the masonry.

2) What is the mass of 1 m³ of sand if the density of sand is 1·6 g/cm³?

3) Find the mass of a block of lead which is 25 cm long, 8 cm wide and 4 cm high. The density of lead is 11·4 g/cm³.

4) Calculate the mass of copper rod 6 cm diameter and 4 m long. The density of copper is 8·9 g/cm³.

5) A cylindrical water tank is 3 m diameter and 2 m long. What mass of water does it contain?

6) The density of petrol is 0·70 g/cm³. What mass of petrol is there in a tank which contains 25 litres?

7) A sheet of copper is 3 m wide and 8 m long. Its thickness is 5 mm. If the density of copper is 9 g/cm³ calculate the mass of the sheet.

8) What is the mass of a steel pipe 20 cm outside diameter and 16 cm inside diameter and 5 m long? Take the density of steel to be 8 g/cm³.

9) A slab of marble is 85 cm long, 59 cm wide and 24 cm thick. If the density of marble is 2·5 g/cm³, calculate the mass of the slab.

10) A stone pillar is 30 cm diameter and 9 m long. If the density of stone is 2·5 g/cm³, calculate the mass of the pillar.

More Difficult Problems

Many problems with volumes and surface areas of solid figures can be solved by forming an equation. The method is shown in Example 18

Example 18   A steel ingot whose volume is 2 m³ is rolled into plate which is 15 mm thick and 1·75 m wide. Calculate the length of the plate in metres.

Using the formula: $V = lbh$

and substituting the given values we have:

$$2 = l \times 1·75 \times 0·015$$

$$l = \frac{2}{1·75 \times 0·015} = 76·19 \text{ m}$$

Hence the length of the plate is 76·19 m.

Exercise 136

1) Calculate the length of a rectangular tank whose volume is 120 cm³ if its width is 8 cm and its height is 3 cm.

2) A cylinder has a volume of 54 m³. If its diameter is 3 m calculate its length.

3) A sphere has a volume of 127 cm³. What is its radius?

4) Calculate the cross-sectional area of a triangular prism whose volume is 90 cm³ and whose length is 18 cm.

5) Find the thickness of a piece of metal if its volume is 1800 cm³ and its length and width are 90 cm and 80 cm respectively.

6) A block of lead is hammered out to make a square sheet 10 mm thick. If the original dimensions of the block are 1·5 m × 1 m × 0·75 m find the dimensions of the square.

7) A steel ingot is in the shape of a cylinder 1·5 m diameter and 3·5 m long. How many metres of square bar of 50 mm side can be rolled from it?

8) Calculate the diameter of a cylinder whose volume is 220 cm³ and whose height is equal to its diameter.

9) An ingot whose volume is 2 m³ is to be made into ball bearings whose diameters are 12 mm. Assuming that there is no wastage how many ball bearings can be made?

10) A cylindrical can holds 18 litres of petrol. Find the depth of petrol if the can has a diameter of 60 cm.

11) A rectangular slab of stone has a mass of 6 kg. Its length is 20 cm and its width is 15 cm. What is its thickness if the density of the stone is 2·5 g/cm³?

12) A sheet of copper has a mass of 18 kg. If the density of copper is 9 g/cm³ and the length of the sheet is $\frac{1}{2}$ m, calculate the cross-sectional area of the sheet.

Summary

1) The volume of a solid figure is measured by seeing how many cubic units it contains. 1 cm³ is the volume contained inside a cube whose side is 1 cm. 1 m³ is the volume contained inside a cube whose side is 1 m. Note that cm³ is the standard abbreviation for cubic centimetres and that m³ stands for cubic metres.

2) Volume of a rectangular solid = length × width × height

3) If a figure has the same cross-section throughout its length then:

Volume = area of cross-section × length

Lateral surface area = perimeter of cross-section × length

4) Volume of a cylinder = π × radius² × height (or length)

Lateral surface area of cylinder = π × diameter × height (or length)

5) Volume of cone = $\frac{1}{3}$ × π × radius² × height

Curved surface of a cone = π × radius × slant height

6) Volume of a pyramid = $\frac{1}{3}$ × area of base × altitude

7) Volume of a sphere = $\frac{4}{3}$ × π × radius³

Surface area of a sphere = 4 × π × radius²

8) The capacity of a container is the volume that it contains. It may be measured in cubic centimetres, cubic metres or litres. 1 litre = 1000 cm³.

9) The density of a substance is the mass per unit volume. Densities are expressed in grammes per cubic centimetre (g/cm³) or kilogrammes per cubic metre (kg/m³).

10) Mass = density × volume of material in the object.

Mental Test 20

1) What is the volume of a rectangular block whose length is 5 cm, whose width is 4 cm and whose height is 2 cm?

2) A triangular prism has a constant cross-section whose area is 8 cm². If its length is 5 cm, what is its volume?

3) A match box is 7 cm wide, 3 cm high and 12 cm long. What is its volume?

4) A block of wood has a cross-section which is a square of 4 cm side. If it is 8 cm long, what is its lateral surface area?

5) What is the volume of the block in Question 4?

6) The density of steel is 8 g/cm³. What is the mass of a piece of steel with a volume of 15 cm³?

7) The mass of a piece of silver is 200 g. If the density of silver is 10 g/cm³ what is the volume of silver?

8) A triangular prism has a constant cross-sectional area. If its volume is 90 cm³ and its length is 9 cm find the cross-sectional area.

9) A cylinder has a volume of 200 cm³ and a length of 25 cm. What is its cross-sectional area?

10) A small tank contains 15 000 cm³

of water. How many litres does it contain?

11) The capacity of a container is 30 litres. How many cubic centimetres does it hold?

12) A solid has a volume of 400 000 mm³. What is the volume in cubic centimetres?

13) What is the thickness of a piece of metal whose volume is 900 cm³ and whose length and breadth are 45 cm and 10 cm respectively?

14) A rectangular block is 200 cm long, 500 cm wide and 50 cm high. What is its volume in cubic metres?

15) A pyramid has a square base of side 6 cm and an altitude of 5 cm. What is its volume?

Self-Test 20

1) A tank has a volume of 8 m³. Hence the volume of the tank is also:
  a 800 cm³   **b** 8000 cm³
  c 80 000 cm³   **d** 8 000 000 cm³

2) The capacity of a container is 50 litres. Hence its capacity is also:
  a 50 000 cm³   **b** 5000 cm³
  c 0·5 m³   **d** 0·05 m³

3) The area of a curved surface of a cylinder is given by:
  a $2 \times \pi \times \text{radius} \times \text{height}$
  b $2 \times \pi \times \text{radius}^2 \times \text{height}$
  c $\pi \times \text{radius} \times \text{height}$
  d $\pi \times \text{radius}^2 \times \text{height}$

4) The volume of a cylinder is given by:
  a $2 \times \pi \times \text{radius} \times \text{height}$
  b $2 \times \pi \times \text{radius}^2 \times \text{height}$
  c $\pi \times \text{radius} \times \text{height}$
  d $\pi \times \text{radius}^2 \times \text{height}$

5) A small cylindrical container has a diameter of 280 mm and a height of 50 mm. It will hold:
  a 3·08 l **b** 30·8 l **c** 6·16 l **d** 61·6 l

6) A cone has a height of 90 mm and a diameter of 140 mm. Hence the volume of the cone is:
  a 462 cm³   **b** 19 800 mm³
  c 462 000 mm³   **d** 19·8 cm³

7) The mass of an object is given by:
  a $\dfrac{\text{density}}{\text{volume}}$ **b** $\dfrac{\text{volume}}{\text{density}}$
  c $\text{density} \times \text{volume}$

8) A block of lead has a volume of 880 cm³. If its mass is 80 g, the density of lead is:
  a 0·9g/cm³   **b** 11 g/cm³
  c 900 kg/m³   **d** 11 000 kg/m³

9) A flask contains 500 litres of oil whose density is 0·7 g/cm³. The mass of oil in the flask is:
  a 350 kg   **b** 35 kg
  c 3500 kg   **d** 3·5 kg

10) The volume of a small box is 504 cm³. Its width is 14 cm and its height is 6 cm. Hence its length is:
  a 6 cm   **b** 36 cm
  c 84 cm   **d** 216 cm

Miscellaneous Excercise

Exercise 137

All these questions are of the type set in examinations. The questions in section A are intended to take only a minute or two to solve but those in section B are intended to take up to 20 minutes to solve.

Section A

1) A cylindrical can of diameter 9 cm holds 5 litres of liquid. Find to the nearest centimetre the height of the can.

2) An ingot containing 8 m³ of molten metal is made into a sheet 5 m wide and 12 mm thick. What is the length of the sheet?

3) What is the volume of a cube of side 8 cm?

4) The cross-section of a triangular prism is constant at 8 cm². If its volume is 160 cm³ calculate its length.

5) How many cubic centimetres are equal to 1 cubic metre?

6) How many litres are there is 5 m³?

7) A triangle has sides 5 cm, 8 cm and 10 cm long. If it forms the constant cross-section of a triangular prism of length 30 cm, find the lateral surface area of the prism.

8) Change 2250 cm into metres.

9) Find the circumference in centimetres of a circle of radius 140 mm.

10) A rectangular table, of area 5 m² is 250 cm wide. What is its length in centimetres?

11) A triangle has a base of 8 cm and a vertical height of 6 cm. Calculate its area.

12) A rectangular room is 8 m long, 5 m wide and 2 m high. Find the volume enclosed by the room.

13) Find the total surface area of a cylinder of height 20 cm and diameter 21 cm.

14) A solid rectangular block has a length of 15 cm, a breadth of 12 cm and a height of 5 cm. What is its total surface area?

15) What is the perimeter of a right-angled triangle whose two shortest sides measure 12 cm and 16 cm?

16) If 1 cm³ of material has a mass of 8 grammes find the mass of a cube of similar material which has a side of 5 cm.

17) A paving stone measures 76 cm by 60 cm. How many are needed to cover an area 38 m by 48 m?

18) Calculate the volume, in cubic centimetres, of a brick 180 mm by 125 mm by 96 mm.

19) A spherical flask holds, when full, 7 litres of liquid. What is the radius of the flask in centimetres?

20) A rectangular block of concrete measuring 45 cm by 25 cm by 15 cm has a mass of 37·125 kg. What is the density of concrete?

21) Find the mass to the nearest kilogramme of a hollow sphere of internal radius 8 cm and external radius 15 cm made from metal whose density is 7·8 g/cm³.

22) A rectangular room is 6 m long, 4 m wide and 2·5 m high. One quarter of the wall space is taken up by windows, doors, etc. The remainder is covered by wallpaper 50 cm wide. What length of wallpaper is required?

Section B

23) The shaded part of Fig. 1 represents a piece of land which is to be fenced completely. The arcs ABC and FED are quadrants of circles of radii 10·5 m and 14 m respectively and with centre *O*. The fencing comes in rolls of length 16 m and whole rolls only are sold. Calculate:
(a) the length of fencing bought, (take $\pi = \frac{22}{7}$),
(b) the length wasted.

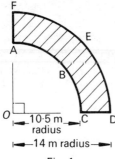

Fig. 1

24) A straight piece of copper tube is 1·2 mm thick; its cross-section is the area between two concentric circles, the radius of the outer circle being 8·5 mm. The mass of the tube is 1·875 kg. Calculate the length of the tube to the nearest millimetre given that 1 cm³ of copper has a mass of 8·86 g.

25) A developing tank of length 24 cm has the cross-section shown in Fig. 2. This consists of a rectangle BCEF and two quadrants of a circle; the dimensions are in centimetres. Calculate the area of the cross-section in square centimetres, correct to three significant figures. If water flows into the tank at a rate of 32 cm³/s, calculate to the nearest second the time taken to fill the tank.

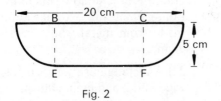

Fig. 2

26) A vertical cross-section of a water channel is shown in Fig. 3, the dimensions being in metres. The surface of the

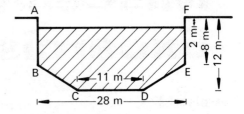

Fig. 3

water is 2 m below AF and water flows along the channel at a rate of 2·2 m/s. Calculate:
(a) The area of the cross-section of water in the channel,
(b) the number of litres, correct to the nearest 1000, of water flowing past the cross-section each minute.

27) Fig. 4 shows a table top made from a rectangular piece of wood measuring originally 1·8 m by 0·9 m, from which the corners have been removed by rounding off with quadrants of circles of radius 35 cm. Calculate:
(a) the area of wood shaved off, in square centimetres,
(b) the perimeter of the table top, in metres.

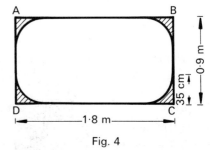

Fig. 4

28) Fig. 5 shows the cross-section of a steel support of length 40 cm. Calculate:

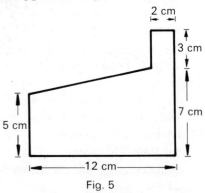

Fig. 5

(a) the area of the cross-section,
(b) the mass of the support to the nearest kilogramme given that the density of steel is 7·79 g/cm³.

29) The hands of a clock are of lengths 2·8 m and 2·1 m. How many more metres does the tip of the minute hand travel than the tip of the hour hand in 90 minutes?

30) Fig. 6 is a diagram representing the cross-section of a glass vessel filled with water. The vessel is cylindrical and open at the top and the thickness of the glass is 8 mm throughout. Externally the vessel is 12·5 cm high and the base diameter is 9·5 cm. Calculate:
(a) the volume of water,
(b) the mass of the empty vessel given that the density of glass is 2·8 g/cm³.

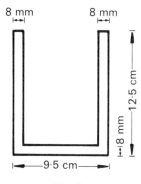

Fig. 6

31) The horizontal cross-section of a garden pool 125 cm deep consists of a rectangle and a semi-circle as shown in Fig.7. Calculate:
(a) the perimeter of the cross-section in metres,
(b) the area of the cross-section in square metres.

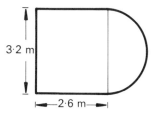

Fig. 7

Water is run into the pool at a rate of 1500 cm³/s. Calculate the time taken to bring the surface of the water 50 cm from the top of the pool.

32) A rectangular block of metal 38 cm long, 29 cm wide and 14 cm thick is melted and cast into a cube. Calculate the length of an edge of the cube, in centimetres, correct to one decimal place.

33) A cylindrical tank holds 24 750 litres of water when full.
(a) What is the capacity of the tank in cubic centimetres?
(b) What is the height of the tank if the diameter of the base is 10 m? Give your answer to the nearest centimetre.

34) A rectangular patio of concrete measuring 6 m long and 5 m wide has a circular pool of 3·5 m diameter set in it. Calculate the area of concrete of the surround of the pool. If the concrete is 5 cm thick and its density is 2·2 g/cm³ calculate the mass of concrete used.

35) A rectangular lawn is 50 m long and 48 m wide and it is surrounded by a path 1·4 m wide. Calculate:
(a) the perimeter of the lawn,
(b) the area of the lawn,
(c) the area of the path.

Tables

Logarithm Tables

N	0	1	2	3	4	5	6	7	8	9
10	0000	0043	0086	0128	0170	0212	0253	0294	0334	0374
11	0414	0453	0492	0531	0569	0607	0645	0682	0719	0755
12	0792	0828	0864	0899	0934	0969	1004	1038	1072	1106
13	1139	1173	1206	1239	1271	1303	1335	1367	1399	1430
14	1461	1492	1523	1553	1584	1614	1644	1673	1703	1732
15	1761	1790	1818	1847	1875	1903	1931	1959	1987	2014
16	2041	2068	2095	2122	2148	2175	2201	2227	2253	2279
17	2304	2330	2355	2380	2405	2430	2455	2480	2504	2529
18	2553	2577	2601	2625	2648	2672	2695	2718	2742	2765
19	2788	2810	2833	2856	2878	2900	2923	2945	2967	2989
20	3010	3032	3054	3075	3096	3118	3139	3160	3181	3201
21	3222	3243	3263	3284	3304	3324	3345	3365	3385	3404
22	3424	3444	3464	3483	3502	3522	3541	3560	3579	3598
23	3617	3636	3655	3674	3692	3711	3729	3747	3766	3784
24	3802	3820	3838	3856	3874	3892	3909	3927	3945	3962
25	3979	3997	4014	4031	4048	4065	4082	4099	4116	4133
26	4150	4166	4183	4200	4216	4232	4249	4265	4281	4298
27	4314	4330	4346	4362	4378	4393	4409	4425	4440	4456
28	4472	4487	4502	4518	4533	4548	4564	4579	4594	4609
29	4624	4639	4654	4669	4683	4698	4713	4728	4742	4757
30	4771	4786	4800	4814	4829	4843	4857	4871	4886	4900
31	4914	4928	4942	4955	4969	4983	4997	5011	5024	5038
32	5051	5065	5079	5092	5105	5119	5132	5145	5159	5172
33	5185	5198	5211	5224	5237	5250	5263	5276	5289	5302
34	5315	5328	5340	5353	5366	5378	5391	5403	5416	5428
35	5441	5453	5465	5478	5490	5502	5514	5527	5539	5551
36	5563	5575	5587	5599	5611	5623	5635	5647	5658	5670
37	5682	5694	5705	5717	5729	5740	5752	5763	5775	5786
38	5798	5809	5821	5832	5843	5855	5866	5877	5888	5899
39	5911	5922	5933	5944	5955	5966	5977	5988	5999	6010
40	6021	6031	6042	6053	6064	6075	6085	6096	6107	6117
41	6128	6138	6149	6160	6170	6180	6191	6201	6212	6222
42	6232	6243	6253	6263	6274	6284	6294	6304	6314	6325
43	6335	6345	6355	6365	6375	6385	6395	6405	6415	6425
44	6435	6444	6454	6464	6474	6484	6493	6503	6513	6522
45	6532	6542	6551	6561	6571	6580	6590	6599	6609	6618
46	6628	6637	6646	6656	6665	6675	6684	6693	6702	6712
47	6721	6730	6739	6749	6758	6767	6776	6785	6794	6803
48	6812	6821	6830	6839	6848	6857	6866	6875	6884	6893
49	6902	6911	6920	6928	6937	6946	6955	6964	6972	6981

Mean Differences

1	2	3	4	5	6	7	8	9
4	8	13	17	21	25	30	34	38
4	8	12	16	20	24	28	32	36
4	8	12	15	19	23	27	31	35
4	7	11	15	18	22	26	30	33
4	7	11	14	18	21	25	28	32
3	7	10	14	17	20	24	27	31
3	7	10	13	16	20	23	26	30
3	6	9	13	16	19	22	25	28
3	6	9	12	15	18	21	24	27
3	6	9	12	15	18	21	24	27
3	6	9	11	14	17	20	23	26
3	6	9	11	14	17	19	22	25
3	5	8	11	13	16	19	21	24
3	5	8	10	13	16	18	21	23
3	5	8	10	13	15	18	20	23
2	5	7	10	12	15	17	20	22
2	5	7	10	12	14	17	19	21
2	5	7	9	12	14	16	19	21
2	5	7	9	11	14	16	18	20
2	4	7	9	11	13	15	18	20
2	4	6	8	11	13	15	17	19
2	4	6	8	10	12	14	16	18
2	4	6	8	10	12	14	15	17
2	4	6	7	9	11	13	15	17
2	4	5	7	9	11	12	14	16
2	3	5	7	9	10	12	14	15
2	3	5	7	8	10	11	13	15
2	3	5	6	8	9	11	13	14
2	3	5	6	8	9	11	12	14
1	3	4	6	7	9	10	12	13
1	3	4	6	7	9	10	11	13
1	3	4	6	7	8	10	11	12
1	3	4	5	7	8	9	11	12
1	3	4	5	6	8	9	10	12
1	3	4	5	6	8	9	10	11
1	2	4	5	6	7	9	10	11
1	2	4	5	6	7	8	10	11
1	2	3	5	6	7	8	9	10
1	2	3	5	6	7	8	9	10
1	2	3	4	5	7	8	9	10
1	2	3	4	5	6	8	9	10
1	2	3	4	5	6	7	8	9
1	2	3	4	5	6	7	8	9
1	2	3	4	5	6	7	8	9
1	2	3	4	5	6	7	8	9
1	2	3	4	5	6	7	8	9
1	2	3	4	5	6	7	7	8
1	2	3	4	5	5	6	7	8
1	2	3	4	4	5	6	7	8
1	2	3	4	4	5	6	7	8

Logarithm Tables

	0	1	2	3	4	5	6	7	8	9	1	2	3	4	5	6	7	8	9
50	6990	6998	7007	7016	7024	7033	7042	7050	7059	7067	1	2	3	3	4	5	6	7	8
51	7076	7084	7093	7101	7110	7118	7126	7135	7143	7152	1	2	3	3	4	5	6	7	8
52	7160	7168	7177	7185	7193	7202	7210	7218	7226	7235	1	2	2	3	4	5	6	7	7
53	7243	7251	7259	7267	7275	7284	7292	7300	7308	7316	1	2	2	3	4	5	6	6	7
54	7324	7332	7340	7348	7356	7364	7372	7380	7388	7396	1	2	2	3	4	5	6	6	7
55	7404	7412	7419	7427	7435	7443	7451	7459	7466	7474	1	2	2	3	4	5	5	6	7
56	7482	7490	7497	7505	7513	7520	7528	7536	7543	7551	1	2	2	3	4	5	5	6	7
57	7559	7566	7574	7582	7589	7597	7604	7612	7619	7627	1	2	2	3	4	5	5	6	7
58	7634	7642	7649	7657	7664	7672	7679	7686	7694	7701	1	1	2	3	4	4	5	6	7
59	7709	7716	7723	7731	7738	7745	7752	7760	7767	7774	1	1	2	3	4	4	5	6	7
60	7782	7789	7796	7803	7810	7818	7825	7832	7839	7846	1	1	2	3	4	4	5	6	6
61	7853	7860	7868	7875	7882	7889	7896	7903	7910	7917	1	1	2	3	4	4	5	6	6
62	7924	7931	7938	7945	7952	7959	7966	7973	7980	7987	1	1	2	3	3	4	5	6	6
63	7993	8000	8007	8014	8021	8028	8035	8041	8048	8055	1	1	2	3	3	4	5	5	6
64	8062	8069	8075	8082	8089	8096	8102	8109	8116	8122	1	1	2	3	3	4	5	5	6
65	8129	8136	8142	8149	8156	8162	8169	8176	8182	8189	1	1	2	3	3	4	5	5	6
66	8195	8202	8209	8215	8222	8228	8235	8241	8248	8254	1	1	2	3	3	4	5	5	6
67	8261	8267	8274	8280	8287	8293	8299	8306	8312	8319	1	1	2	3	3	4	5	5	6
68	8325	8331	8338	8344	8351	8357	8363	8370	8376	8382	1	1	2	3	3	4	4	5	6
69	8388	8395	8401	8407	8414	8420	8426	8432	8439	8445	1	1	2	2	3	4	4	5	6
70	8451	8457	8463	8470	8476	8482	8488	8494	8500	8506	1	1	2	2	3	4	4	5	6
71	8513	8519	8525	8531	8537	8543	8549	8555	8561	8567	1	1	2	2	3	4	4	5	5
72	8573	8579	8585	8591	8597	8603	8609	8615	8621	8627	1	1	2	2	3	4	4	5	5
73	8633	8639	8645	8651	8657	8663	8669	8675	8681	8686	1	1	2	2	3	4	4	5	5
74	8692	8698	8704	8710	8716	8722	8727	8733	8739	8745	1	1	2	2	3	3	4	5	5
75	8751	8756	8762	8768	8774	8779	8785	8791	8797	8802	1	1	2	2	3	3	4	5	5
76	8808	8814	8820	8825	8831	8837	8842	8848	8854	8859	1	1	2	2	3	3	4	5	5
77	8865	8871	8876	8882	8887	8893	8899	8904	8910	8915	1	1	2	2	3	3	4	4	5
78	8921	8927	8932	8938	8943	8949	8954	8960	8965	8971	1	1	2	2	3	3	4	4	5
79	8976	8982	8987	8993	8998	9004	9009	9015	9020	9025	1	1	2	2	3	3	4	4	5
80	9031	9036	9042	9047	9053	9058	9063	9069	9074	9079	1	1	2	2	3	3	4	4	5
81	9085	9090	9096	9101	9106	9112	9117	9122	9128	9133	1	1	2	2	3	3	4	4	5
82	9138	9143	9149	9154	9159	9165	9170	9175	9180	9186	1	1	2	2	3	3	4	4	5
83	9191	9196	9201	9206	9212	9217	9222	9227	9232	9238	1	1	2	2	3	3	4	4	5
84	9243	9248	9253	9258	9263	9269	9274	9279	9284	9289	1	1	2	2	3	3	4	4	5
85	9294	9299	9304	9309	9315	9320	9325	9330	9335	9340	1	1	2	2	3	3	4	4	5
86	9345	9350	9355	9360	9365	9370	9375	9380	9385	9390	1	1	2	2	3	3	4	4	5
87	9395	9400	9405	9410	9415	9420	9425	9430	9435	9440	0	1	1	2	2	3	3	4	4
88	9445	9450	9455	9460	9465	9469	9474	9479	9484	9489	0	1	1	2	2	3	3	4	4
89	9494	9499	9504	9509	9513	9518	9523	9528	9533	9538	0	1	1	2	2	3	3	4	4
90	9542	9547	9552	9557	9562	9566	9571	9576	9581	9586	0	1	1	2	2	3	3	4	4
91	9590	9595	9600	9605	9609	9614	9619	9624	9628	9633	0	1	1	2	2	3	3	4	4
92	9638	9643	9647	9652	9657	9661	9666	9671	9675	9680	0	1	1	2	2	3	3	4	4
93	9685	9689	9694	9699	9703	9708	9713	9717	9722	9727	0	1	1	2	2	3	3	4	4
94	9731	9736	9741	9745	9750	9754	9759	9763	9768	9773	0	1	1	2	2	3	3	4	4
95	9777	9782	9786	9791	9795	9800	9805	9809	9814	9818	0	1	1	2	2	3	3	4	4
96	9823	9827	9832	9836	9841	9845	9850	9854	9859	9863	0	1	1	2	2	3	3	4	4
97	9868	9872	9877	9881	9886	9890	9894	9899	9903	9908	0	1	1	2	2	3	3	4	4
98	9912	9917	9921	9926	9930	9934	9939	9943	9948	9952	0	1	1	2	2	3	3	4	4
99	9956	9961	9965	9969	9974	9978	9983	9987	9991	9996	0	1	1	2	2	3	3	3	4

Antilogarithm Tables

	0	1	2	3	4	5	6	7	8	9	1	2	3	4	5	6	7	8	9
0.00	1000	1002	1005	1007	1009	1012	1014	1016	1019	1021	0	0	1	1	1	1	2	2	2
0.01	1023	1026	1028	1030	1033	1035	1038	1040	1042	1045	0	0	1	1	1	1	2	2	2
0.02	1047	1050	1052	1054	1057	1059	1062	1064	1067	1069	0	0	1	1	1	1	2	2	2
0.03	1072	1074	1076	1079	1081	1084	1086	1089	1091	1094	0	0	1	1	1	1	2	2	2
0.04	1096	1099	1102	1104	1107	1109	1112	1114	1117	1119	0	1	1	1	1	2	2	2	2
0.05	1122	1125	1127	1130	1132	1135	1138	1140	1143	1146	0	1	1	1	1	2	2	2	2
0.06	1148	1151	1153	1156	1159	1161	1164	1167	1169	1172	0	1	1	1	1	2	2	2	2
0.07	1175	1178	1180	1183	1186	1189	1191	1194	1197	1199	0	1	1	1	1	2	2	2	2
0.08	1202	1205	1208	1211	1213	1216	1219	1222	1225	1227	0	1	1	1	1	2	2	2	3
0.09	1230	1233	1236	1239	1242	1245	1247	1250	1253	1256	0	1	1	1	1	2	2	2	3
0.10	1259	1262	1265	1268	1271	1274	1276	1279	1282	1285	0	1	1	1	1	2	2	2	3
0.11	1288	1291	1294	1297	1300	1303	1306	1309	1312	1315	0	1	1	1	2	2	2	2	3
0.12	1318	1321	1324	1327	1330	1334	1337	1340	1343	1346	0	1	1	1	2	2	2	2	3
0.13	1349	1352	1355	1358	1361	1365	1368	1371	1374	1377	0	1	1	1	2	2	2	3	3
0.14	1380	1384	1387	1390	1393	1396	1400	1403	1406	1409	0	1	1	1	2	2	2	3	3
0.15	1413	1416	1419	1422	1426	1429	1432	1435	1439	1442	0	1	1	1	2	2	2	3	3
0.16	1445	1449	1452	1455	1459	1462	1466	1469	1472	1476	0	1	1	1	2	2	2	3	3
0.17	1479	1483	1486	1489	1493	1496	1500	1503	1507	1510	0	1	1	1	2	2	2	3	3
0.18	1514	1517	1521	1524	1528	1531	1535	1538	1542	1545	0	1	1	1	2	2	2	3	3
0.19	1549	1552	1556	1560	1563	1567	1570	1574	1578	1581	0	1	1	1	2	2	3	3	3
0.20	1585	1589	1592	1596	1600	1603	1607	1611	1614	1618	0	1	1	1	2	2	3	3	3
0.21	1622	1626	1629	1633	1637	1641	1644	1648	1652	1656	0	1	1	2	2	2	3	3	3
0.22	1660	1663	1667	1671	1675	1679	1683	1687	1690	1694	0	1	1	2	2	2	3	3	3
0.23	1698	1702	1706	1710	1714	1718	1722	1726	1730	1734	0	1	1	2	2	2	3	3	4
0.24	1738	1742	1746	1750	1754	1758	1762	1766	1770	1774	0	1	1	2	2	2	3	3	4
0.25	1778	1782	1786	1791	1795	1799	1803	1807	1811	1816	0	1	1	2	2	2	3	3	4
0.26	1820	1824	1828	1832	1837	1841	1845	1849	1854	1858	0	1	1	2	2	3	3	3	4
0.27	1862	1866	1871	1875	1879	1884	1888	1892	1897	1901	0	1	1	2	2	3	3	3	4
0.28	1905	1910	1914	1919	1923	1928	1932	1936	1941	1945	0	1	1	2	2	3	3	4	4
0.29	1950	1954	1959	1963	1968	1972	1977	1982	1986	1991	0	1	1	2	2	3	3	4	4
0.30	1995	2000	2004	2009	2014	2018	2023	2028	2032	2037	0	1	1	2	2	3	3	4	4
0.31	2042	2046	2051	2056	2061	2065	2070	2075	2080	2084	0	1	1	2	2	3	3	4	4
0.32	2089	2094	2099	2104	2109	2113	2118	2123	2128	2133	0	1	1	2	2	3	3	4	4
0.33	2138	2143	2148	2153	2158	2163	2168	2173	2178	2183	0	1	1	2	2	3	3	4	4
0.34	2188	2193	2198	2203	2208	2213	2218	2223	2228	2234	1	1	2	2	3	3	4	4	5
0.35	2239	2244	2249	2254	2259	2265	2270	2275	2280	2286	1	1	2	2	3	3	4	4	5
0.36	2291	2296	2301	2307	2312	2317	2323	2328	2333	2339	1	1	2	2	3	3	4	4	5
0.37	2344	2350	2355	2360	2366	2371	2377	2382	2388	2393	1	1	2	2	3	3	4	4	5
0.38	2399	2404	2410	2415	2421	2427	2432	2438	2443	2449	1	1	2	2	3	3	4	4	5
0.39	2455	2460	2466	2472	2477	2483	2489	2495	2500	2506	1	1	2	2	3	3	4	5	5
0.40	2512	2518	2523	2529	2535	2541	2547	2553	2559	2564	1	1	2	2	3	4	4	5	5
0.41	2570	2576	2582	2588	2594	2600	2606	2612	2618	2624	1	1	2	2	3	4	4	5	5
0.42	2630	2636	2642	2649	2655	2661	2667	2673	2679	2685	1	1	2	2	3	4	4	5	6
0.43	2692	2698	2704	2710	2716	2723	2729	2735	2742	2748	1	1	2	3	3	4	4	5	6
0.44	2754	2761	2767	2773	2780	2786	2793	2799	2805	2812	1	1	2	3	3	4	4	5	6
0.45	2818	2825	2831	2838	2844	2851	2858	2864	2871	2877	1	1	2	3	3	4	5	5	6
0.46	2884	2891	2897	2904	2911	2917	2924	2931	2938	2944	1	1	2	3	3	4	5	5	6
0.47	2951	2958	2965	2972	2979	2985	2992	2999	3006	3013	1	1	2	3	3	4	5	5	6
0.48	3020	3027	3034	3041	3048	3055	3062	3069	3076	3083	1	1	2	3	4	4	5	6	6
0.49	3090	3097	3105	3112	3119	3126	3133	3141	3148	3155	1	1	2	3	4	4	5	6	6

Antilogarithm Tables

	0	1	2	3	4	5	6	7	8	9	1	2	3	4	5	6	7	8	9
0.50	3162	3170	3177	3184	3192	3199	3206	3214	3221	3228	1	1	2	3	4	4	5	6	7
0.51	3236	3243	3251	3258	3266	3273	3281	3289	3296	3304	1	2	2	3	4	5	5	6	7
0.52	3311	3319	3327	3334	3342	3350	3357	3365	3373	3381	1	2	2	3	4	5	5	6	7
0.53	3388	3396	3404	3412	3420	3428	3436	3443	3451	3459	1	2	2	3	4	5	6	6	7
0.54	3467	3475	3483	3491	3499	3508	3516	3524	3532	3540	1	2	2	3	4	5	6	6	7
0.55	3548	3556	3565	3573	3581	3589	3597	3606	3614	3622	1	2	2	3	4	5	6	7	7
0.56	3631	3639	3648	3656	3664	3673	3681	3690	3698	3707	1	2	3	3	4	5	6	7	8
0.57	3715	3724	3733	3741	3750	3758	3767	3776	3784	3793	1	2	3	3	4	5	6	7	8
0.58	3802	3811	3819	3828	3837	3846	3855	3864	3873	3882	1	2	3	4	4	5	6	7	8
0.59	3890	3899	3908	3917	3926	3936	3945	3954	3963	3972	1	2	3	4	5	5	6	7	8
0.60	3981	3990	3999	4009	4018	4027	4036	4046	4055	4064	1	2	3	4	5	6	6	7	8
0.61	4074	4083	4093	4102	4111	4121	4130	4140	4150	4159	1	2	3	4	5	6	7	8	9
0.62	4169	4178	4188	4198	4207	4217	4227	4236	4246	4256	1	2	3	4	5	6	7	8	9
0.63	4266	4276	4285	4295	4305	4315	4325	4335	4345	4355	1	2	3	4	5	6	7	8	9
0.64	4365	4375	4385	4395	4406	4416	4426	4436	4446	4457	1	2	3	4	5	6	7	8	9
0.65	4467	4477	4487	4498	4508	4519	4529	4539	4550	4560	1	2	3	4	5	6	7	8	9
0.66	4571	4581	4592	4603	4613	4624	4634	4645	4656	4667	1	2	3	4	5	6	7	9	10
0.67	4677	4688	4699	4710	4721	4732	4742	4753	4764	4775	1	2	3	4	5	7	8	9	10
0.68	4786	4797	4808	4819	4831	4842	4853	4864	4875	4887	1	2	3	4	6	7	8	9	10
0.69	4893	4909	4920	4932	4943	4955	4966	4977	4989	5000	1	2	3	5	6	7	8	9	10
0.70	5012	5023	5035	5047	5058	5070	5082	5093	5105	5117	1	2	4	5	6	7	8	9	11
0.71	5129	5140	5152	5164	5176	5188	5200	5212	5224	5236	1	2	4	5	6	7	8	10	11
0.72	5248	5260	5272	5284	5297	5309	5321	5333	5346	5358	1	2	4	5	6	7	9	10	11
0.73	5370	5383	5395	5408	5420	5433	5445	5458	5470	5483	1	3	4	5	6	8	9	10	11
0.74	5495	5508	5521	5534	5546	5559	5572	5585	5598	5610	1	3	4	5	6	8	9	10	12
0.75	5623	5636	5649	5662	5675	5689	5702	5715	5728	5741	1	3	4	5	7	8	9	10	12
0.76	5754	5768	5781	5794	5808	5821	5834	5848	5861	5875	1	3	4	5	7	8	9	11	12
0.77	5888	5902	5916	5929	5943	5957	5970	5984	5998	6012	1	3	4	5	7	8	10	11	12
0.78	6026	6039	6053	6067	6081	6095	6109	6124	6138	6152	1	3	4	6	7	8	10	11	13
0.79	6166	6180	6194	6209	6223	6237	6252	6266	6281	6295	1	3	4	6	7	9	10	11	13
0.80	6310	6324	6339	6353	6368	6383	6397	6412	6427	6442	1	3	4	6	7	9	10	12	13
0.81	6457	6471	6486	6501	6516	6531	6546	6561	6577	6592	2	3	5	6	8	9	11	12	14
0.82	6607	6622	6637	6653	6668	6683	6699	6714	6730	6745	2	3	5	6	8	9	11	12	14
0.83	6761	6776	6792	6808	6823	6839	6855	6871	6887	6902	2	3	5	6	8	9	11	13	14
0.84	6918	6934	6950	6966	6982	6998	7015	7031	7047	7063	2	3	5	6	8	10	11	13	15
0.85	7079	7096	7112	7129	7145	7161	7178	7194	7211	7228	2	3	5	7	8	10	12	13	15
0.86	7244	7261	7278	7295	7311	7328	7345	7362	7379	7396	2	3	5	7	8	10	12	13	15
0.87	7413	7430	7447	7464	7482	7499	7516	7534	7551	7568	2	3	5	7	9	10	12	14	16
0.88	7586	7603	7621	7638	7656	7674	7691	7709	7727	7745	2	4	5	7	9	11	12	14	16
0.89	7762	7780	7798	7816	7834	7852	7870	7889	7907	7925	2	4	5	7	9	11	13	14	16
0.90	7943	7962	7980	7998	8017	8035	8054	8072	8091	8110	2	4	6	7	9	11	13	15	17
0.91	8128	8147	8166	8185	8204	8222	8241	8260	8279	8299	2	4	6	8	9	11	13	15	17
0.92	8318	8337	8356	8375	8395	8414	8433	8453	8472	8492	2	4	6	8	10	12	14	15	17
0.93	8511	8531	8551	8570	8590	8610	8630	8650	8670	8690	2	4	6	8	10	12	14	16	18
0.94	8710	8730	8750	8770	8790	8810	8831	8851	8872	8892	2	4	6	8	10	12	14	16	18
0.95	8913	8933	8954	8974	8995	9016	9036	9057	9078	9099	2	4	6	8	10	12	15	17	19
0.96	9120	9141	9162	9183	9204	9226	9247	9268	9290	9311	2	4	6	8	11	13	15	17	19
0.97	9333	9354	9376	9397	9419	9441	9462	9484	9506	9528	2	4	7	9	11	13	15	17	20
0.98	9550	9572	9594	9616	9638	9661	9683	9705	9727	9750	2	4	7	9	11	13	16	18	20
0.99	9772	9795	9817	9840	9863	9886	9908	9931	9954	9977	2	5	7	9	11	14	16	18	20

Table of Squares

x	0	1	2	3	4	5	6	7	8	9	1 2 3	4 5 6	7 8 9
1·0	1·000	1·020	1·040	1·061	1·082	1·103	1·124	1·145	1·166	1·188	2 4 6	8 10 13	15 17 19
1·1	1·210	1·232	1·254	1·277	1·300	1·323	1·346	1·369	1·392	1·416	2 5 7	9 11 14	16 18 21
1·2	1·440	1·464	1·488	1·513	1·538	1·563	1·588	1·613	1·638	1·664	2 5 7	10 12 15	17 20 22
1·3	1·690	1·716	1·742	1·769	1·796	1·823	1·850	1·877	1·904	1·932	3 5 8	11 13 16	19 22 24
1·4	1·960	1·988	2·016	2·045	2·074	2·103	2·132	2·161	2·190	2·220	3 6 9	12 14 17	20 23 26
1·5	2·250	2·280	2·310	2·341	2·372	2·403	2·434	2·465	2·496	2·528	3 6 9	12 15 19	22 25 28
1·6	2·560	2·592	2·624	2·657	2·690	2·723	2·756	2·789	2·822	2·856	3 7 10	13 16 20	23 26 30
1·7	2·890	2·924	2·958	2·993	3·028	3·063	3·098	3·133	3·168	3·204	3 7 10	14 17 21	24 28 31
1·8	3·240	3·276	3·312	3·349	3·386	3·423	3·460	3·497	3·534	3·572	4 7 11	15 18 22	26 30 33
1·9	3·610	3·648	3·686	3·725	3·764	3·803	3·842	3·881	3·920	3·960	4 8 12	16 19 23	27 31 35
2·0	4·000	4·040	4·080	4·121	4·162	4·203	4·244	4·285	4·326	4·368	4 8 12	16 20 25	29 33 37
2·1	4·410	4·452	4·494	4·537	4·580	4·623	4·666	4·709	4·752	4·796	4 9 13	17 21 26	30 34 39
2·2	4·840	4·884	4·928	4·973	5·018	5·063	5·108	5·153	5·198	5·244	4 9 13	18 22 27	31 36 40
2·3	5·290	5·336	5·382	5·429	5·476	5·523	5·570	5·617	5·664	5·712	5 9 14	19 23 28	33 38 42
2·4	5·760	5·808	5·856	5·905	5·954	6·003	6·052	6·101	6·150	6·200	5 10 15	20 24 29	34 39 44
2·5	6·250	6·300	6·350	6·401	6·452	6·503	6·554	6·605	6·656	6·708	5 10 15	20 25 31	36 41 46
2·6	6·760	6·812	6·864	6·917	6·970	7·023	7·076	7·129	7·182	7·236	5 11 16	21 26 32	37 42 48
2·7	7·290	7·344	7·398	7·453	7·508	7·563	7·618	7·673	7·728	7·784	5 11 16	22 27 33	38 44 49
2·8	7·840	7·896	7·952	8·009	8·066	8·123	8·180	8·237	8·294	8·352	6 11 17	23 28 34	40 46 51
2·9	8·410	8·468	8·526	8·585	8·644	8·703	8·762	8·821	8·880	8·940	6 12 18	24 29 35	41 47 53
3·0	9·000	9·060	9·120	9·181	9·242	9·303	9·364	9·425	9·486	9·548	6 12 18	24 30 37	43 49 55
3·1	9·610	9·672	9·734	9·797	9·860	9·923	9·986	10·05	10·11	10·18	6 13 19	25 31 38	44 50 57
3·2	10·24	10·30	10·37	10·43	10·50	10·56	10·63	10·69	10·76	10·82	1 1 2	3 3 4	5 5 6
3·3	10·89	10·96	11·02	11·09	11·16	11·22	11·29	11·36	11·42	11·49	1 1 2	3 3 4	5 5 6
3·4	11·56	11·63	11·70	11·76	11·83	11·90	11·97	12·04	12·11	12·18	1 1 2	3 3 4	5 6 6
3·5	12·25	12·32	12·39	12·46	12·53	12·60	12·67	12·74	12·82	12·89	1 1 2	3 4 4	5 6 6
3·6	12·96	13·03	13·10	13·18	13·25	13·32	13·40	13·47	13·54	13·62	1 1 2	3 4 4	5 6 7
3·7	13·69	13·76	13·84	13·91	13·99	14·06	14·14	14·21	14·29	14·36	1 2 2	3 4 4	5 6 7
3·8	14·44	14·52	14·59	14·67	14·75	14·82	14·90	14·98	15·05	15·13	1 2 2	3 4 5	5 6 7
3·9	15·21	15·29	15·37	15·44	15·52	15·60	15·68	15·76	15·84	15·92	1 2 2	3 4 5	6 6 7
4·0	16·00	16·08	16·16	16·24	16·32	16·40	16·48	16·56	16·65	16·73	1 2 2	3 4 5	6 6 7
4·1	16·81	16·89	16·97	17·06	17·14	17·22	17·31	17·39	17·47	17·56	1 2 2	3 4 5	6 7 7
4·2	17·64	17·72	17·81	17·89	17·98	18·06	18·15	18·23	18·32	18·40	1 2 3	3 4 5	6 7 8
4·3	18·49	18·58	18·66	18·75	18·84	18·92	19·01	19·10	19·18	19·27	1 2 3	3 4 5	6 7 8
4·4	19·36	19·45	19·54	19·62	19·71	19·80	19·89	19·98	20·07	20·16	1 2 3	4 4 5	6 7 8
4·5	20·25	20·34	20·43	20·52	20·61	20·70	20·79	20·88	20·98	21·07	1 2 3	4 5 5	6 7 8
4·6	21·16	21·25	21·34	21·44	21·53	21·62	21·72	21·81	21·90	22·00	1 2 3	4 5 6	7 7 8
4·7	22·09	22·18	22·28	22·37	22·47	22·56	22·66	22·75	22·85	22·94	1 2 3	4 5 6	7 8 9
4·8	23·04	23·14	23·23	23·33	23·43	23·52	23·62	23·72	23·81	23·91	1 2 3	4 5 6	7 8 9
4·9	24·01	24·11	24·21	24·30	24·40	24·50	24·60	24·70	24·80	24·90	1 2 3	4 5 6	7 8 9
5·0	25·00	25·10	25·20	25·30	25·40	25·50	25·60	25·70	25·81	25·91	1 2 3	4 5 6	7 8 9
5·1	26·01	26·11	26·21	26·32	26·42	26·52	26·63	26·73	26·83	26·94	1 2 3	4 5 6	7 8 9
5·2	27·04	27·14	27·25	27·35	27·46	27·56	27·67	27·77	27·88	27·98	1 2 3	4 5 6	7 8 9
5·3	28·09	28·20	28·30	28·41	28·52	28·62	28·73	28·84	28·94	29·05	1 2 3	4 5 6	7 9 10
5·4	29·16	29·27	29·38	29·48	29·59	29·70	29·81	29·92	30·03	30·14	1 2 3	4 5 7	8 9 10

Table of Squares

x	0	1	2	3	4	5	6	7	8	9	1	2	3	4	5	6	7	8	9
5·5	30·25	30·36	30·47	30·58	30·69	30·80	30·91	31·02	31·14	31·25	1	2	3	4	6	7	8	9	10
5·6	31·36	31·47	31·58	31·70	31·81	31·92	32·04	32·15	32·26	32·38	1	2	3	5	6	7	8	9	10
5·7	32·49	32·60	32·72	32·83	32·95	33·06	33·18	33·29	33·41	33·52	1	2	3	5	6	7	8	9	10
5·8	33·64	33·76	33·87	33·99	34·11	34·22	34·34	34·46	34·57	34·69	1	2	4	5	6	7	8	9	11
5·9	34·81	34·93	35·05	35·16	35·28	35·40	35·52	35·64	35·76	35·88	1	2	4	5	6	7	8	10	11
6·0	36·00	36·12	36·24	36·36	36·48	36·60	36·72	36·84	36·97	37·09	1	2	4	5	6	7	9	10	11
6·1	37·21	37·33	37·45	37·58	37·70	37·82	37·95	38·07	38·19	38·32	1	2	4	5	6	7	9	10	11
6·2	38·44	38·56	38·69	38·81	38·94	39·06	39·19	39·31	39·44	39·56	1	3	4	5	6	8	9	10	11
6·3	39·69	39·82	39·94	40·07	40·20	40·32	40·45	40·58	40·70	40·83	1	3	4	5	6	8	9	10	11
6·4	40·96	41·09	41·22	41·34	41·47	41·60	41·73	41·86	41·99	42·12	1	3	4	5	6	8	9	10	12
6·5	42·25	42·38	42·51	42·64	42·77	42·90	43·03	43·16	43·30	43·43	1	3	4	5	7	8	9	10	12
6·6	43·56	43·69	43·82	43·96	44·09	44·22	44·36	44·49	44·62	44·76	1	3	4	5	7	8	9	11	12
6·7	44·89	45·02	45·16	45·29	45·43	45·56	45·70	45·83	45·97	46·10	1	3	4	5	7	8	9	11	12
6·8	46·24	46·38	46·51	56·65	46·79	46·92	47·06	47·20	47·33	47·47	1	3	4	5	7	8	10	11	12
6·9	47·61	47·75	47·89	48·02	48·16	48·30	48·44	48·58	48·72	48·86	1	3	4	6	7	8	10	11	13
7·0	49·00	49·14	49·28	49·42	49·56	49·70	49·84	49·98	50·13	50·27	1	3	4	6	7	8	10	11	13
7·1	50·41	50·55	50·69	50·84	50·98	51·12	51·27	51·41	51·55	51·70	1	3	4	6	7	9	10	11	13
7·2	51·84	51·98	52·13	52·27	52·42	52·56	52·71	52·85	53·00	53·14	1	3	4	6	7	9	10	12	13
7·3	53·29	53·44	53·58	53·73	53·88	54·02	54·17	54·32	54·46	54·61	1	3	4	6	7	9	10	12	13
7·4	54·76	54·91	55·06	55·20	55·35	55·50	55·65	55·80	55·95	56·10	1	3	4	6	7	9	10	12	13
7·5	56·25	56·40	56·55	56·70	56·85	57·00	57·15	57·30	57·46	57·61	2	3	5	6	8	9	11	12	14
7·6	57·76	57·91	58·06	58·22	58·37	58·52	58·68	58·83	58·98	59·14	2	3	5	6	8	9	11	12	14
7·7	59·29	59·44	59·60	59·75	59·91	60·06	60·22	60·37	60·53	60·68	2	3	5	6	8	9	11	12	14
7·8	60·84	61·00	61·15	61·31	61·47	61·62	61·78	61·94	62·09	62·25	2	3	5	6	8	9	11	13	14
7·9	62·41	62·57	62·73	62·88	63·04	63·20	63·36	63·52	63·68	63·84	2	3	5	6	8	10	11	13	14
8·0	64·00	64·16	64·32	64·48	64·64	64·80	64·96	65·12	65·29	65·45	2	3	5	6	8	10	11	13	14
8·1	65·61	65·77	65·93	66·10	66·26	66·42	67·59	66·75	66·91	67·08	2	3	5	7	8	10	11	13	15
8·2	67·24	67·40	67·57	67·73	67·90	68·06	68·23	68·39	68·56	68·72	2	3	5	7	8	10	12	13	15
8·3	68·89	69·06	69·22	69·39	69·56	69·72	69·89	70·06	70·22	70·39	2	3	5	7	8	10	12	13	15
8·4	70·56	70·73	70·90	71·06	71·23	71·40	71·57	71·74	71·91	72·08	2	3	5	7	8	10	12	14	15
8·5	72·25	72·42	72·59	72·76	72·93	73·10	73·27	73·44	73·62	73·79	2	3	5	7	9	10	12	14	15
8·6	73·96	74·13	74·30	74·48	74·65	74·82	75·00	75·17	75·34	75·52	2	3	5	7	9	10	12	14	16
8·7	75·69	75·86	76·04	76·21	76·39	76·56	76·74	76·91	77·09	77·26	2	4	5	7	9	11	12	14	16
8·8	77·44	77·62	77·79	77·97	78·15	78·32	78·50	78·68	78·85	79·03	2	4	5	7	9	11	12	14	16
8·9	79·21	79·39	79·57	79·74	79·92	80·10	80·28	80·46	80·64	80·82	2	4	5	7	9	11	13	14	16
9·0	81·00	81·18	81·36	81·54	81·72	81·90	82·08	82·26	82·45	82·63	2	4	5	7	9	11	13	14	16
9·1	82·81	82·99	83·17	83·36	83·54	83·72	83·91	84·09	84·27	84·46	2	4	5	7	9	11	13	15	16
9·2	84·64	84·82	85·01	85·19	85·38	85·56	85·75	85·93	86·12	86·30	2	4	6	7	9	11	13	15	17
9·3	86·49	86·68	86·86	87·05	87·24	87·42	87·61	87·80	87·98	88·17	2	4	6	7	9	11	13	15	17
9·4	88·36	88·55	88·74	88·92	89·11	89·30	89·49	89·68	89·87	90·06	2	4	6	8	9	11	13	15	17
9·5	90·25	90·44	90·63	90·82	91·01	91·20	91·39	91·58	91·78	91·97	2	4	6	8	10	11	13	15	17
9·6	92·16	92·35	92·54	92·74	92·93	93·12	93·32	93·51	93·70	93·90	2	4	6	8	10	12	14	15	17
9·7	94·09	94·28	94·48	94·67	94·87	95·06	95·26	95·45	95·65	95·84	2	4	6	8	10	12	14	16	18
9·8	96·04	96·24	96·43	96·63	96·83	97·02	97·22	97·42	97·61	97·81	2	4	6	8	10	12	14	16	18
9·9	98·01	98·21	98·41	98·60	98·80	99·00	99·20	99·40	99·60	99·80	2	4	6	8	10	12	14	16	18

Table of Square Roots from 1—10

	·0	·1	·2	·3	·4	·5	·6	·7	·8	·9	1	2	3	4	5	6	7	8	9
1·0	1·000	1·005	1·010	1·015	1·020	1·025	1·030	1·034	1·039	1·044	0	1	1	2	2	3	3	4	4
1·1	1·049	1·054	1·058	1·063	1·068	1·072	1·077	1·082	1·086	1·091	0	1	1	2	2	3	3	4	4
1·2	1·095	1·100	1·105	1·109	1·114	1·118	1·122	1·127	1·131	1·136	0	1	1	2	2	3	3	4	4
1·3	1·140	1·145	1·149	1·153	1·158	1·162	1·166	1·170	1·175	1·179	0	1	1	2	2	3	3	3	4
1·4	1·183	1·187	1·192	1·196	1·200	1·204	1·208	1·212	1·217	1·221	0	1	1	2	2	3	3	3	4
1·5	1·225	1·229	1·233	1·237	1·241	1·245	1·249	1·253	1·257	1·261	0	1	1	2	2	2	3	3	4
1·6	1·265	1·269	1·273	1·277	1·281	1·285	1·288	1·292	1·296	1·300	0	1	1	2	2	2	3	3	3
1·7	1·304	1·308	1·311	1·315	1·319	1·323	1·327	1·330	1·334	1·338	0	1	1	1	2	2	3	3	3
1·8	1·342	1·345	1·349	1·353	1·356	1·360	1·364	1·367	1·371	1·375	0	1	1	1	2	2	3	3	3
1·9	1·378	1·382	1·386	1·389	1·393	1·396	1·400	1·404	1·407	1·411	0	1	1	1	2	2	3	3	3
2·0	1·414	1·418	1·421	1·425	1·428	1·432	1·435	1·439	1·442	1·446	0	1	1	1	2	2	2	3	3
2·1	1·449	1·453	1·456	1·459	1·463	1·466	1·470	1·473	1·476	1·480	0	1	1	1	2	2	2	3	3
2·2	1·483	1·487	1·490	1·493	1·497	1·500	1·503	1·507	1·510	1·513	0	1	1	1	2	2	2	3	3
2·3	1·517	1·520	1·523	1·526	1·530	1·533	1·536	1·539	1·543	1·546	0	1	1	1	2	2	2	2	3
2·4	1·549	1·552	1·556	1·559	1·562	1·565	1·568	1·572	1·575	1·578	0	1	1	1	2	2	2	2	3
2·5	1·581	1·584	1·587	1·591	1·594	1·597	1·600	1·603	1·606	1·609	0	1	1	1	2	2	2	2	3
2·6	1·612	1·616	1·619	1·622	1·625	1·628	1·631	1·634	1·637	1·640	0	1	1	1	2	2	2	2	3
2·7	1·643	1·646	1·649	1·652	1·655	1·658	1·661	1·664	1·667	1·670	0	1	1	1	2	2	2	2	3
2·8	1·673	1·676	1·679	1·682	1·685	1·688	1·691	1·694	1·697	1·700	0	1	1	1	2	2	2	2	3
2·9	1·703	1·706	1·709	1·712	1·715	1·718	1·720	1·723	1·726	1·729	0	1	1	1	1	2	2	2	3
3·0	1·732	1·735	1·738	1·741	1·744	1·746	1·749	1·752	1·755	1·758	0	1	1	1	1	2	2	2	3
3·1	1·761	1·764	1·766	1·769	1·772	1·775	1·778	1·780	1·783	1·786	0	1	1	1	1	2	2	2	3
3·2	1·789	1·792	1·794	1·797	1·800	1·803	1·806	1·808	1·811	1·814	0	1	1	1	1	2	2	2	2
3·3	1·817	1·819	1·822	1·825	1·828	1·830	1·833	1·836	1·838	1·841	0	1	1	1	1	2	2	2	2
3·4	1·844	1·847	1·849	1·852	1·855	1·857	1·860	1·863	1·865	1·868	0	1	1	1	1	2	2	2	2
3·5	1·871	1·873	1·876	1·879	1·881	1·884	1·887	1·889	1·892	1·895	0	1	1	1	1	2	2	2	2
3·6	1·897	1·900	1·903	1·905	1·908	1·910	1·913	1·916	1·918	1·921	0	1	1	1	1	2	2	2	2
3·7	1·924	1·926	1·929	1·931	1·934	1·936	1·939	1·942	1·944	1·947	0	1	1	1	1	2	2	2	2
3·8	1·949	1·952	1·954	1·957	1·960	1·962	1·965	1·967	1·970	1·972	0	1	1	1	1	2	2	2	2
3·9	1·975	1·977	1·980	1·982	1·985	1·987	1·990	1·992	1·995	1·997	0	0	1	1	1	1	2	2	2
4·0	2·000	2·002	2·005	2·007	2·010	2·012	2·015	2·017	2·020	2·022	0	0	1	1	1	1	2	2	2
4·1	2·025	2·027	2·030	2·032	2·035	2·037	2·040	2·042	2·045	2·047	0	0	1	1	1	1	2	2	2
4·2	2·049	2·052	2·054	2·057	2·059	2·062	2·064	2·066	2·069	2·071	0	0	1	1	1	1	2	2	2
4·3	2·074	2·076	2·078	2·081	2·083	2·086	2·088	2·090	2·093	2·095	0	0	1	1	1	1	1	2	2
4·4	2·098	2·100	2·102	2·105	2·107	2·110	2·112	2·114	2·117	2·119	0	0	1	1	1	1	1	2	2
4·5	2·121	2·124	2·126	2·128	2·131	2·133	2·135	2·138	2·140	2·142	0	0	1	1	1	1	1	2	2
4·6	2·145	2·147	2·149	2·152	2·154	2·156	2·159	2·161	2·163	2·166	0	0	1	1	1	1	1	2	2
4·7	2·168	2·170	2·173	2·175	2·177	2·179	2·182	2·184	2·186	2·189	0	0	1	1	1	1	1	2	2
4·8	2·191	2·193	2·195	2·198	2·200	2·202	2·205	2·207	2·209	2·211	0	0	1	1	1	1	1	2	2
4·9	2·214	2·216	2·218	2·220	2·223	2·225	2·227	2·229	2·232	2·234	0	0	1	1	1	1	1	2	2
5·0	2·236	2·238	2·241	2·243	2·245	2·247	2·249	2·252	2·254	2·256	0	0	1	1	1	1	1	2	2
5·1	2·258	2·261	2·263	2·265	2·267	2·269	2·272	2·274	2·276	2·278	0	0	1	1	1	1	1	2	2
5·2	2·280	2·283	2·285	2·287	2·289	2·291	2·293	2·296	2·298	2·300	0	0	1	1	1	1	1	2	2
5·3	2·302	2·304	2·307	2·309	2·311	2·313	2·315	2·317	2·319	2·322	0	0	1	1	1	1	1	2	2
5·4	2·324	2·326	2·328	2·330	2·332	2·335	2·337	2·339	2·341	2·343	0	0	1	1	1	1	1	2	2

Table of Square Roots from 1—10

	·0	·1	·2	·3	·4	·5	·6	·7	·8	·9	1	2	3	4	5	6	7	8	9
5·5	2·345	2·347	2·349	2·352	2·354	2·356	2·358	2·360	2·362	2·364	0	0	1	1	1	1	1	2	2
5·6	2·366	2·369	2·371	2·373	2·375	2·377	2·379	2·381	2·383	2·385	0	0	1	1	1	1	1	2	2
5·7	2·387	2·390	2·392	2·394	2·396	2·398	2·400	2·402	2·404	2·406	0	0	1	1	1	1	1	2	2
5·8	2·408	2·410	2·412	2·415	2·417	2·419	2·421	2·423	2·425	2·427	0	0	1	1	1	1	1	2	2
5·9	2·429	2·431	2·433	2·435	2·437	2·439	2·441	2·443	2·445	2·447	0	0	1	1	1	1	1	2	2
6·0	2·449	2·452	2·454	2·456	2·458	2·460	2·462	2·464	2·466	2·468	0	0	1	1	1	1	1	2	2
6·1	2·470	2·472	2·474	2·476	2·478	2·480	2·482	2·484	2·486	2·488	0	0	1	1	1	1	1	2	2
6·2	2·490	2·492	2·494	2·496	2·498	2·500	2·502	2·504	2·506	2·508	0	0	1	1	1	1	1	2	2
6·3	2·510	2·512	2·514	2·516	2·518	2·520	2·522	2·524	2·526	2·528	0	0	1	1	1	1	1	2	2
6·4	2·530	2·532	2·534	2·536	2·538	2·540	2·542	2·544	2·546	2·548	0	0	1	1	1	1	1	2	2
6·5	2·550	2·551	2·553	2·555	2·557	2·559	2·561	2·563	2·565	2·567	0	0	1	1	1	1	1	2	2
6·6	2·569	2·571	2·573	2·575	2·577	2·579	2·581	2·583	2·585	2·587	0	0	1	1	1	1	1	2	2
6·7	2·588	2·590	2·592	2·594	2·596	2·598	2·600	2·602	2·604	2·606	0	1	1	1	1	1	1	2	2
6·8	2·608	2·610	2·612	2·613	2·615	2·617	2·619	2·621	2·623	2·625	0	0	1	1	1	1	1	2	2
6·9	2·627	2·629	2·631	2·632	2·634	2·636	2·638	2·640	2·642	2·644	0	0	1	1	1	1	1	2	2
7·0	2·646	2·648	2·650	2·651	2·653	2·655	2·657	2·659	2·661	2·663	0	0	1	1	1	1	1	2	2
7·1	2·665	2·666	2·668	2·670	2·672	2·674	2·676	2·678	2·680	2·681	0	0	1	1	1	1	1	2	2
7·2	2·683	2·685	2·687	2·689	2·691	2·693	2·694	2·696	2·698	2·700	0	0	1	1	1	1	1	2	2
7·3	2·702	2·704	2·706	2·707	2·709	2·711	2·713	2·715	2·717	2·718	0	0	1	1	1	1	1	2	2
7·4	2·720	2·722	2·724	2·726	2·728	2·729	2·731	2·733	2·735	2·737	0	0	1	1	1	1	1	2	2
7·5	2·739	2·740	2·742	2·744	2·746	2·748	2·750	2·751	2·753	2·755	0	0	1	1	1	1	1	2	2
7·6	2·757	2·759	2·760	2·762	2·764	2·766	2·768	2·769	2·771	2·773	0	0	1	1	1	1	1	2	2
7·7	2·775	2·777	2·778	2·780	2·782	2·784	2·786	2·787	2·789	2·791	0	0	1	1	1	1	1	2	2
7·8	2·793	2·795	2·796	2·798	2·800	2·802	2·804	2·805	2·807	2·809	0	0	1	1	1	1	1	2	2
7·9	2·811	2·812	2·814	2·816	2·818	2·820	2·821	2·823	2·825	2·827	0	0	1	1	1	1	1	2	2
8·0	2·828	2·830	2·832	2·834	2·835	2·837	2·839	2·841	2·843	2·844	0	0	1	1	1	1	1	2	2
8·1	2·846	2·848	2·850	2·851	2·853	2·855	2·857	2·858	2·860	2·862	0	0	1	1	1	1	1	2	2
8·2	2·864	2·865	2·867	2·869	2·871	2·872	2·874	2·876	2·877	2·879	0	0	1	1	1	1	1	2	2
8·3	2·881	2·883	2·884	2·886	2·888	2·890	2·891	2·893	2·895	2·897	0	0	1	1	1	1	1	2	2
3·4	2·898	2·900	2·902	2·903	2·905	2·907	2·909	2·910	2·912	2·914	0	0	1	1	1	1	1	2	2
8·5	2·915	2·917	2·919	2·921	2·922	2·924	2·926	2·927	2·929	2·931	0	0	1	1	1	1	1	2	2
8·6	2·933	2·934	2·936	2·938	2·939	2·941	2·943	2·944	2·946	2·948	0	0	1	1	1	1	1	2	2
8·7	2·950	2·951	2·953	2·955	2·956	2·958	2·960	2·961	2·963	2·965	0	0	1	1	1	1	1	2	2
8·8	2·966	2·968	2·970	2·972	2·973	2·975	2·977	2·978	2·980	2·982	0	0	1	1	1	1	1	2	2
8·9	2·983	2·985	2·987	2·988	2·990	2·992	2·993	2·995	2·997	2·998	0	0	1	1	1	1	1	2	2
9·0	3·000	3·002	3·003	3·005	3·007	3·008	3·010	3·012	3·013	3·015	0	0	0	1	1	1	1	1	1
9·1	3·017	3·018	3·020	3·022	3·023	3·025	3·027	3·028	3·030	3·032	0	0	0	1	1	1	1	1	1
9·2	3·033	3·035	3·036	3·038	3·040	3·041	3·043	3·045	3·046	3·048	0	0	0	1	1	1	1	1	1
9·3	3·050	3·051	3·053	3·055	3·056	3·058	3·059	3·061	3·063	3·064	0	0	0	1	1	1	1	1	1
9·4	3·066	3·068	3·069	3·071	3·072	3·074	3·076	3·077	3·079	3·081	0	0	0	1	1	1	1	1	1
9·5	3·082	3·084	3·085	3·087	3·089	3·090	3·092	3·094	3·095	3·097	0	0	0	1	1	1	1	1	1
9·6	3·098	3·100	3·102	3·103	3·105	3·106	3·108	3·110	3·111	3·113	0	0	0	1	1	1	1	1	1
9·7	3·114	3·116	3·118	3·119	3·121	3·122	3·124	3·126	3·127	3·129	0	0	0	1	1	1	1	1	1
9·8	3·130	3·132	3·134	3·135	3·137	3·138	3·140	3·142	3·143	3·145	0	0	0	1	1	1	1	1	1
9·9	3·146	3·148	3·150	3·151	3·153	3·154	3·156	3·158	3·159	3·161	0	0	0	1	1	1	1	1	1

Table of Square Roots from 10—100

x	·0	·1	·2	·3	·4	·5	·6	·7	·8	·9	1	2	3	4	5	6	7	8	9
10	3·162	3·178	3·194	3·209	3·225	3·240	3·256	3·271	3·286	3·302	2	3	5	6	8	10	11	13	14
11	3·317	3·332	3·347	3·362	3·376	3·391	3·406	3·421	3·435	3·450	1	3	4	6	7	9	10	12	13
12	3·464	3·479	3·493	3·507	3·521	3·536	3·550	3·564	3·578	3·592	1	3	4	6	7	8	10	11	13
13	3·606	3·619	3·633	3·647	3·661	3·674	3·688	3·701	3·715	3·728	1	3	4	5	7	8	10	11	12
14	3·742	3·755	3·768	3·782	3·795	3·808	3·821	3·834	3·847	3·860	1	3	4	5	7	8	9	10	12
15	3·873	3·886	3·899	3·912	3·924	3·937	3·950	3·962	3·975	3·987	1	3	4	5	6	8	9	10	11
16	4·000	4·012	4·025	4·037	4·050	4·062	4·074	4·087	4·099	4·111	1	2	4	5	6	7	9	10	11
17	4·123	4·135	4·147	4·159	4·171	4·183	4·195	4·207	4·219	4·231	1	2	4	5	6	7	8	10	11
18	4·243	4·254	4·266	4·278	4·290	4·301	4·313	4·324	4·336	4·347	1	2	3	5	6	7	8	9	10
19	4·359	4·370	4·382	4·393	4·405	4·416	4·427	4·438	4·450	4·461	1	2	3	5	6	7	8	9	10
20	4·472	4·483	4·494	4·506	4·517	4·528	4·539	4·550	4·561	4·572	1	2	3	4	6	7	8	9	10
21	4·583	4·593	4·604	4·615	4·626	4·637	4·648	4·658	4·669	4·680	1	2	3	4	5	6	8	9	10
22	4·690	4·701	4 712	4·722	4·733	4·743	4·754	4·764	4·775	4·785	1	2	3	4	5	6	7	8	10
23	4·796	4·806	4·817	4·827	4·837	4·848	4·858	4·868	4·879	4·889	1	2	3	4	5	6	7	8	9
24	4·899	4·909	4·919	4·930	4·940	4·950	4·960	4·970	4·980	4·990	1	2	3	4	5	6	7	8	9
25	5·000	5·010	5·020	5·030	5·040	5·050	5·060	5·070	5·079	5·089	1	2	3	4	5	6	7	8	9
26	5·099	5·109	5·119	5·128	5·138	5·148	5·158	5·167	5·177	5·187	1	2	3	4	5	6	7	8	9
27	5·196	5·206	5·215	5·225	5·235	5·244	5·254	5·263	5·273	5·282	1	2	3	4	5	6	7	8	9
28	5·292	5·301	5·310	5·320	5·329	5·339	5·348	5·357	5·367	5·376	1	2	3	4	5	6	7	7	8
29	5·385	5·394	5·404	5·413	5·422	5·431	5·441	5·450	5·459	5·468	1	2	3	4	5	5	6	7	8
30	5·477	5·486	5·495	5·505	5·514	5·523	5·532	5·541	5·550	5·559	1	2	3	4	5	5	6	7	8
31	5·568	5·577	5·586	5·595	5·604	5·612	5·621	5·630	5·639	5·648	1	2	3	4	4	5	6	7	8
32	5·657	5·666	5·675	5·683	5·692	5·701	5·710	5·718	5·727	5·736	1	2	3	4	4	5	6	7	8
33	5·745	5·753	5·762	5·771	5·779	5·788	5·797	5·805	5·814	5·822	1	2	3	3	4	5	6	7	8
34	5·831	5·840	5·848	5·857	5·865	5·874	5·882	5·891	5·899	5·908	1	2	3	3	4	5	6	7	8
35	5·916	5·925	5·933	5·941	5·950	5·958	5·967	5·975	5·983	5·992	1	2	2	3	4	5	6	7	8
36	6·000	6·008	6·017	6·025	6·033	6·042	6·050	6·058	6·066	6·075	1	2	2	3	4	5	6	7	7
37	6·083	6·091	6·099	6·107	6·116	6·124	6·132	6·140	6·148	6·156	1	2	2	3	4	5	6	6	7
38	6·164	6·173	6·181	6·189	6·197	6·205	6·213	6·221	6·229	6·237	1	2	2	3	4	5	6	6	7
39	6·245	6·253	6·261	6·269	6·277	6·285	6·293	6·301	6·309	6·317	1	2	2	3	4	5	6	6	7
40	6·325	6·332	6·340	6·348	6·356	6·364	6·372	6·380	6·387	6·395	1	2	2	3	4	5	6	6	7
41	6·403	6·411	6·419	6·427	6·434	6·442	6·450	6·458	6·465	6·473	1	2	2	3	4	5	5	6	7
42	6·481	6·488	6·496	6·504	6·512	6·519	6·527	6·535	6·542	6·550	1	2	2	3	4	5	5	6	7
43	6·557	6·565	6·573	6·580	6·588	6·595	6·603	6·611	6·618	6·626	1	2	2	3	4	5	5	6	7
44	6·633	6·641	6·648	6·656	6·663	6·671	6·678	6·686	6·693	6·701	1	2	2	3	4	4	5	6	7
45	6·708	6·716	6·723	6·731	6·738	6·745	6·753	6·760	6·768	6·775	1	1	2	3	4	4	5	6	7
46	6·782	6·790	6·797	6·804	6·812	6·819	6·826	6·834	6·841	6·848	1	1	2	3	4	4	5	6	7
47	6·856	6·863	6·870	6·877	6·885	6·892	6·899	6·907	6·914	6·921	1	1	2	3	4	4	5	6	6
48	6·928	6·935	6·943	6·950	6·957	6·964	6·971	6·979	6·986	6·993	1	1	2	3	4	4	5	6	6
49	7·000	7·007	7·014	7·021	7·029	7·036	7·043	7·050	7·057	7·064	1	1	2	3	4	4	5	6	6
50	7·071	7·078	7·085	7·092	7·099	7·106	7·113	7·120	7·127	7·134	1	1	2	3	4	4	5	6	6
51	7·141	7·148	7·155	7·162	7·169	7·176	7·183	7·190	7·197	7·204	1	1	2	3	4	4	5	6	6
52	7·211	7·218	7·225	7·232	7·239	7·246	7·253	7·259	7·266	7·273	1	1	2	3	3	4	5	6	6
53	7·280	7·287	7·294	7·301	7·308	7·314	7·321	7·328	7·335	7·342	1	1	2	3	3	4	5	5	6
54	7·348	7·355	7·362	7·369	7·376	7·382	7·389	7·396	7·403	7·409	1	1	2	3	3	4	5	5	6

Table of Square Roots from 10—100

x	·0	·1	·2	·3	·4	·5	·6	·7	·8	·9	1	2	3	4	5	6	7	8	9
55	7·416	7·423	7·430	7·436	7·443	7·450	7·457	7·463	7·470	7·477	1	1	2	3	3	4	5	5	6
56	7·483	7·490	7·497	7·503	7·510	7·517	7·523	7·530	7·537	7·543	1	1	2	3	3	4	5	5	6
57	7·550	7·556	7·563	7·570	7·576	7·583	7·589	7·596	7·603	7·609	1	1	2	3	3	4	5	5	6
58	7·616	7·622	7·629	7·635	7·642	7·649	7·655	7·662	7·668	7·675	1	1	2	3	3	4	5	5	6
59	7·681	7·688	7·694	7·701	7·707	7·714	7·720	7·727	7·733	7·740	1	1	2	3	3	4	5	5	6
60	7·746	7·752	7·759	7·765	7·772	7·778	7·785	7·791	7·797	7·804	1	1	2	3	3	4	4	5	6
61	7·810	7·817	7·823	7·829	7·836	7·842	7·849	7·855	7·861	7·868	1	1	2	2	3	4	4	5	5
62	7·874	7·880	7·887	7·893	7·899	7·906	7·912	7·918	7·925	7·931	1	1	2	2	3	4	4	5	5
63	7·937	7·944	7·950	7·956	7·962	7·969	7·975	7·981	7·987	7·994	1	1	2	2	3	4	4	5	5
64	8·000	8·006	8·012	8·019	8·025	8·031	8·037	8·044	8·050	8·056	1	1	2	2	3	4	4	5	5
65	8·062	8·068	8·075	8·081	8·087	8·093	8·099	8·106	8·112	8·118	1	1	2	2	3	4	4	5	5
66	8·124	8·130	8·136	8·142	8·149	8·155	8·161	8·167	8·173	8·179	1	1	2	2	3	4	4	5	5
67	8·185	8·191	8·198	8·204	8·210	8·216	8·222	8·228	8·234	8 240	1	1	2	2	3	4	4	5	5
68	8·246	8·252	8·258	8·264	8·270	8·276	8·283	8·289	8·295	8·301	1	1	2	2	3	4	4	5	5
69	8·307	8·313	8·319	8·325	8·331	8·337	8·343	8·349	8·355	8·361	1	1	2	2	3	4	4	5	5
70	8·367	8·373	8·379	8·385	8·390	8·396	8·402	8·408	8·414	8·420	1	1	2	2	3	4	4	5	5
71	8·426	6·432	8·438	8·444	8·450	8·456	8·462	8·468	8·473	8·479	1	1	2	2	3	3	4	5	5
72	8·485	8·491	8·497	8·503	8·509	8·515	8·521	8·526	8·532	8·538	1	1	2	2	3	3	4	5	5
73	8·544	8·550	8·556	8·562	8·567	8·573	8·579	8·585	8·591	8 597	1	1	2	2	3	3	4	5	5
74	8·602	8·608	8·614	8·620	8·626	8·631	8·637	8·643	8·649	8·654	1	1	2	2	3	3	4	5	5
75	8·660	8·666	8·672	8·678	8·683	8·689	8·695	8·701	8·706	8·712	1	1	2	2	3	3	4	4	5
76	8·718	8·724	8·729	8·735	8·741	8·746	8·752	8·758	8·764	8·769	1	1	2	2	3	3	4	4	5
77	8·775	8·781	8·786	8·792	8·798	8·803	8·809	8·815	8·820	8·826	1	1	2	2	3	3	4	4	5
78	8·832	8·837	8·843	8·849	8·854	8·860	8·866	8·871	8·877	8·883	1	1	2	2	3	3	4	4	5
79	8·888	8·894	8·899	8·905	8·911	8·916	8·922	8·927	8·933	8·939	1	1	2	2	3	3	4	4	5
80	8·944	8·950	8·955	8·961	8·967	8·972	8·978	8·983	8·989	8·994	1	1	2	2	3	3	4	4	5
81	9·000	9·006	9·011	9·017	9·022	9·028	9·033	9·039	9·044	9·050	1	1	2	2	3	3	4	4	5
82	9·055	9·061	9·066	9·072	9·077	9·083	9·088	9·094	9·099	9·105	1	1	2	2	3	3	4	4	5
83	9·110	9·116	9·121	9·127	9·132	9·138	9·143	9·149	9·154	9·160	1	1	2	2	3	3	4	4	5
84	9·165	9·171	9·176	9·182	9·187	9·192	9·198	9·203	9·209	9·214	1	1	2	2	3	3	4	4	5
85	9·220	9·225	9·230	9·236	9·241	9·247	9·252	9·257	9·263	9·268	1	1	2	2	3	3	4	4	5
86	9·274	9·279	9·284	9·290	9·295	9·301	9·306	9·311	9·317	9·322	1	1	2	2	3	3	4	4	5
87	9·327	9·333	9·338	9·343	9·349	9·354	9·359	9·365	9·370	9·375	1	1	2	2	3	3	4	4	5
88	9·381	9·386	9·391	9·397	9·402	9·407	9·413	9·418	9·423	9·429	1	1	2	2	3	3	4	4	5
89	9·434	9·439	9·445	9·450	9·455	9·460	9·466	9·471	9·476	9·482	1	1	2	2	3	3	4	4	5
90	9·487	9·492	9·497	9·503	9·508	9·513	9·518	9·524	9·529	9·534	1	1	2	2	3	3	4	4	5
91	9·539	9·545	9·550	9·555	9·560	9·566	9·571	9·576	9·581	9·586	1	1	2	2	3	3	4	4	5
92	9·592	9·597	9·602	9·607	9·612	9·618	9·623	9·628	9·633	9·638	1	1	2	2	3	3	4	4	5
93	9·644	9·649	9·654	9·659	9·664	9·670	9·675	9·680	9·685	9·690	1	1	2	2	3	3	4	4	5
94	9·695	9·701	9·706	9·711	9·716	9·721	9·726	9·731	9·737	9·742	1	1	2	2	3	3	4	4	5
95	9·747	9·752	9·757	9·762	9·767	9·772	9·778	9·783	9·788	9·793	1	1	2	2	3	3	4	4	5
96	9·798	9·803	9·808	9·813	9·818	9·823	9·829	9·834	9·839	9·844	1	1	2	2	3	3	4	4	5
97	9·849	9·854	9·859	9·864	9·869	9·874	9·879	9·884	9·889	9·894	1	1	2	2	3	3	4	4	5
98	9·899	9·905	9·910	9·915	9·920	9·925	9·930	9·935	9·940	9·945	1	1	2	2	3	3	4	4	5
99	9·950	9·955	9·960	9·965	9·970	9·975	9·980	9·985	9·990	9·995	0	1	1	2	2	3	4	4	4

Table of Reciprocals of Numbers from 1—10

Numbers in difference columns to be *subtracted*, not added

	0	1	2	3	4	5	6	7	8	9	1	2	3	4	5	6	7	8	9
1.0	1.0000	0.9901	0.9804	0.9709	0.9615	0.9524	0.9434	0.9346	0.9259	0.9174									
1.1	0.9091	0.9009	0.8929	0.8850	0.8772	0.8696	0.8621	0.8547	0.8475	0.8403									
1.2	0.8333	0.8264	0.8197	0.8130	0.8065	0.8000	0.7937	0.7874	0.7813	0.7752									
1.3	0.7692	0.7634	0.7576	0.7519	0.7463	0.7407	0.7353	0.7299	0.7246	0.7194									
1.4	0.7143	0.7092	0.7042	0.6993	0.6944	0.6897	0.6849	0.6803	0.6757	0.6711									
1.5	0.6667	0.6623	0.6579	0.6536	0.6494	0.6452	0.6410	0.6369	0.6329	0.6289	4	8	12	17	21	25	29	33	37
1.6	0.6250	0.6211	0.6173	0.6135	0.6098	0.6061	0.6024	0.5988	0.5952	0.5917	4	7	11	15	18	22	26	29	33
1.7	0.5882	0.5848	0.5814	0.5780	0.5747	0.5714	0.5682	0.5650	0.5618	0.5587	3	7	10	13	16	20	23	26	29
1.8	0.5556	0.5525	0.5495	0.5464	0.5435	0.5405	0.5376	0.5348	0.5319	0.5291	3	6	9	12	15	18	20	23	26
1.9	0.5263	0.5236	0.5208	0.5181	0.5155	0.5128	0.5102	0.5076	0.5051	0.5025	3	5	8	11	13	16	18	21	24
2.0	0.5000	0.4975	0.4950	0.4926	0.4902	0.4878	0.4854	0.4831	0.4808	0.4785	2	5	7	10	12	14	17	19	21
2.1	0.4762	0.4739	0.4717	0.4695	0.4673	0.4651	0.4630	0.4608	0.4587	0.4566	2	4	6	9	11	13	15	17	19
2.2	0.4545	0.4525	0.4505	0.4484	0.4464	0.4444	0.4425	0.4405	0.4386	0.4367	2	4	6	8	10	12	14	16	18
2.3	0.4348	0.4329	0.4310	0.4292	0.4274	0.4255	0.4237	0.4219	0.4202	0.4184	2	4	5	7	9	11	13	14	16
2.4	0.4167	0.4149	0.4132	0.4115	0.4098	0.4082	0.4065	0.4049	0.4032	0.4016	2	3	5	7	8	10	12	13	15
2.5	0.4000	0.3984	0.3968	0.3953	0.3937	0.3922	0.3906	0.3891	0.3876	0.3861	2	3	5	6	8	9	11	12	14
2.6	0.3846	0.3831	0.3817	0.3802	0.3788	0.3774	0.3759	0.3745	0.3731	0.3717	1	3	4	6	7	9	10	11	13
2.7	0.3704	0.3690	0.3676	0.3663	0.3650	0.3636	0.3623	0.3610	0.3597	0.3584	1	3	4	5	7	8	9	11	12
2.8	0.3571	0.3559	0.3546	0.3534	0.3521	0.3509	0.3497	0.3484	0.3472	0.3460	1	2	4	5	6	7	9	10	11
2.9	0.3448	0.3436	0.3425	0.3413	0.3401	0.3390	0.3378	0.3367	0.3356	0.3344	1	2	3	5	6	7	8	9	10
3.0	0.3333	0.3322	0.3311	0.3300	0.3289	0.3279	0.3268	0.3257	0.3247	0.3236	1	2	3	4	5	6	8	9	10
3.1	0.3226	0.3215	0.3205	0.3195	0.3185	0.3175	0.3165	0.3155	0.3145	0.3135	1	2	3	4	5	6	7	8	9
3.2	0.3125	0.3115	0.3106	0.3096	0.3086	0.3077	0.3067	0.3058	0.3049	0.3040	1	2	3	4	5	6	7	8	9
3.3	0.3030	0.3021	0.3012	0.3003	0.2994	0.2985	0.2976	0.2967	0.2959	0.2950	1	2	3	4	4	5	6	7	8
3.4	0.2941	0.2933	0.2924	0.2915	0.2907	0.2899	0.2890	0.2882	0.2874	0.2865	1	2	3	3	4	5	6	7	8
3.5	0.2857	0.2849	0.2841	0.2833	0.2825	0.2817	0.2809	0.2801	0.2793	0.2786	1	2	2	3	4	5	6	6	7
3.6	0.2778	0.2770	0.2762	0.2755	0.2747	0.2740	0.2732	0.2725	0.2717	0.2710	1	2	2	3	4	5	5	6	7
3.7	0.2703	0.2695	0.2688	0.2681	0.2674	0.2667	0.2660	0.2653	0.2646	0.2639	1	1	2	3	4	4	5	6	6
3.8	0.2632	0.2625	0.2618	0.2611	0.2604	0.2597	0.2591	0.2584	0.2577	0.2571	1	1	2	3	3	4	5	5	6
3.9	0.2564	0.2558	0.2551	0.2545	0.2538	0.2532	0.2525	0.2519	0.2513	0.2506	1	1	2	3	3	4	4	5	6
4.0	0.2500	0.2494	0.2488	0.2481	0.2475	0.2469	0.2463	0.2457	0.2451	0.2445	1	1	2	2	3	4	4	5	5
4.1	0.2439	0.2433	0.2427	0.2421	0.2415	0.2410	0.2404	0.2398	0.2392	0.2387	1	1	2	2	3	3	4	5	5
4.2	0.2381	0.2375	0.2370	0.2364	0.2358	0.2353	0.2347	0.2342	0.2336	0.2331	1	1	2	2	3	3	4	4	5
4.3	0.2326	0.2320	0.2315	0.2309	0.2304	0.2299	0.2294	0.2288	0.2283	0.2278	1	1	2	2	3	3	4	4	5
4.4	0.2273	0.2268	0.2262	0.2257	0.2252	0.2247	0.2242	0.2237	0.2232	0.2227	1	1	2	2	3	3	4	4	5
4.5	0.2222	0.2217	0.2212	0.2208	0.2203	0.2198	0.2193	0.2188	0.2183	0.2179	0	1	1	2	2	3	3	4	4
4.6	0.2174	0.2169	0.2165	0.2160	0.2155	0.2151	0.2146	0.2141	0.2137	0.2132	0	1	1	2	2	3	3	4	4
4.7	0.2128	0.2123	0.2119	0.2114	0.2110	0.2105	0.2101	0.2096	0.2092	0.2088	0	1	1	2	2	3	3	4	4
4.8	0.2083	0.2079	0.2075	0.2070	0.2066	0.2062	0.2058	0.2053	0.2049	0.2045	0	1	1	2	2	3	3	3	4
4.9	0.2041	0.2037	0.2033	0.2028	0.2024	0.2020	0.2016	0.2012	0.2008	0.2004	0	1	1	2	2	2	3	3	4
5.0	0.2000	0.1996	0.1992	0.1988	0.1984	0.1980	0.1976	0.1972	0.1969	0.1965	0	1	1	2	2	2	3	3	4
5.1	0.1961	0.1957	0.1953	0.1949	0.1946	0.1942	0.1938	0.1934	0.1931	0.1927	0	1	1	2	2	2	3	3	3
5.2	0.1923	0.1919	0.1916	0.1912	0.1908	0.1905	0.1901	0.1898	0.1894	0.1890	0	1	1	1	2	2	3	3	3
5.3	0.1887	0.1883	0.1880	0.1876	0.1873	0.1869	0.1866	0.1862	0.1859	0.1855	0	1	1	1	2	2	2	3	3
5.4	0.1852	0.1848	0.1845	0.1842	0.1838	0.1835	0.1832	0.1828	0.1825	0.1821	0	1	1	1	2	2	2	3	3

Table of Reciprocals of Numbers from 1—10

Numbers in difference columns to be *subtracted*, not added

	0	1	2	3	4	5	6	7	8	9	1 2 3	4 5 6	7 8 9
5.5	0.1818	0.1815	0.1812	0.1808	0.1805	0.1802	0.1799	0.1795	0.1792	0.1789	0 1 1	1 2 2	2 3 3
5.6	0.1786	0.1783	0.1779	0.1776	0.1773	0.1770	0.1767	0.1764	0.1761	0.1757	0 1 1	1 2 2	2 3 3
5.7	0.1754	0.1751	0.1748	0.1745	0.1742	0.1739	0.1736	0.1733	0.1730	0.1727	0 1 1	1 2 2	2 2 3
5.8	0.1724	0.1721	0.1718	0.1715	0.1712	0.1709	0.1706	0.1704	0.1701	0.1698	0 1 1	1 1 2	2 2 3
5.9	0.1695	0.1692	0.1689	0.1686	0.1684	0.1681	0.1678	0.1675	0.1672	0.1669	0 1 1	1 1 2	2 2 3
6.0	0.1667	0.1664	0.1661	0.1658	0.1656	0.1653	0.1650	0.1647	0.1645	0.1642	0 1 1	1 1 2	2 2 2
6.1	0.1639	0.1637	0.1634	0.1631	0.1629	0.1626	0.1623	0.1621	0.1618	0.1616	0 1 1	1 1 2	2 2 2
6.2	0.1613	0.1610	0.1608	0.1605	0.1603	0.1600	0.1597	0.1595	0.1592	0.1590	0 1 1	1 1 2	2 2 2
6.3	0.1587	0.1585	0.1582	0.1580	0.1577	0.1575	0.1572	0.1570	0.1567	0.1565	0 0 1	1 1 1	2 2 2
6.4	0.1563	0.1560	0.1558	0.1555	0.1553	0.1550	0.1548	0.1546	0.1543	0.1541	0 0 1	1 1 1	2 2 2
6.5	0.1538	0.1536	0.1534	0.1531	0.1529	0.1527	0.1524	0.1522	0.1520	0.1517	0 0 1	1 1 1	2 2 2
6.6	0.1515	0.1513	0.1511	0.1508	0.1506	0.1504	0.1502	0.1499	0.1497	0.1495	0 0 1	1 1 1	2 2 2
6.7	0.1493	0.1490	0.1488	0.1486	0.1484	0.1481	0.1479	0.1477	0.1475	0.1473	0 0 1	1 1 1	2 2 2
6.8	0.1471	0.1468	0.1466	0.1464	0.1462	0.1460	0.1458	0.1456	0.1453	0.1451	0 0 1	1 1 1	1 2 2
6.9	0.1449	0.1447	0.1445	0.1443	0.1441	0.1439	0.1437	0.1435	0.1433	0.1431	0 0 1	1 1 1	1 2 2
7.0	0.1429	0.1427	0.1425	0.1422	0.1420	0.1418	0.1416	0.1414	0.1412	0.1410	0 0 1	1 1 1	1 2 2
7.1	0.1408	0.1406	0.1404	0.1403	0.1401	0.1399	0.1397	0.1395	0.1393	0.1391	0 0 1	1 1 1	1 2 2
7.2	0.1389	0.1387	0.1385	0.1383	0.1381	0.1379	0.1377	0.1376	0.1374	0.1372	0 0 1	1 1 1	1 2 2
7.3	0.1370	0.1368	0.1366	0.1364	0.1362	0.1361	0.1359	0.1357	0.1355	0.1353	0 0 1	1 1 1	1 1 2
7.4	0.1351	0.1350	0.1348	0.1346	0.1344	0.1342	0.1340	0.1339	0.1337	0.1335	0 0 1	1 1 1	1 1 2
7.5	0.1333	0.1332	0.1330	0.1328	0.1326	0.1325	0.1323	0.1321	0.1319	0.1318	0 0 1	1 1 1	1 1 2
7.6	0.1316	0.1314	0.1312	0.1311	0.1309	0.1307	0.1305	0.1304	0.1302	0.1300	0 0 1	1 1 1	1 1 2
7.7	0.1299	0.1297	0.1295	0.1294	0.1292	0.1290	0.1289	0.1287	0.1285	0.1284	0 0 0	1 1 1	1 1 1
7.8	0.1282	0.1280	0.1279	0.1277	0.1276	0.1274	0.1272	0.1271	0.1269	0.1267	0 0 0	1 1 1	1 1 1
7.9	0.1266	0.1264	0.1263	0.1261	0.1259	0.1258	0.1256	0.1255	0.1253	0.1252	0 0 0	1 1 1	1 1 1
8.0	0.1250	0.1248	0.1247	0.1245	0.1244	0.1242	0.1241	0.1239	0.1238	0.1236	0 0 0	1 1 1	1 1 1
8.1	0.1235	0.1233	0.1232	0.1230	0.1229	0.1227	0.1225	0.1224	0.1222	0.1221	0 0 0	1 1 1	1 1 1
8.2	0.1220	0.1218	0.1217	0.1215	0.1214	0.1212	0.1211	0.1209	0.1208	0.1206	0 0 0	1 1 1	1 1 1
8.3	0.1205	0.1203	0.1202	0.1200	0.1199	0.1198	0.1196	0.1195	0.1193	0.1192	0 0 0	1 1 1	1 1 1
8.4	0.1190	0.1189	0.1188	0.1186	0.1185	0.1183	0.1182	0.1181	0.1179	0.1178	0 0 0	1 1 1	1 1 1
8.5	0.1176	0.1175	0.1174	0.1172	0.1171	0.1170	0.1168	0.1167	0.1166	0.1164	0 0 0	1 1 1	1 1 1
8.6	0.1163	0.1161	0.1160	0.1159	0.1157	0.1156	0.1155	0.1153	0.1152	0.1151	0 0 0	1 1 1	1 1 1
8.7	0.1149	0.1148	0.1147	0.1145	0.1144	0.1143	0.1142	0.1140	0.1139	0.1138	0 0 0	1 1 1	1 1 1
8.8	0.1136	0.1135	0.1134	0.1133	0.1131	0.1130	0.1129	0.1127	0.1126	0.1125	0 0 0	1 1 1	1 1 1
8.9	0.1124	0.1122	0.1121	0.1120	0.1119	0.1117	0.1116	0.1115	0.1114	0.1112	0 0 0	0 1 1	1 1 1
9.0	0.1111	0.1110	0.1109	0.1107	0.1106	0.1105	0.1104	0.1103	0.1101	0.1100	0 0 0	0 1 1	1 1 1
9.1	0.1099	0.1098	0.1096	0.1095	0.1094	0.1093	0.1092	0.1091	0.1089	0.1088	0 0 0	0 1 1	1 1 1
9.2	0.1087	0.1086	0.1085	0.1083	0.1082	0.1081	0.1080	0.1079	0.1078	0.1076	0 0 0	0 1 1	1 1 1
9.3	0.1075	0.1074	0.1073	0.1072	0.1071	0.1070	0.1068	0.1067	0.1066	0.1065	0 0 0	0 1 1	1 1 1
9.4	0.1064	0.1063	0.1062	0.1060	0.1059	0.1058	0.1057	0.1056	0.1055	0.1054	0 0 0	0 1 1	1 1 1
9.5	0.1053	0.1052	0.1050	0.1049	0.1048	0.1047	0.1046	0.1045	0.1044	0.1043	0 0 0	0 1 1	1 1 1
9.6	0.1042	0.1041	0.1040	0.1038	0.1037	0.1036	0.1035	0.1034	0.1033	0.1032	0 0 0	0 1 1	1 1 1
9.7	0.1031	0.1030	0.1029	0.1028	0.1027	0.1026	0.1025	0.1024	0.1022	0.1021	0 0 0	0 1 1	1 1 1
9.8	0.1020	0.1019	0.1018	0.1017	0.1016	0.1015	0.1014	0.1013	0.1012	0.1011	0 0 0	0 1 1	1 1 1
9.9	0.1010	0.1009	0.1008	0.1007	0.1006	0.1005	0.1004	0.1003	0.1002	0.1001	0 0 0	0 1 1	1 1 1

Table of Simple Interest

Appreciation of £1 for periods from 1 year to 25 years

Year	5%	6%	7%	8%	9%	10%	11%	12%	13%	14%
1	1·050	1·060	1·070	1·080	1·090	1·100	1·110	1·120	1·130	1·140
2	1·100	1·120	1·140	1·160	1·180	1·200	1·220	1·240	1·260	1·280
3	1·150	1·180	1·210	1·240	1·270	1·300	1·330	1·360	1·390	1·420
4	1·200	1·240	1·280	1·320	1·360	1·400	1·440	1·480	1·520	1·560
5	1·250	1·300	1·350	1·400	1·450	1·500	1·550	1·600	1·650	1·700
6	1·300	1·360	1·420	1·480	1·540	1·600	1·660	1·720	1·780	1·840
7	1·350	1·420	1·490	1·560	1·630	1·700	1·770	1·840	1·910	1·980
8	1·400	1·480	1·560	1·640	1·720	1·800	1·880	1·960	2·040	2·120
9	1·450	1·540	1·630	1·720	1·810	1·900	1·990	2·080	2·170	2·260
10	1·500	1·600	1·700	1·800	1·900	2·000	2·100	2·200	2·300	2·400
11	1·550	1·660	1·770	1·880	1·990	2·100	2·210	2·320	2·430	2·540
12	1·600	1·720	1·840	1·960	2·080	2·200	2·320	2·440	2·560	2·680
13	1·650	1·780	1·910	2·040	2·170	2·300	2·430	2·560	2·690	2·820
14	1·700	1·840	1·980	2·120	2·260	2·400	2·540	2·680	2·820	2·960
15	1·750	1·900	2·050	2·200	2·350	2·500	2·650	2·800	2·950	3·100
16	1·800	1·960	2·120	2·280	2·440	2·600	2·760	2·920	3·080	3·240
17	1·850	2·020	2·190	2·360	2·530	2·700	2·870	3·040	3·210	3·380
18	1·900	2·080	2·260	2·440	2·620	2·800	2·980	3·160	3·340	3·520
19	1·950	2·140	2·330	2·520	2·710	2·900	3·090	3·280	3·470	3·660
20	2·000	2·200	2·400	2·600	2·800	3·000	3·200	3·400	3·600	3·800
21	2·050	2·260	2·470	2·680	2·890	3·100	3·310	3·520	3·730	3·940
22	2·100	2·320	2·540	2·760	2·980	3·200	3·420	3·640	3·860	4·080
23	2·150	2·380	2·610	2·840	3·070	3·300	3·530	3·760	3·990	4·220
24	2·200	2·440	2·680	2·920	3·160	3·400	3·640	3·880	4·120	4·360
25	2·250	2·500	2·750	3·000	3·250	3·500	3·750	4·000	4·250	4·500

Table of Compound Interest

Appreciation of £1 for periods from 1 year to 25 years

Year	5%	6%	7%	8%	9%	10%	11%	12%	13%	14%
1	1·050	1·060	1·070	1·080	1·090	1·100	1·110	1·120	1·130	1·140
2	1·103	1·124	1·145	1·166	1·188	1·210	1·232	1·254	1·277	1·300
3	1·158	1·191	1·225	1·260	1·295	1·331	1·368	1·405	1·443	1·482
4	1·216	1·262	1·311	1·360	1·412	1·464	1·518	1·574	1·603	1·689
5	1·276	1·338	1·403	1·469	1·539	1·611	1·685	1·762	1·842	1·925
6	1·340	1·419	1·501	1·587	1·677	1·772	1·870	1·974	2·082	2·195
7	1·407	1·504	1·606	1·714	1·828	1·949	2·076	2·211	2·353	2·502
8	1·477	1·594	1·718	1·851	1·993	2·144	2·304	2·476	2·658	2·853
9	1·551	1·689	1·838	1·999	2·172	2·358	2·558	2·773	3·004	3·252
10	1·629	1·791	1·967	2·159	2·367	2·594	2·839	3·106	3·395	3·707
11	1·710	1·898	2·105	2·332	2·580	2·853	3·152	3·479	3·836	4·226
12	1·796	2·012	2·252	2·518	2·813	3·138	3·498	3·896	4·335	4·818
13	1·886	2·133	2·410	2·720	3·066	3·452	3·883	4·363	4·898	5·492
14	1·980	2·261	2·579	2·937	3·342	3·797	4·310	4·887	5·535	6·261
15	2·079	2·397	2·759	3·172	3·642	4·177	4·785	5·474	6·254	7·130
16	2·183	2·540	2·952	3·426	3·970	4·595	5·311	6·130	7·067	8·137
17	2·292	2·693	3·159	3·700	4·328	5·054	5·895	6·866	7·986	9·276
18	2·407	2·854	3·380	3·996	4·717	5·560	6·544	7·690	9·024	10·575
19	2·527	3·026	3·617	4·316	5·142	6·116	7·263	8·613	10·197	12·056
20	2·653	3·207	3·870	4·661	5·604	6·727	8·062	9·646	11·523	13·743
21	2·786	3·400	4·141	5·034	6·109	7·400	8·949	10·804	13·021	15·668
22	2·925	3·604	4·430	5·437	6·659	8·140	9·934	12·100	14·714	17·861
23	3·072	3·820	4·741	5·871	7·258	8·954	11·026	13·552	16·627	20·362
24	3·225	4·049	5·072	6·341	7·911	9·850	12·239	15·179	18·788	23·212
25	3·386	4·292	5·427	6·848	8·623	10·835	13·585	17·000	21·231	26·462

Answers

ANSWERS TO CHAPTER 1

Exercise 1
1) 457 2) 9536 3) 7777 4) 3008
5) 705 6) 30 028 7) 5090 8) 4904
9) 125 906 10) 3 800 007
11) 95 827 000 12) 300 000 009
13) two hundred and twenty five
14) eight thousand three hundred and twenty one
15) three thousand and seventeen
16) three thousand nine hundred and sixty
17) one thousand eight hundred and seven
18) twenty thousand and four
19) seventeen thousand
20) one hundred and ninety eight thousand, three hundred and seventy six
21) two hundred thousand and five
22) seven million, three hundred and sixty five thousand, two hundred and thirty one
23) twenty seven million, three hundred and nine

Exercise 2
1) 351 2) 4570 3) 58 190
4) 8 579 649 5) 126 331

Exercise 3
1) 32 2) 335 3) 14 4) 1558
5) 9226

Exercise 4
1) 11 2) 32 3) 36 4) 18

Exercise 5
1) 6 2) 35 3) 54 4) 32
5) 63 6) 15 7) 81 8) 42

Exercise 6
1) 928 2) 9334 3) 1 010 829
4) 4 483 887 5) 1 022 656

Exercise 7
1) 246 2) 56 3) 433 remainder 3
4) 1842 remainder 1 5) 624 remainder 5

Exercise 8
1) 546 remainder 4 2) 1264
3) 309 remainder 1 4) 909 remainder 2
5) 903 remainder 1 6) 1701
7) 59 817 8) 5923

Exercise 9
1) 13 2) 10 3) 57 4) 7
5) 35 6) 15 7) 45 8) 74
9) 13 10) 20

Mental test 1
1) 28 2) 42 3) 350 4) 46
5) 11 6) 9 7) 62 8) 5
9) 25 10) 65 11) 84 12) 133
13) 819 14) 21 15) 103 16) 2799
17) 217 18) 143 19) 108 20) 23

Self-test 1
1) b 2) a 3) e 4) a
5)(a) 22 676 (b) 22 527 (c) 15 891
6)(a) b (b) c (c) a 7)(a) 1105
(b) 1316 (c) 6116 (d) 261 (e) 114
(f) 903 8)(a) 114 786
(b) 7 625 868 (c) 37 883 967
(d) 23 114 250 (e) 56 770 371
(f) 57 566 124 9)(a) 11 587
(b) 539 (c) 48 (d) 18 10)(a) 17
(b) 12 (c) 6 (d) 72 11)(a) 4
(b) 5 (c) 9 (d) 4 (e) 11
(f) 4, 8, 16 12)(a) b (b) a (c) b
(d) c (e) a 13) true 14) false
15) false 16) true 17) false 18) true
19) false 20) true

ANSWERS TO CHAPTER 2

Exercise 10
1) $\frac{21}{28}$ 2) $\frac{12}{20}$ 3) $\frac{25}{30}$ 4) $\frac{7}{63}$
5) $\frac{8}{12}$ 6) $\frac{4}{24}$ 7) $\frac{24}{64}$ 8) $\frac{25}{35}$

Exercise 11
1) $\frac{1}{2}$ 2) $\frac{3}{5}$ 3) $\frac{1}{8}$ 4) $\frac{3}{5}$
5) $\frac{7}{8}$ 6) $\frac{3}{4}$ 7) $\frac{5}{7}$ 8) $\frac{18}{35}$
9) $\frac{2}{3}$ 10) $\frac{2}{3}$

Exercise 12
1) $3\frac{1}{2}$ 2) 2 3) $2\frac{1}{5}$ 4) $1\frac{1}{11}$
5) $2\frac{5}{8}$ 6) $\frac{19}{8}$ 7) $\frac{51}{10}$ 8) $\frac{26}{3}$
9) $\frac{127}{20}$ 10) $\frac{31}{7}$

Exercise 13

1) 24 2) 60 3) 12 4) 24
5) 40 6) 100 7) 160 8) 120
9) 420 10) 5040

Exercise 14

1) $\frac{1}{2}, \frac{7}{12}, \frac{2}{3}$ and $\frac{5}{6}$ 2) $\frac{3}{4}, \frac{6}{7}, \frac{7}{8}$ and $\frac{9}{10}$
3) $\frac{11}{20}, \frac{3}{5}, \frac{7}{10}$ and $\frac{13}{16}$ 4) $\frac{3}{5}, \frac{5}{8}, \frac{13}{20}$ and $\frac{3}{4}$
5) $\frac{9}{14}, \frac{11}{16}, \frac{7}{10}$ and $\frac{3}{4}$ 6) $\frac{3}{8}, \frac{2}{5}, \frac{5}{9}$ and $\frac{4}{7}$

Exercise 15

1) $\frac{5}{6}$ 2) $\frac{13}{10} = 1\frac{3}{10}$ 3) $1\frac{1}{8}$
4) $\frac{11}{20}$ 5) $2\frac{1}{8}$ 6) $1\frac{47}{120}$ 7) $4\frac{15}{16}$
8) $14\frac{4}{15}$ 9) $13\frac{23}{56}$ 10) $10\frac{2}{3}$ 11) $11\frac{5}{16}$
12) $10\frac{13}{15}$

Exercise 16

1) $\frac{1}{6}$ 2) $\frac{2}{15}$ 3) $\frac{1}{6}$ 4) $\frac{1}{2}$
5) $\frac{1}{24}$ 6) $\frac{7}{8}$ 7) $2\frac{2}{7}$ 8) $1\frac{1}{5}$
9) $2\frac{19}{40}$ 10) $\frac{51}{160}$ 11) $\frac{41}{80}$

Exercise 17

1) $1\frac{3}{8}$ 2) $\frac{7}{20}$ 3) $6\frac{7}{8}$ 4) $\frac{2}{3}$
5) $8\frac{13}{80}$ 6) $12\frac{9}{40}$ 7) $2\frac{21}{80}$ 8) $8\frac{23}{32}$
9) $3\frac{7}{8}$ 10) $3\frac{31}{100}$

Exercise 18

1) $\frac{8}{15}$ 2) $\frac{15}{28}$ 3) $\frac{10}{27}$ 4) $1\frac{19}{36}$
5) $4\frac{9}{10}$ 6) $6\frac{2}{3}$ 7) $1\frac{32}{45}$ 8) $2\frac{53}{56}$

Exercise 19

1) $1\frac{1}{3}$ 2) 4 3) $\frac{7}{16}$ 4) $1\frac{1}{2}$
5) $\frac{1}{24}$ 6) 4 7) $6\frac{3}{4}$ 8) $8\frac{1}{4}$
9) 12 10) 100 11) 3 12) 2

Exercise 20

1) $\frac{3}{5}$ 2) 8 3) $1\frac{1}{3}$ 4) $1\frac{1}{2}$
5) $\frac{2}{3}$ 6) $\frac{25}{26}$ 7) $1\frac{1}{5}$ 8) $3\frac{5}{6}$

Exercise 21

1) $3\frac{13}{14}$ 2) 5 3) $2\frac{1}{2}$ 4) $\frac{5}{6}$
5) $\frac{2}{3}$ 6) $2\frac{1}{2}$ 7) $1\frac{2}{5}$ 8) $\frac{2}{3}$
9) $\frac{1}{6}$ 10) $\frac{3}{25}$

Mental test 2

1) $\frac{5}{8}$ 2) $\frac{11}{20}$ 3) $\frac{3}{10}$ 4) $\frac{7}{8}$
5) 1 6) $\frac{7}{12}$ 7) $\frac{1}{10}$ 8) $\frac{2}{7}$
9) $\frac{3}{8}$ 10) 8 11) 12 12) $\frac{1}{8}$
13) $\frac{1}{3}$ 14) $\frac{1}{2}$ 15) $\frac{5}{6}$

Self-test 2

1) b 2) a and e 3) c 4) a
5) d 6) a 7) c and d 8) e
9) b 10) d 11) b 12) c
13) c 14) b, c 15) b 16) true
17) false 18) true 19) true 20) true
21) true 22) true 23) true 24) true
25) false

ANSWERS TO CHAPTER 3

Exercise 22

1) 0·7 2) 0·37 3) 0·589 4) 0·009
5) 0·03 6) 0·017 7) 8·06 8) 24·0209
9) 50·008 10) $\frac{2}{10}$ 11) $4\frac{6}{10}$ 12) $3\frac{58}{100}$
13) $437\frac{25}{100}$ 14) $\frac{4}{1000}$ 15) $\frac{36}{1000}$ 16) $400\frac{29}{1000}$
17) $\frac{1}{1000}$ 18) $\frac{329}{10000}$

Exercise 23

1) 3 2) 11·5 3) 24·04 4) 58·616
5) 54·852 6) 4·12 7) 15·616 8) 0·339
9) 0·812 10) 5·4109

Exercise 24

1) 41, 410, 4100 2) 24·2, 242, 2420
3) 0·46, 4·6, 46 4) 3·5, 35, 350
5) 1·486, 14·86, 148·6
6) 0·017 53, 0·1753, 1·753
7) 48·53 8) 9 9) 1700·6 10) 5639·6

Exercise 25

1) 0·36, 0·036, 0·0036
2) 6·4198, 0·641 98, 0·064 198
3) 0·007, 0·0007, 0·000 07
4) 51·04, 5·104, 0·5104
5) 0·0352, 0·003 52, 0·000 352
6) 0·054 7) 0·002 05 8) 0·004
9) 0·000 008 6 10) 0·062 742 8

Exercise 26

1) 743·0266 2) 0·951 534
3) 0·2888 4) 7·411 25
5) 0·001 376

Exercise 27

1) 1·33   2) 0·016   3) 189·74   4) 4·1066
5) 43·2

Exercise 28

1) 24·8658, 24·87, 25
2) 0·008 357, 0·008 36, 0·0084
3) 4·9785, 4·98, 5   4) 22   5) 35·60
6) 28 388 000, 28 000 000
7) 4·1498, 4·150, 4·15   8) 9·20

Exercise 29

1) $200 \times 0.005 = 1$ 2) $32 \times 0.25 = 8$
3) $0.7 \times 0.1 \times 2 = 0.14$
4) $80 \div 20 = 4$ 5) $0.06 \div 0.003 = 20$
6) $30 \times 30 \times 0.03 = 27$
7) $\dfrac{0.7 \times 0.006}{0.03} = 0.14$ 8) $\dfrac{30 \times 30}{10 \times 3} = 30$

Exercise 30

1) 0·25   2) 0·75   3) 0·375   4) 0·6875
5) 0·5   6) 0·6667   7) 0·6563   8) 0·4531
9) 1·8333   10) 2·4375   11) 0·333   12) 0·778
13) 0·133   14) 0·189   15) 0·356   16) 0·232
17) 0·525   18) 0·384   19) 0·328   20) 0·567

Exercise 31

1) $\frac{1}{5}$ 2) $\frac{9}{20}$ 3) $\frac{5}{16}$ 4) $2\frac{11}{20}$
5) $\frac{3}{400}$ 6) $2\frac{1}{8}$ 7) 0·0001
8) 0·001 875

Mental test 3

1) 5   2) 1·77   3) 33·41   4) 1·22
5) 2·12   6) 0·08   7) 11·5   8) 5·81
9) 5·72   10) 0·48   11) 9·27   12) 0·12
13) 0·15   14) 2·4   15) 1·3

Self-test 3

1) b   2) b   3) d   4) a
5) c   6) d   7) c   8) d
9) c   10) a   11) false   12) false
13) true   14) false   15) false   16) false
17) true   18) true   19) true   20) true

ANSWERS TO CHAPTER 4

Exercise 32

1) 2·25   2) 4·41   3) 73·96   4) 9·923
5) 58·98   6) 27·35   7) 18·18   8) 62·67
9) 64·27   10) 75·76   11) 529   12) 1648

13) 9 566 000   14) 12 610   15) 9628
16) 0·000 361   17) 0·5317
18) 0·000 017 80   19) 0·08032
20) 0·000 000 334 6

Exercise 33

1) 1·844   2) 2·862   3) 2·294   4) 3·039
5) 2·649   6) 1·735   7) 5·916   8) 9·445
9) 7·292   10) 9·110   11) 8·901   12) 7·072
13) 30   14) 26·94   15) 84·51   16) 298·3
17) 62·81   18) 29 890   19) 0·3921   20) 0·04121
21) 0·1987   22) 0·02798   23) 0·04447

Exercise 34

1) 10   2) 15   3) 49   4) 24
5) 120   6) 30   7) 336   8) 2520

Exercise 35

1) $\frac{2}{3}$ 2) $\frac{3}{4}$ 3) $\frac{5}{7}$ 4) $\frac{2}{3}$
5) $\frac{9}{10}$ 6) $\frac{2}{3}$ 7) $\frac{5}{8}$ 8) $\frac{5}{7}$
9) $\frac{4}{5}$ 10) $\frac{1}{6}$ 11) 13   12) 12
13) 3   14) 9   15) 6

Exercise 36

1) 0·2941   2) 0·1221   3) 0·1900   4) 0·1082
5) 0·1426   6) 0·028 57   7) 0·011 21
8) 0·018 81   9) 0·001 111
10) 0·000 14   11) 6·506   12) 588·9
13) 25·34   14) 1277   15) 505·6

Exercise 37

1) 0·004 283   2) 53·12
3) 0·000 016   4) 0·3449
5) 0·2311   6) 7·458   7) 0·001 023
8) 0·005 163   9) 5·801   10) 9·881
11) 0·2230   12) 0·3465   13) 13·73   14) 0·0654

Mental test 4

1) 169   2) 0·04   3) 900   4) 0·0025
5) 160 000   6) 40   7) 0·5
8) 300   9) 0·04   10) 13   11) 4
12) 20   13) 42   14) $\frac{2}{3}$ 15) 0·05
16) 5   17) 0·002   18) 20

Self-test 4

1) c   2) a   3) b   4) b
5) a   6) c   7) b   8) c
9) a   10) b   11) b   12) b
13) b   14) c   15) b   16) b
17) b   18) c

ANSWERS TO CHAPTER 5

Exercise 38

1) 15	2) -12	3) -32	4) 14
5) -24	6) 26	7) -18	8) 23

Exercise 39

1) -5	2) -9	3) 5	4) 5
5) -1	6) 0	7) -4	8) 7

Exercise 40

1) 2	2) 3	3) 14	4) 4
5) 1	6) -5	7) -5	8) 16

Exercise 41

1) -42	2) -42	3) 42	4) 42
5) -48	6) 4	7) 120	8) 9

Exercise 42

1) -3	2) -3	3) 3	4) 3
5) -2	6) -1	7) 2	8) -1
9) -2	10) 12	11) -1	12) -2
13) -8	14) -3		

Mental test 5

1) 12	2) 4	3) -25	4) -17
5) -4	6) -8	7) -17	8) 4
9) 6	10) -18	11) -16	12) -3
13) 4	14) 6	15) 3	16) 3
17) 11	18) -4	19) -11	20) 7
21) 20	22) -20	23) -20	24) 20
25) 25	26) 64	27) -18	28) 2
29) 2	30) -2	31) 3	32) -2
33) 3	34) -1	35) -1	36) -6

Self-test 5

1) false	2) true	3) false	4) true
5) true	6) false	7) false	8) true
9) true	10) true		

ANSWERS TO CHAPTER 6

Exercise 43

1) 2^{11}	2) 3^{11}	3) 5^{13}	4) 3^8
5) 7^3	6) 3^8	7) 2^4	8) 10^4
9) 3^8	10) 2^2	11) 5^{12}	12) $3^2 \times 5^8$
13) 10^{12}	14) $2^4 \times 3^8 \times 5^{12}$	15) $\dfrac{3^3}{4^3}$	
16) $\dfrac{5^8}{7^{12}}$	17) $\frac{1}{10}$	18) $\frac{1}{4}$	19) $\frac{1}{81}$

20) $\frac{1}{16}$	21) $\frac{1}{25}$	22) 2	23) 3
24) 2	25) 2	26) 1	27) 1
28) 1	29) $\frac{1}{4}$	30) $\frac{1}{5}$	

Exercise 44

1)(a) $1 \cdot 96 \times 10$ (b) $3 \cdot 85 \times 10^2$
  (c) $5 \cdot 9876 \times 10^4$ (d) $1 \cdot 5 \times 10^6$
  (e) $1 \cdot 3 \times 10^{-2}$ (f) $3 \cdot 85 \times 10^{-3}$
  (g) $6 \cdot 98 \times 10^{-4}$ (h) $2 \cdot 385 \times 10^{-2}$
2)(a) 150   (b) 47 000
  (c) 3 600 000   (d) 9450
  (e) 0·25   (f) 0·004
  (g) 0·000 08   (h) 0·04
3)(a) $2 \cdot 1 \times 10^3$ (b) $9 \cdot 95 \times 10^3$
  (c) $8 \cdot 58 \times 10^4$
4)(a) $2 \cdot 1 \times 10^{-2}$ (b) $8 \cdot 72 \times 10^{-3}$
  (c) $2 \cdot 11 \times 10^{-4}$

Exercise 45

1) 0·5563	2) 0·6812	3) 0·5340	4) 0·9238
5) 0·9624	6) 0·6218	7) 0·9194	8) 0·7865
9) 0·4588	10) 0·7557		

Exercise 46

1)(a) 1   (b) 4   (c) 4   (d) 2
  (e) 5   (f) 1   (g) 0   (h) 2
  (i) 3   (j) 2
2)(a) 0·8451, 1·8451, 2·8451, 3·8451, 4·8451
  (b) 0·4914, 1·4914, 2·4914, 3·4914, 6·4914
  (c) 1·6839, 5·6839, 0·6839, 2·6839
  (d) 3·8974, 0·8974, 1·8974, 4·8974
  (e) 0·0013, 1·0013, 3·0013, 2·0013

Exercise 47

1) 2·089, 208·9, 20 890, 20·89
2) 1884, 1·884, 18 840, 1 884 000
3) 3·969, 39·69, 39 690, 396·9
4) 7850, 7·850, 785·0, 78 500
5) 2·399   6) 18·32   7) 1473   8) 365·6

Exercise 48

1) 362·1	2) 17 970	3) 148 900	4) 3783
5) 1·941	6) 2·599	7) 9·907	8) 1·566
9) 71·93	10) 9·338	11) 25·67	12) 1·898

Exercise 49

1) 393·2	2) 863·4	3) 1·596	4) 102·1
5) 49·82	6) 1·213	7) 1·647	8) 2·398
9) 2·486	10) 1·888	11) 15·19	12) 56 130

Exercise 50

1) $0 \cdot 4498,\ \bar{1} \cdot 4498,\ \bar{2} \cdot 4498,\ \bar{3} \cdot 4498$

2) 0·6625, $\bar{1}$·6625, $\bar{3}$·6625, $\bar{5}$·6625
3) $\bar{2}$·9898, $\bar{4}$·9898, $\bar{1}$·9898
4) $\bar{5}$·7690, $\bar{2}$·7690, $\bar{4}$·7690
5) 0·2714 6) 0·006 606
7) 0·000 3537 8) 0·030 70
9) 0·000 000 034 03 10) 0·1052

Exercise 51

1) 0 2) 1 3) $\bar{4}$ 4) $\bar{4}$
5) 1 6) $\bar{2}$ 7) $\bar{3}$ 8) $\bar{9}$
9) $\bar{3}$ 10) $\bar{2}$ 11) $\bar{1}$ 12) $\bar{3}$
13) $\bar{3}$ 14) $\bar{3}$ 15) 3 16) 5
17) 0 18) 3 19) $\bar{3}$ 20) 3

Exercise 52

1) 0·1 2) 2·3 3) $\bar{2}$·9 4) 0·1
5) 1·1 6) $\bar{2}$·7 7) $\bar{4}$·1 8) $\bar{2}$·0
9) $\bar{2}$·2 10) 1·1 11) $\bar{1}$·2 12) $\bar{4}$·5
13) 4·4 14) 2·3 15) $\bar{2}$·9172 16) 0·2340
17) $\bar{9}$·1650 18) 5·1 19) $\bar{3}$·2 20) 0·4
21) $\bar{2}$·3 22) $\bar{2}$·5 23) 4·2 24) $\bar{2}$·1
25) $\bar{2}$·9 26) $\bar{1}$·5 27) $\bar{4}$·5 28) $\bar{2}$·5
29) $\bar{1}$·8 30) $\bar{1}$·8 31) 6·9094 32) $\bar{1}$·6204
33) $\bar{4}$·5424 34) 2·1238

Exercise 53

1) $\bar{2}$·8 2) $\bar{9}$·3 3) $\bar{1}$·4 4) $\bar{4}$·4
5) $\bar{1}$·0 6) $\bar{1}$·3 7) $\bar{1}$·3 8) $\bar{1}$·6
9) $\bar{1}$·5 10) $\bar{2}$·7 11) 0·047 20
12) 0·2992 13) 0·000 001 814 14) 0·5069
15) 0·4119 16) 0·092 10 17) 0·9305
18) 0·000 474 8 19) 0·4894
20) 0·000 019 24

Mental test 6

1) 3^6 2) 5^{10} 3) 2^{14} 4) 4^6
5) 3^6 6) $3^8 \times 5^{12}$ 7) 7^{30} 8) $\frac{9}{16}$
9) 0·01 10) 0·25 11) 0·2 12) 1
13) 2 14) 3 15) 2 16) 2
17) 1 18) 1·9 19) 5·8 20) 2·1

Self-test 6

1) a 2) b 3) a 4) c
5) c 6) b 7) d 8) a
9) b 10) d 11) a 12) c

ANSWERS TO MISCELLANEOUS EXERCISE

Exercise 54

1) $\frac{3}{4}$ 2) 2·16 3) $1\frac{1}{3}$ 4) 0·123
5) $1\frac{1}{2}$ 6) 0·56 7) 830 8) $\frac{1}{4}$

9) 80 10) 1 11) 0·3159 12) $\frac{5}{6}$
13)(a) 3·272 (b) 56 440
14) 15 15) 10·296 16) 0·001 024
17) 4 18) 0·5718 19) 10^4 20) 1·38
21) 59·37 and 0·1684
22)(i) 9·0321 (ii) 9·03
23) $\frac{32}{77}$ 24) 310·5 25) 0·024 26) $1\frac{1}{2}$
27) 0·016 28) 35·4, 35·445, 40 29) 0·785
30) 96 31) $20\frac{1}{4}$ 32) 0·625 33) 1·00
34) $\frac{7}{72}$ 35) 1·284 36) 10·050 37) $\frac{47}{50}$
38) 6·7 39) 1·3 40) 14
41)(i) $\frac{3}{4}, \frac{4}{5}, \frac{7}{8}, \frac{8}{9}$ (ii) 0·925 (iii) $\frac{1}{30}$
42)(a) 628·2 (b) 6·452
43)(a) 0·6773 (b) 0·3548
44)(a) 0·000 427 0 (b) 2342 (c) 37·05
45)(i) $9·487 \times 10^2$ (ii) 0·3802 (iii) 1·806
46) 0·3903 47) 0·070 18
48)(a) 0·4348 (b) 0·043 17
49) $2·356 \times 10^5$
50)(a) 0·8720 (b) 0·4391

ANSWERS TO CHAPTER 7

Exercise 55

1)(a) 5 630 (b) 680 (c) 17 698
(d) 5·92 (e) 0·68 (f) 6·895
(g) 0·073 (h) 45·97 (i) 0·798
(j) 0·005
2)(a) 9·753 (b) 0·259 (c) 0·058
(d) 0·029 85 (e) 0·790 685
3)(a) 468 (b) 78·2 (c) 516 000 (d) 389·7
(e) 8·8
4)(a) 1234 (b) 580 000 (c) 258
(d) 3890 (e) 52
5)(a) 0·530 (b) 35
(c) 0·002 473 (d) 0·597 600
6)(a) 56 (b) 0·096 (c) 8 630 (d) 81
(e) 0·584

Exercise 56

1) 4507 2) 1·393 3) 6·2 cm 4) 19·7675
5) 4·25 kg 6) 74 kg 7) 14·01 km
8) 42·45 m

Exercise 57

1) 39·95 m 2) 505·6 m
3) 18·98 m 4) 51 pieces; 42 cm
5) 36 6) 1 053 kg 7) 6 8) 12·6 m

Exercise 58

1) 48 m 2) 148·8 m 3) 27 m 4) 6·02 m
5) 5 rolls 6) 6 rolls 7) 6·53 m

Mental test 7

1) 15·45 m 2) 57·9 cm 3) 9 700 4) 376
5) 5·98 m 6) 1·80 m 7) 9 g 8) 14 m
9) 1 560 kg 10) 200 11) 200 kg
12) 25

Self-test 7

1) true 2) false 3) false 4) false
5) false 6) true 7) true 8) true
9) false 10) true 11) true 12) true
13) false 14) false 15) true

ANSWERS TO CHAPTER 8

Exercise 59

1) 68 p, 63 p, 58½ p
2) 216 p, 359½ p, 1768 p
3) £0·35, £0·78½, £0·06, £0·03
4) £2·46, £9·83½, £265·32
5)(a) £10·06 (b) £215·58
 (c) £5·42½ (d) £2·35 (e) £2·00½
6)(a) £2·24 (b) £7·93
 (c) £68·61½ (d) £0·78 (e) £2·09½

Exercise 63

1) £1·80 2) £6·37½ 3) £16·98½ 4) £168·84
5) 13 p 6) 21½ p 7) £1·30½ 8) £2·16½

Exercise 64

1) £22·50+£101·25+£159·00+£64·00 =
£346·75
2) £124·00+£31·50+£40·80+£12·50 =
£208·80
3) £29·25+£61·20+£51·45+£46·80 =
£188·70
4) £13·92+£136·50+£117·30+£225·00+
£109·00 = £601·72
5) £19·80+£9·00+£61·75+£22·44+£13·92
= £126·91

Mental test 8

1) £7·23 2) 60 p 3) £120 4) 7½ p
5) 1½ p 6) £3 7) 20 p 8) £4·95
9) £7·92 10) £15

Self-test 8

1) true 2) true 3) false 4) true
5) true 6) false 7) true 8) true
9) true 10) true

ANSWERS TO CHAPTER 9

Exercise 65

1) $\frac{8}{3}$ 2) $\frac{2}{3}$ 3) $\frac{3}{1}$ 4) $\frac{3}{5}$
5) $\frac{2}{3}$ 6) $\frac{3}{20}$ 7) $\frac{25}{4}$ 8) 150 m
9) £192 10) $\frac{6}{1}$

Exercise 66

1) £500 and £300 2) £64 and £16
3) £50, £40 and £30 4) £280
5) 15, 22·5 and 37·5 kg
6) 84, 294, 462 mm 7) £6258 and £4470
8) £3·60

Exercise 67

1) £4·80 2) £4·24 3) 87½ p, £48·12½
4) £1·75 5) 33·17 litres
6) 18⅓, 36⅔, 2, 40, 1 7) £224 8) 7 hours

Exercise 68

1) 13½ days 2) 3⅓ days
3) 160 rev/min 4) 6 5) 20 men

Exercise 69

1) 79·35 2) 3025 3) 64·96 4) £109·85
5) £6·46 6) 7884·93 7) 53·39 8) £3·433
9) 9 krona = £1 10) £3·95

Exercise 70

1) £2000 and £4000 2) £10 000 and £12 000
3) £27 000, £30 000 and £36 000 4) £2400
5) £2250 and £3000

Mental test 9

1) ½ 2) $\frac{8}{3}$ 3) $\frac{8}{1}$ 4) 100 cm
5) £105 6) £420 and £180 7) £30
8) 100 kg 9) £2·80 10) 50 p 11) 5 hours
12) 20 days 13) 10 14) 600
15) 1500 lira = £1

Self-test 9

1) true 2) false 3) true 4) true
5) true 6) false 7) true 8) false
9) true 10) true 11) false 12) true
13) true 14) false 15) false 16) **b**
17) **d** 18) **a** 19) **b** 20) **c**
21) **c** 22) **a**

ANSWERS TO CHAPTER 10

Exercise 71

1) 70   2) 55   3) 36   4) 80
5) 62   6) 25   7) 90   8) 95

Exercise 72

1) 70   2) 73   3) 68   4) 81·3
5) 92·7   6) 33·3   7) 81·9

Exercise 73

1) 0·32   2) 0·78   3) 0·06   4) 0·24
5) 0·315   6) 0·482   7) 0·025   8) 0·0125
9) 0·0395   10) 0·201

Exercise 74

1)(a) 10   (b) 24   (c) 6   (d) 2·4
   (e) 21·315   (f) 2·516
2)(a) 12·5 (b) 20   (c) 16   (d) 16·29
   (e) 45·45
3) 60%; 27   4) 115 cm   5) $88\frac{2}{3}$ cm
6)(a) £7·20   (b) £13·20 (c) £187·50
7)(a) 2·083% are bad
  (b) 3·077% are absent
  (c) 87·76% eat lunches
8) 39 643   9) 150 kg   10) 600

Exercise 75

1) 25%   2)(a) 20%   (b) $16\frac{2}{3}$%
3)(a) $13\frac{1}{3}$%   (b) 9·95%
4) 20%   5) $33\frac{1}{3}$%   6) $12\frac{1}{2}$%   7) 17·65%
8) 10%

Exercise 76

1) 20%   2) 25%   3) £1·50   4) £58·50
5) £3·75   6) £16   7) £70   8) £6
9) £225   10) £1385

Exercise 77

1) £300   2) £62·50; $33\frac{1}{3}$%; £187·50
3) 28·57%   4) 25%   5) £24 000
6) 53·85%; £185·50   7) 23·08%
8) 20%

Exercise 78

1)(a) £8000; £15 000 (b) 21·05%; 39·47%
   (c) 34·78%; 65·22%
2)(a) £30   (b) 12%
3) £26 200; 16·03%
4)(a) £70   (b) 20%   (c) 31·82%
5)(a) £15 000   (b) £4230   (c) £10 770

(d) 23·93%   (e) 35·9%

Exercise 79

1) £12·60   2) £28·50   3) 18 p   4) £4·25
5) £265·05

Exercise 80

1) £168   2) £10   3) £200   4) 30%
5) £304·50   6) £182·40
7) £200   8) £1164   9) £10
10) £578·42   11) £898·61
12) £12

Mental test 10

1) 80%   2) 0·3   3) $\frac{1}{8}$ 4) 89%
5) 24   6) 3·5   7) £3·20   8) £6
9) 25%   10) £10   11) 20%   12) £36
13) £100   14) 20%   15) 25%   16) £15 000
17) £10 000   18) £20 000
19) £1·50   20) £27

Self-test 10

1) true   2) false   3) true   4) false
5) false   6) true   7) true   8) true
9) false   10) true   11) true   12) false
13) false   14) false   15) false
16) **a, b** and **d**   17) **b**   18) **a**
19) **c**   20) **b**   21) **c**   22) **b**
23) **b**   24) **c** and **d**   25) **d**

ANSWERS TO CHAPTER 11

Exercise 82

1) 9   2) 3   3) 3   4) 18
5) 45   6) 6   7) 45   8) 30
9) 23   10) 26   11) 33   12) 33
13) 28   14) 1   15) $\frac{3}{4}$ 16) 5
17) 5   18) 7·7

Exercise 83

1) 4   2) 81   3) 54   4) 32
5) 1152   6) 74   7) 20   8) 3024
9) 3   10) 18·96

Exercise 84

1) 6   2) 5   3) 6   4) 7
5) 10   6) 13   7) 4   8) 5
9) 4   10) 6   11) 20   12) 18
13) 32   14) 4   15) 6   16) 3
17) 9   18) 2   19) 2   20) 2
21) $\frac{1}{3}$ 22) $1\frac{1}{2}$

Exercise 85

1) 17	2) 160	3) 18·852	4) 252
5) 0·2	6) 400	7) 21	8) 180
9) 1875	10) 6		

Exercise 86

1) ½	2) 5	3) 3	4) 4
5) 100	6) 8·593	7) 2·546	8) 6

Mental test 11

1) 4	2) 2	3) 3	4) 3
5) 3	6) 4	7) 10	8) 15
9) 19	10) 2	11) 2	12) 3
13) 6	14) 12	15) 12	16) 4
17) 20	18) 14	19) 9	20) 4

Self-test 11

1) true	2) false	3) true	4) true
5) false	6) false	7) false	8) false
9) true	10) true	11) true	12) false
13) true	14) false	15) true	16) true
17) true	18) false	19) true	20) true

ANSWERS TO CHAPTER 12

Exercise 87

1) £126	2) £20	3) 4 years
4) 5 months		5) 2½ years
6) 7%	7) 9%	8) £320 9) £0·30
10) £66		11) £14·56
12)(a) £189	(b) £275	(c) £3200
(d) £10 010	(e) £1701	

Exercise 88

1) £117·20	2) £331	3) £2567	4) £9450
5) £2506	6) £432; £542		7) £2765
8) $3011			

Exercise 89

1) £175·35 2) £342·50 3) £2215   4) £9471
5) £1631·70

Exercise 90

1) £6655   2) £3271   3) £5260   4) £2440
5) £1007

Mental test 12

1) £10	2) £18	3) £60	4) £12
5) £21	6) £245	7) £550	8) £162

Self-test 12

1) d	2) b	3) a	4) c
5) d	6) b	7) d	8) a
9) a	10) c	11) c	12) c
13) d	14) a		

ANSWERS TO MISCELLANEOUS EXERCISE

Exercise 91

1) 107·95 francs   2) 93 p   3) 3 years
4) £13·13   5) 23·50 francs   6) £34·00
7) £1811·25   8) £450   9) 22 p
10) 133·65 11) £85 and £59·50   12) £64·84
13) 7   14) £7·84   15) £8·03   16) 7
17) 11·1% 18) £2·24   19) £6·60   20) £23·75
21) £49·45 22) £103·07   23) £87·07
24) —   25) £13·45 26) 5%   27) 5
28) 50   29) 695·2   30) 11%   31) £6931
32) 2·9 p   33) £110·53
34) £10 000 and £3600   35) 18·75%
36) £159·60 and £146·40   37) £8000
38) £20 900; £14 896   39) £1132 40) £6·43
41) £20 240
42) £7560, £5248 and £4592; £996

ANSWERS TO CHAPTER 13

Exercise 92

1) £33·60   2) £44·85   3) £28·86   4) £55·20
5) £1·12   6) 75 p   7) 80 p   8) 92 p

Exercise 93

1) £32·64   2) £72   3) £81·22
4) 94 p per hour   5) 6 hours 6) 6 hours

Exercise 94

1) £7   2) £7·95   3) £14·50   4) £15·66½

Exercise 95

1) £13   2) £55·50   3) £13; £47
4) £122·50

Exercise 96

1) £180   2) £131   3) £238   4) £300
5) £423

Exercise 97

1) £35·59   2) £102·80 3) £57·95; £39·00

4) £2382·64   5) £249·28

Mental test 13

1) 70 p   2) £48   3) £5   4) £1·80
5) £9   6) £15   7) £200   8) £38
9) £32   10) £18

Self-test 13

1) c   2) a   3) d   4) c
5) b   6) a   7) d   8) c

ANSWERS TO CHAPTER 14

Exercise 98

1) £63   2) £120   3) 90 p
4) 31·25 p in the £1   5) £1 161 000
6) 9·1 p in the £1   7) £85 000
8) £87 960; 55 p   9) £39 100
10) 2·9 p in the £1

Exercise 99

1) £9·17   2) £8·37   3) £146·40 4) £56·40
5) £109·05 6) £16·67

Exercise 100

1) £7·44   2) £14·37½ 3) £25·80   4) £19·40
5) £2·25   6) £9·54   7) 73 p

Exercise 101

1) £420   2) £200   3) £958·65 4) £813·7
5) £657

Mental test 14

1) £75   2) £40 000 3) 50 p in the £1
4) £150   5) £20   6) £7   7) £96
8) £40   9) £15   10) £32   11) £600
12) £1200

Self-test 14

1) c   2) a   3) d   4) b
5) b   6) a   7) c   8) c
9) d   10) d

ANSWERS TO CHAPTER 15

Exercise 102

1) £22·40 2) 730   3) £14·75 4) 345
5) £40·32 6) Method (ii)   7) £12·56
8) £17·40

Exercise 103

1) £300   2) £422·96; 3·52 p   3) 2·988 p
4) 4036 p 5) £120   6) £25   7) £12

Exercise 104

1) £24·75 2) £71·68 3) 16%   4) 12%
5) £23·96 6) £272·40; £32·40   7) £10·09
8) £25·83

Mental test 15

1) £50   2) £35   3) £11·50 4) 500
5) £40   6) £11   7) £56   8) 10 p

Self-test 15

1) d   2) b   3) a   4) c
5) c   6) b   7) d   8) a

ANSWERS TO CHAPTER 16

Exercise 105

1)(a) £1256   (b) £351   (c) £165·20
2)(a) £174·60   (b) £304·50 (c) £573·30
3)(a) £24   (b) £81   (c) £637·50
4)(a) £22·50   (b) £125   (c) £96
5)(a) 10·8%   (b) 2·35% (c) 6·12%
6) £80; 10·67%   7) £738; £63; 8·54%
8) 32 p   9) £1125   10) 4·4%   11) 46·4%
12) £11 800

Exercise 106

1)(a) £400   (b) £362·32 (c) £583·33
2)(a) £28   (b) £60   (c) £20
3) £681·82; £40·91; 6·82%
4) £240   5) £300   6) £218·18 7) £90
8) £4444·44; £66·67   9) £29·64 less
10)(a) £1515·38   (b) £2561   (c) £78

Exercise 107

1)(a) 40 p in the £1   (b) 9·1 p in the £1
(c) 33·57 p in the £1
2)(a) £2100   (b) £510·24
(c) £2978·82
3) 44·68 p in the £1   4) 20·32 p in the £1
5) £3589·40

Mental test 16

1) £50   2) £60   3) £16   4) £20
5) £200   6) £315   7) £6   8) £25
9) £8   10) £2·10   11) 30 p in the £1
12) £400

Self-test 16

1) d   2) b   3) a   4) b
5) a   6) c   7) c   8) b

ANSWERS TO MISCELLANEOUS EXERCISE

Exercise 108

1) £15·75   2) £2·10   3) £129·80 4) £3339
5) £120   6) £15·68 7) 50p in the £1
8) £60   9) £980   10) £2100; £180
11) £1824 12) 67·22 13) £3133·50
14) £7·11 15) £17·36 16) 24·5p in the £1
17) £335·56   18) £62·80 19) £2750
20) £2·80 21) 464   22) £6·96 23) £14·72
24) 8
25) £18 000; 70p in the £1; 4p in the £1
26) £10·50; £37·50; 8·33p
27) £321·42; 62·66%   28) £84·10
29)(a) 36·67p in the £1
   (b) £898·42   (c) £1810·74
30)(a) £5515   (b) £1956·75
   (c) 28·1%
31)(a) 72·5p in the £1 (b) £113·10 (c) £33 800
32) £300   33) £1125; 4⅛%
34) £81; £234   35) £426
36)(a) 17   (b) £0·80
37(a) £1065   (b) £109·50
38) £546; 5·9p   39) £24·37½
40)(a) £1145   (b) £343·50 (c) £6·60

ANSWERS TO CHAPTER 17

Exercise 109

1) 22·24   2) 115   3) 12·2 kg 4) £38·40
5) £28·30 6) 324   7) 97·6
8) 14 years 6 months 9) 76   10) 9·13p

Exercise 110

1) 75 km/h   2) 4 hours
3) 350 km   4) 26 km/h
5) 75 km/h   6) 80 km/h
7) 5 hours   8) 38·4 km/h

Exercise 111

1) 16p   2) 25·71p 3) £1·17   4) 73·8p
5) £2·27 6) 23·25p

Exercise 112

1) 29·83 cm   2) £42·45 3) £14·56
4) 23 mm 5) £1·93

---

6)(a) 5   (b) 8·5   (c) 8
7) 63; 63 8) 8

Mental test 17

1) 6   2) 5   3) 2400   4) 85 g
5) 160   6) 6p   7) 40 km/h
8) 150 km 9) 3 hours
10) 76·8 p/kg   11) 21·2p 12) 8
13) 2·0   14) 4

Self-test 17

1) d   2) b   3) a   4) b
5) d   6) a   7) a   8) c
9) c   10) b   11) d   12) b

ANSWERS TO CHAPTER 18

Exercise 113

2) 254   4) £1·71   5) 63, 9·5

Exercise 114

1) 202 francs, £19·6   2) £326   3) £30·40
4) 6   8) 7·64

Exercise 115

1)(a) 50 km/h   (b) 100 km (c) 3 hours
2) 180 km, ⅔ hour   3) 40 km/h
4) 35 km, 10 km/h   5) 22·1 km/h

Exercise 116

1) 640
2)(a) 4100   (b) 1000   (c) £4400
3) 400   4) 15 years   5) 80 km

Exercise 117

7) Length of bar   24·95 24·96 24·97 24·98
   Frequency   1   1   4   4
   Length of bar   24·99 25·00 25·01 25·02
   Frequency   5   5   7   6
   Length of bar   25·03 25·04 25·05
   Frequency   4   2   1
8) Mark   3   4   5   6   7   8   9
   Frequency 1   3   4   6   7   5   4
9) 29·85   11) 29·91   12) £31·90, £32·20

ANSWERS TO MISCELLANEOUS EXERCISE

Exercise 118

1) 22 litres 2) 162·5 kg   3) 153 cm

4) £48   5) 2·4 km/h
6) 4·40 p.m.   7) 15; 15   8) 13⅔
9) 56·36 km/h   10) 53·75 km/h
11) 81 km/h   12) £99·95½; £5197·66
13) £2650; 20 000 km   14) £1·60
15) 36 cm; 25 years   16) £1·55; £2·07
17) $9·84; £11·22   18) 1810 cm³
19) 0·998 95   20) 10·3525
21)(a) 16·01 cm   (b) 16·08 cm
22)(a) 7 cm   (b) 8·5 cm (c) 9·6 cm
23)(a) 8·2 m   (b) 7·2 m   (c) 5 secs.

ANSWERS TO CHAPTER 19

Exercise 119

1)(a) 56 cm²   (b) 220 mm²
   (c) 630 m²
2) 1·036 m²   3) 1·7424 m²
4) 28·42 m²   5) 62 m²   6) 174 m²
7)(a) 53·55 m²   (b) 45·03 m²   (c) 8·52 m²
8)(a) 1200 mm²   (b) 275 mm²
   (c) 259·5 mm²   (d) 774 mm²
   (e) 1050 mm²   (f) 1094 mm²

Exercise 120

1) 6 m   2) 8·3 m   3) 10 m²   4) 5·5 m
5) 60 cm   6) 144 cm²; 12 cm   7) 2400
8) 66 m²

Exercise 121

1) 56 cm²   2) 0·0455 m²   3) 4 m
4) 7·2 cm   5) 23·4 cm²

Exercise 122

1) 135°   2) 54°   3) 60°   4) 63°
5) 18°   6) 135°   7) 288°   8) 288'
9) 108°   10) 90°

Exercise 123

1) 7·071 cm   2) 50 mm
3) 4·472 cm
4)(a) 7·810 cm   (b) 9·644 cm
   (c) 51·96 mm   (d) 82·61 mm
5) 4·243 cm   6) 8·544 cm

Exercise 124

1) 6·021 cm   2) 13·229 cm
3) 28·496 cm   4) 8·314 cm
5) 7·101 cm

Exercise 125

1) 108 cm²   2) 22·125 cm²

3) 13·416 cm²   4) 9·617 cm²
5) 93·46 cm²

Exercise 126

1) 40 cm²   2) 94·24 cm²   3) 10 cm
4) 30·615 cm²   5) 198 mm²

Exercise 127

1) 132 cm   2) 2200 mm   3) 270·2 m
4) 19·86 cm   5) 88 cm
6) 267·1 mm   7) 26·47 m
8) 4400 mm   9) 88 m
10) 10·18 m   11) 30·16 m
12) 2 m   13) 35 cm 14) 304·3 mm

Exercise 128

1) 616 cm²   2) 385 000
3) 24·99 m²   4) 1386 cm²
5) 47·55 m²   6) 30 670 mm²
7) 141·4 cm²   8) 581·3 mm²
9) 116·3 m²   10) 289·8 m²

Exercise 129

1) 3·142 cm; 6·284 cm²
2) 15·71 cm; 78·55 cm²
3) 3·142 cm; 4·713 cm²
4) 3·959 m; 5·345 m²
5) 238·3 mm; 9292·5 mm²
6) 39·10 cm²

Exercise 130

1) 21·45 cm²   2) 5·363 cm²
3) 13·728 cm²   4) 7·722 cm²
5) 211·9 cm²

Mental test 19

1) 40 cm²   2) 6 m   3) 6 cm   4) 96 cm²
5) 20 mm   6) 16 cm²   7) 4 m   8) 10 cm
9) 30 cm² 10) 44 cm   11) 88 cm   12) 154 cm²

Self test 19

1) b and c 2) a and c   3) b and d 4) b
5) c   6) b and d 7) d   8) a
9) b   10) b and c

ANSWERS TO CHAPTER 20

Exercise 131

1) 140 cm³   2) 225 000 mm³
3) 7700 cm³   4) 31 420 mm³

5) 73·28 cm³   6) 0·0087 m³
7) 3·8556 cm³   8) 300 cm³
9) 23·1 m³   10) 22 622 cm³

Exercise 132

1) 47·5 m²   2) 1960 cm²
3) 77·4 m²   4) 4·522 m²
5) 15·91 m²   6) 86·28 m²
7) 82·92 m²

Exercise 133

1) 50·27 cm³; 62·84 cm²
2) 264 cm²; 199·5 cm³ 3) 20·78 cm³
4) 288 cm³
5) 523·7 cm³; 314·2 cm²
6) 1527 cm³
7) 30 470 cm³; 4210 cm²
8) 4295 cm³

Exercise 134

1) 2800 litres   2) 39600 litres
3) 9·426 m³; 9426 litres
4) 7·855 litres   5) 15·375 litres
6) 384 ml; 96   7) 31·81 ml; 15·7
8) 9000 litres   9) 11·31 litres
10) 3·620 litres   11) 150 seconds
12)(a) 0·053 m³/s   (b) 3181 l/min
13) 180 000 l/min
14) 35·35 m³; 707 000 seconds
15) 3·82 cm/min

Exercise 135

1) 600 g   2) 1600 kg 3) 9·12 kg
4) 100·7 kg   5) 14 139 kg
6) 17·50 kg   7) 1080 kg
8 452·4 kg   9) 300·9 kg
10) 1591 kg

Exercise 136

1) 5 cm   2) 7·638 m 3) 3·118 cm

4) 5 cm²   5) 2·5 mm 6) 10·61 m 7) 2474 m
8) 6·542 cm   9) 2 211 000
10) 6·365 cm   11) 8 cm 12) 40 cm²

Mental test 20

1) 40 cm³ 2) 40 cm³ 3) 252 cm³
4) 128 cm²   5) 128 cm³
6) 120 g   7) 20 cm³ 8) 10 cm² 9) 8 cm²
10) 15 litres   11) 30 000 cm³
12) 400 cm³   13) 2 cm   14) 5 m³
15) 60 cm³

Self-test 20

1) d   2) a, d   3) a   4) d
5) a   6) a, c   7) c   8) a, c
9) a   10) a

ANSWERS TO MISCELLANEOUS EXERCISE

Exercise 137

1) 79 cm   2) 133·3 m   3) 512 cm³
4) 20 cm   5) 1 000 000   6) 5000
7) 690 cm²   8) 22·50 m
9) 88 cm   10) 200 cm 11) 24 cm² 12) 80 m³
13) 2012 cm²   14) 630 cm²
15) 48 cm   16) 1000 g 17) 4000
18) 2160 cm³   19) 11·87 cm
20) 2·2 g/cm³   21) 94 kg   22) 75 m
23) 3 rolls; 2·5 m   24) 3553 mm
25) 89·3 cm²; 67 seconds
26) 246 m²; 32 472 000 litres
27) 1050 cm²; 4·8 m   28) 80 cm²; 25 kg
29) 24·75 m   30) 573·5 cm³; 874·8 g
31)(a) 13·43 m; 12·34 m²; 6170 seconds
32) 24·9 cm
33)(a) 24 750 000 cm³   (b) 32 cm
34) 20·38 m²; 2242 kg
35) 196 m; 2400 m²; 282·2 m²

Index